Marketing in an Audiology Practice

Marketing in an Audiology Practice

Brian Taylor, AuD

5521 Ruffin Road
San Diego, CA 92123

e-mail: info@pluralpublishing.com
Website: http://www.pluralpublishing.com

FSC
www.fsc.org
MIX
Paper from
responsible sources
FSC® C011935

Typeset in 11/13 Garamond by Flanagan's Publishing Services, Inc.
Printed in the United States of America by McNaughton & Gunn, Inc.

Library of Congress Cataloging-in-Publication Data

Marketing in an audiology practice / [edited by] Brian Taylor.
    p. ; cm.
  Includes bibliographical references and index.
  ISBN 978-1-59756-569-1 (alk. paper)—ISBN 1-59756-569-5 (alk. paper)
  I. Taylor, Brian, 1966- , editor.
  [DNLM: 1. Audiology. 2. Marketing of Health Services—methods.
3. Practice Management, Medical—economics. WV 21]
  RF291
  617.80068—dc23
                                                    2014048441

CONTENTS

INTRODUCTION

This is not, I repeat, not, a marketing textbook. It is an audiology book that will demonstrate how marketing and branding are instrumental to the long-term sustainability of an audiology or hearing instrument dispensing practice. It is written for two audiences: graduate students who often do not get enough exposure to business-related coursework during their graduate school tenure and experienced audiologists who are looking for some material of a practical nature. Its primary intent is to support audiologists who aspire to own or operate their own practice.

Although the word *marketing* appears in the title of this textbook, this book is in many ways more about branding than marketing, at least when you consider how marketing is traditionally defined. If you're interested in learning the details of direct mail advertising, lead generation tactics, or telemarketing programs, you will find plenty of practical tidbits here but not many of the arcane details you are more likely to encounter if you took a university-level business management or marketing course. Rather, the aim of this book is to provide you, the reader, with an overview of all aspects of marketing, public relations, and branding within the context of a real-world audiology practice. For the experienced clinician or practice manager, probably the best use of this book would be to keep it in your office and, when need arises, to find some insights on marketing strategies and tactics. On the other hand, if you are a doctorate candidate, the hope is that this book is part of a broader business course you are required to take. Whatever your reason for reading this book, let's get started with some fundamental concepts related to marketing in your audiology practice.

No matter the scale and scope of your practice, no matter the location or target market, there are a few core management principles worthy of consideration before you begin reading this book. As an audiologist with practical knowledge in business management, I have had the privilege of working with a variety of audiology practices around the world. The most successful practices, those that have a sustainable business model with extremely happy and content employees and even happier, contented patients, talk about and implement the following four principles.

1. Have a vision: A practice that clearly defines its mission and values is more likely to offer its community a unique service that stands apart from the competition. This process begins with the owner and other key stakeholders defining and defending a distinctive offering to the marketplace. This distinctive offering is likely to involve some combination of service delivery and professionalism that is attractive to a segment of the market. The function of marketing is matching your vision to a segment of your market who desires your unique offering. This includes observing unfolding circumstances in a rapidly changing marketplace and possibly relying on some guidance and insights from independent consultants from outside the industry.

2. Create a plan: Practices that take that vision and put it into action with clear goals and priorities have a chance to stand out from the crowd. This requires the integration of information and respect for the culture of your organization. The function of a marketing plan is to ensure that the entire staff understands their role and responsibility for communicating your brand message and attracting patients to your practice.

3. Take action: The most thoughtful, meticulous plan is wasted if it is not put into action. The ability to take a specific course of action around a single initiative, manically focusing on that initiative until results are achieved, separates the cream of the crop from the mediocre. For many practitioners, it is relatively easy to set goals, but often there is not a thorough action plan. The most successful practices have the courage and discipline to see their plan through by taking a serious of actions.

4. Measure results and modify their plans: Practices that carefully chose a handful of key metrics that are relevant for continuous improvement in both the patient care and finan-

cial part of their business are often the most successful. In addition to using just a few key metrics, they use these data to modify their plans and actions to stay ahead of the competition and further fine-tune the day-to-day activities that define their business.

Applying these four principles is likely to help you achieve "category of one" status. Together, these principles comprise your brand identity. This is critical because the first law of marketing, according to Al Ries and Jack Trout (2009), authors of the *22 Immutable Laws of Marketing*, is to achieve "category of one" status. They call this the law of leadership—their first immutable law—to be known in your marketplace as the first (or best) at something.

For audiologists and hearing instrument specialists, all striving to attract the same small pool of patients, it is very challenging—sometimes even next to impossible—to create this elusive "category of one" status. This book is intended to help you get on the path to achieving it. Chapter 1 addresses the all-important matters of building a brand and having a clear marketing strategy. Chapter 2 delves into human behavior and how certain consumer choices can be triggered through advertising messaging. Chapter 3 provides a comprehensive overview of an actual working marketing plan that has been implemented by an experienced private practice audiologist, while Chapter 4 brings a fresh perspective on advertising. Chapter 5 discusses how and why audiologists need to build relationships with the gatekeepers of health care, the primary care physicians and their staff, using the best available science that shows a relationship between age-related hearing loss and other chronic medical conditions. The book culminates with Chapter 6, a review of how social media can be deployed in a busy practice, and Chapter 7, marketing principles applied to a nonprofit hospital or clinic.

Before getting into the specifics of marketing, it's worth spending some time addressing how marketing fits into the broader context of operating a successful practice. We can examine this through the lens of the practice development hierarchy of needs. Marketing in your practice is interconnected with all other aspects of your business, as this next section will demonstrate.

WHY MARKETING MATTERS: THE HIERARCHY OF PRACTICE NEEDS

If you went to an American college or university in the past 50 years, there's a good chance you took Psychology 101. If you took that course, you probably remember names like Freud, Jung, Piaget, and Maslow. Each was the architect of a highly influential movement within their field of study, including psychologist Abraham Maslow (1908–1970), who created a theory associated with how individuals reach their full potential as human beings. The foundation of his theory rested on the fact that certain biological needs had to be satisfied before self-esteem and other similar needs were met. He used the term *self-actualization*, which is at the top of the pyramid to describe the innate desire human beings have to lead a fulfilling life. At the time he created this theory, commonly known as Maslow's hierarchy of needs, the prevailing attitude among psychologists was to develop theories of human behavior around the disordered state of individuals. The real genius behind Maslow's hierarchy of needs is that he studied normal human behavior, rather than disordered behavior, to arrive at his theory of the self. Maslow's view of the normal human self has had a profound effect on a number of fields, including business.

Managers and owners can apply Maslow's hierarchy of needs to their business as shown in Figure 0–1. In order for your business to reach its full potential as a center of excellence, you can apply a similar hierarchical approach. By studying what successful professionals have done to build their practice, you can apply Maslow's hierarchy to ensure that the fundamentals of your business are sound.

The practice development hierarchy of needs is a pathway to greater success. Let's spend a little more time examining this concept as it relates to practice management and marketing. Notice that the most fundamental need of your practice, which is customers, is at the bottom of the pyramid. Without fulfilling these basic needs of your customers, the needs listed directly above it (staff) will not be met. To reach a higher level in the hierarchy, managers need to continue to improve their skills to reach the highest level, which is self-actualization. When self-

Figure 0–1. Maslow's hierarchy of needs.

actualization is finally reached, you are likely to have a highly profitable practice that is known throughout your community for providing a consistently high-quality service experience for each patient. Additionally, reaching the highest level of the hierarchy provides a level of contentment, allowing you to take time away from your practice without losing sleep. Let's review each level of the hierarchy and examine some of the details pertaining to each.

Level 1: The Base of the Pyramid: Customers

As business management pioneer Peter Drucker (2009) so eloquently stated, "The purpose of a business is to create a customer."

In order for any business to have a shot at survival, it needs to create customers, which is primarily a function of marketing. Most businesses view marketing as a funnel in which advertising is used to create awareness and desire that eventually leads to a few people agreeing to purchase your product or service. The marketing funnel is shown in Figure 0–2. For most businesses, the fundamentals of the funnel hold true, but for hearing aid dispensing and the practice of audiology, there are some critical differences. Considering that approximately 60% of hearing aid purchases are to previous buyers of the product, as well as the relatively low volume of the market relative to other products and services, word-of-mouth referrals take on greater importance in our industry.

Consequently, relationship marketing tactics need to be centered on public relations and community outreach programs, in addition to mining your existing database (assuming you are not a startup business) of patients to cull sales opportunities. This issue will be discussed in detail in several of these chapters. Table 0–1 provides you with list of relationship marketing tactics you must incorporate into your marketing plan.

With the rise of social media, it's essential to add Facebook or its equivalent to your marketing plan. Because Facebook users are able to "like" and make comments on your page, it becomes

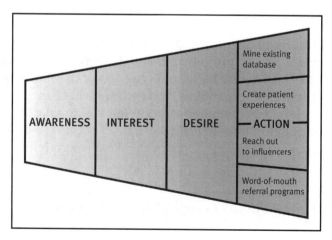

Figure 0–2. The marketing funnel.

Table 0–1. A Checklist of Relationship Marketing Tactics

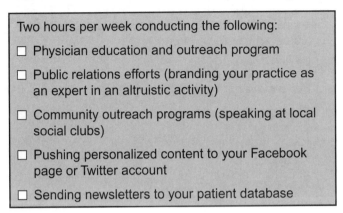

Two hours per week conducting the following:

☐ Physician education and outreach program

☐ Public relations efforts (branding your practice as an expert in an altruistic activity)

☐ Community outreach programs (speaking at local social clubs)

☐ Pushing personalized content to your Facebook page or Twitter account

☐ Sending newsletters to your patient database

a virtual billboard for your practice. Given the importance of word-of-mouth referrals, the viral effects of Facebook make it a word-of-mouth referral engine on steroids. This concept will be covered in considerable detail in Chapter 6.

Many practices take the time to develop and execute a marketing plan, but a considerable number of practices fail to create and execute a sales plan. Although this book is focused on marketing, it would be unwise to ignore the important role "sales" has on the sustainability of any business. Too many audiologists have a "if I build it they will come mentality." The reality is all products need a distribution system—consumers need to be educated, informed, and even inspired to seek out and purchase your offerings. Sales and marketing are the vehicles to do this.

Whereas a marketing plan is designed to "pull" people into your clinic, a sales plan is geared to "push" people into making a purchase once they are in your clinic. A good sales plan institutionalizes how you ferry a patient through your practice once the patient decides to place a phone call or visit your practice. To many audiologists, the word *selling* might seem harsh, but the reality is effective marketing and selling skills are essential for any product or service. Marketing and selling boil down to distributing your offering to a target audience. Yes, even essential techniques like motivational interviewing are part of an effective sales plan. Table 0–2 describes the

Table 0–2. A Checklist of Components of a Sales Plan

Essential elements of a sales plan include documented processes of the following:
☐ Answering the phone
☐ Scheduling appointments
☐ Greeting the patient
☐ Testing and fitting the patient
☐ Asking for the sale
☐ Follow-up and aftercare services

essential elements of a sales plan. An effective marketing plan complements each of the items found on the checklist. For example, if you have a unique aftercare service or a stellar front office assistant who stands out from the crowd, these clinical or "sales" tactics can be baked into your marketing plan and branding strategy. It is simply not enough to have the service: You have to make sure your target audience knows that it exists and give them a compelling, emotionally compelling reason to buy it.

Not Just Customers, but the Right Customers

A common mistake many practices make is "trying to be all things to all people." In other words, many practices blindly attempt to market to all patients, regardless of age, interest, or need, without paying enough attention to the specific type of patients they want to service. One way to avoid this mistake is to ask, "What do I want my practice to be known for?" There are five possible answers to that question: price, technology, convenience, customer service, and memorable experience. When asked, most practices report they want to be known for providing either legendary customer service or a memorable patient experience. Therefore, once you've decided on the vision of your practice, it's imperative to build plans and set goals, which support your vision. Whatever your vision, it must be supported by a structured and actionable marketing plan with measurable key performance indicators. Chapter 3, authored by Dr. Karen Jacobs, will address how your marketing plan interconnects with your strategy and vision.

Level 2: Staff

A well-designed marketing plan is essential, but it simply will not replace great people, who you hire and train to execute your strategy and run your office systems. The second fundamental component in the practice development hierarchy is your ability to hire, train, coach, and mentor your staff. Once you have determined a hiring profile, it is your responsibility to develop your staff. Table 0–3 provides a general overview of how you can develop your staff. Since several MarkeTrak surveys have suggested that the interaction between office staff and the patient is such an integral part of your value proposition, it's imperative

Table 0–3. Essential Elements of Building a Staff

Staff development checklist

- ☐ Clearly define the job
- ☐ Match skills to job requirements using a computer-based career profiling tool
- ☐ Interview effectively
- ☐ Conduct weekly one-on-one meetings to foster an effective relationship with each staff member
- ☐ Talk about performance: provide prompt, constructive feedback
- ☐ Identify areas of improvement and opportunities to improve through coaching and mentoring
- ☐ Delegate responsibilities when possible

that your have a highly motivated and engaging staff. Your job is to create the environment for that to occur.

Level 3: Infrastructure and Work Flow

Once you've built solid programs and plans for customers and staff, the next level in the practice development hierarchy is building a solid office infrastructure and clinic work flow. Office infrastructure is generally thought to be the computers you use to run your back office, billing, and appointment scheduler. Beyond simply having office systems (e.g., computers) available to your staff to use, Level 3 infrastructure relates to how you use these tools every day in your clinic. The two terms best describing office infrastructure and clinic work flow are *efficiency* and *effectiveness*. Efficiency is doing things right; effectiveness is doing the right things. Both are essential components of infrastructure and work flow. Table 0–4 lists several elements of office infrastructure you are required to lead.

Level 4: Manager Vigilance

Let's place your marketing strategy and plan in the larger context of running a business. Regardless of your business plan, there are seven actions all effective managers must engage in with their staff to be profitable and grow. If you look around

Table 0–4. Components of Infrastructure

☐ Billing and coding: back office systems

☐ Clinical protocols

☐ Office work flow

☐ Database management

☐ Accounting and bookkeeping systems

☐ Appointment scheduling

the Internet, there is no shortage of consultants who want to help you improve the culture, profitability, and growth of your business. This book is intended to provide some guidance and insight on how to market your audiology practice. It is up to you, however, to implement this plan within the framework of managing a business.

When you get right down to it, the action required to move a business up the hierarchy needs to come from the manager. The essence of effective management is summarized in Figure 0–3. The key ingredients of vigilant management are focus and action. Without taking some type of action, your business is doomed to fail. And, without the proper focus, your actions will be wasted. Following the steps on the wheel will help you focus and take action. There's really no special or unique talent needed to achieve Level 4. As Peter Drucker (2009) said, "No institution can possibly survive if it needs geniuses or supermen to manage it. It must be organized in such a way as to be able to get along under a leadership composed of average human beings." Effective management of your customers, staff, and infrastructure is actually quite ordinary, dull, and predictable. Vigilant managers

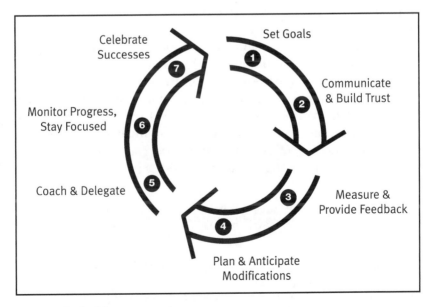

Figure 0–3. Management process.

have the ability to coalesce their staff and complete all tasks on the management wheel. Executing a thoughtful, data-driven marketing plan is no exception.

Level 5: Self-Actualization of Your Business

Without the first four components of the hierarchy, the highest level—self-actualization of your business—will not be achieved. *Self-actualization* is a highly subjective term that ostensibly means you are content with the status and performance of your business. It might mean you could leave for an extended period of time and not worry about the day-to-day operation of your business, it could mean you are ready to sell it to someone, or it might even mean you are proud to be the local provider of choice for hearing care services. Self-actualization means you define success on your own terms and conditions. Without the first four elements of the hierarchy, it is impossible to obtain. Every small business owner and clinician needs guidance and support from time to time in their quest to get to the highest rung on the ladder—self-actualization. This book hopes to emphasize that a comprehensive marketing plan is a foundation to obtaining Level 5 status.

Given the myriad challenges associated with generating office traffic to an audiology practice—factors such as stigma, inconvenience, and costs—it is imperative that you build a sustainable brand identity, create a dynamic marketing plan based on sound data you have collected about the marketplace, and have the discipline to implement the plan, measure results, and modify your course of action as the needs of your target audience undoubtedly change. Happy reading!

REFERENCES

Drucker, P. (2009). *The essential Drucker (Collins business essentials).* New York, NY: HarperCollins.

Ries, A., & Trout, J. (2009). *The 22 immutable laws of marketing.* New York, NY: HarperCollins.

CONTRIBUTORS

Curtis J. Alcock
Founder
Audira, an online think tank for hearing
Exeter, United Kingdom
Chapter 2

Geoffrey Cooling, MISHAA
Co-Founder
Audiology Engine
Dublin, Ireland
Chapter 4

Karen Ann Jacobs, AuD
Owner-Operator
AVA Hearing Center
Grand Rapids, Michigan
Chapter 3

Donald W. Nielsen, PhD
Fellow, Knowles Hearing Center
Independent Consultant
Former Director, Audiology Clinic and Translational
    Research
Northwestern University
Former Professor and Chair, Speech and Hearing
    Department
Washington University
Dublin, Ohio
Chapter 7

Brian Taylor, AuD
Director of Practice Development and Clinical Affairs
Unitron
Editor-in-chief, *Audiology Practices*
Academy of Doctors of Audiology
http://www.audiologist.org
Minneapolis, Minnesota
Chapters 1, 5, and 6

Robert Tysoe, DIP
Business Administration and Marketing
Richardsons Business College, Sydney, Australia
Founder and Marketing Consultant
Hearing Healthcare Marketing Co.
Portland, Oregon
Chapter 5

1

DEVELOPING A STRATEGY AND BRAND FOR YOUR PRACTICE: PILLAR-OF-COMMUNITY MARKETING

Brian Taylor

Something is happening in our practices, and although we cannot be certain what it is, it probably has something to do with customers having an abundance of information at their fingertips, more choices, and access to improved technology—all a direct result of a global economy. In every industry, power is shifting from sellers to buyers. The business of audiology is no different. For our profession, the "seller" is the clinical audiologist providing expert services and guidance, mainly centered on the hearing aid, while the "buyer" is the patient who has unprecedented access to information and an abundance of choices. The purpose of Chapter 1 is to provide audiologists, hearing instruments specialists, and others associated with these professions practical guidance on the development of a strategy and brand in this era of economic change and uncertainty. The pertinent question is the following: How will our value to the marketplace evolve in the context of these larger forces, such as globalization and digital innovation? In today's era of economic uncertainty, there is an abundance of challenges facing many hearing aid dispensing practices, including trying to understand the wants and needs of their potential buyers and how they approach the buying process. By the end of this chapter, you should have a better idea of the importance of pillar-of-community marketing and how to put it into action.

Every business, practice, and medical center has a brand. Brand is the name, design, symbol, or any other feature that identifies and differentiates one business's product or service from those of another business. In a profession such as audiology, brand is probably best described as your reputation and status among the patients within your community. One of the things that sets a local brand, like an audiology practice, from, let's say, Coca-Cola is reach. Coca-Cola is a product that can be purchased anywhere—and the target audience for a sweet, fizzy beverage is far greater than that of hearing care services. On the other hand, even though audiologists dispense medical devices that can be obtained virtually anywhere on the planet, the delivery of a service experience that accompanies the hearing aids has the potential to be totally unique to the audiologist delivering it. Through the lens of the service delivery experience provided to patients, your brand is you!

Since your brand is you, let's take a look at the current status of the industry and how its evolution may be affecting your brand. For various reasons, the industry has been plagued with an inability to convert qualified leads into loyal patients. First, there is the relatively small number of people in need of the services of an audiologist. Consider that about 10% of adults have enough hearing loss to warrant the use of amplification. Also, consider that many of these hearing-impaired adults with acquired hearing loss already own hearing aids, especially those with moderate to severe hearing loss. Among the nonowners of amplification, some will be in denial for the proverbial 7 to 10 years, whereas others in this group refuse to try hearing aids because of stigma or because they simply cannot afford them. Recently published benchmarking studies suggest that the typical practice often attracts less than 100 motivated hearing-impaired individuals over a 3- to 4-month window of time. Additionally, the typical practice may have only fitted 100 patients with hearing aids over the course of the entire year.

Consider that once a motivated hearing-impaired prospect inquires about your product and services, many practices are faced with a litany of potential landmines that can diminish the overall productivity of their business, not to mention the final outcome of the fitting. Among these landmines are the following:

- An inability to schedule appointments for prospects inquiring about services
- An inability to convert qualified prospects into hearing aid users (Taylor, 2009)
- A combined hearing aid in-the-drawer, return for credit, and low daily use rate of 30% (Kochkin, 2009)
- Lower than expected benefit from hearing aids for patients who experience a minimalist clinical protocol (Kochkin et al., 2010)

If those statistics aren't enough to rankle you, also consider that over the past 5 to 10 years, two gradual societal transformations have occurred. These slow-moving societal transformations have occurred largely beyond the purview of the audiology community. It is only recently that both have begun to have a growing presence within our own industry.

The first transformation is related to the increasing availability of low-cost digital technology. In the hearing care sector, this is evident in the growing number of over-the-counter personal sound amplification products (PSAPs). Although PSAPs have been available for quite some time, it is relatively recently that they have become available through third-party insurance providers and big-box electronic outlets. The second societal transformation is the rise of big-box retail and their disruptive business model, which maximizes operational efficiency and offers consumers goods at extremely low prices. Many segments of the "mom-and-pop shop" economy have been unable to directly compete on price with big-box retail, and it is a relatively recent occurrence that audiology practices have been faced with these new market players. Both directly and indirectly, these innovations—PSAPs and big-box retail—present hurdles that have a direct impact on your brand reputation, which we discuss later in this chapter.

THE AGE OF DISRUPTIVE INNOVATION

We associate disruptive innovation with technology, such as PSAPs. PSAPs, along with the rise of big-box retail represent a growing trend in disruptive innovation that has challenged virtually every industry at one time or another since the Industrial Revolution. Recently, however, the combination of low-cost electronics and the Internet has enabled disruptive innovations to challenge many elective medical procedure markets, including hearing care and audiology.

According to Christensen (2003), there are two types of disruptive innovations. Low-end disruptions target customers who do not need or desire to have the full performance valued by customers already using the product or technology. Low-end disruption commonly overtakes a traditional product or technology when the rate of product improvement exceeds the rate at which customers can adapt to new performance features. Low-cost cameras and laptop computers with limited features are two prime examples of low-end disruptive technology.

The second type of disruptive innovation is referred to as a new market disruption. This occurs when the needs of a specific group of customers go underserved for a prolonged period of time. Thus, a new and often less expensive technology can capture untapped sectors of the market. One example of a new market disruption is the Sony pocket radio, which introduced a large group of teenagers who could not afford or lacked the space for a tabletop radio to the pleasures of rock and roll in the late 1950s.

Over-the-counter PSAPs and amplifier apps downloaded to a smartphone represent both low-end and new market disruptions. Given the relative low market penetration rates of hearing aid adaptation, 30% "failure rate," and cost barriers associated with hearing aid use for some individuals, audiologists need to understand and potentially find ways to unleash the power of disruptive technology in their practices to grow their business without cannibalizing their existing core patient base. More effective marketing and branding strategies are needed in order for audiologists to find an audience for their services.

A significant part of branding and marketing involves understanding your target audience. Audiologists may begin the process of embracing disruptive innovations through a better understanding of market segmentation and identifying their target audience. Traditionally, market segmentation involves compartmentalizing patients based on age, degree of hearing loss, or income. Once segmented along age, hearing loss, or income, audiologists can devise marketing strategies to reach various segments of the market. To leverage the concept of disruptive innovation, however, audiologists must segment their patients in a different way. By asking, "What jobs do hearing-impaired patients hire me to do?" audiologists can begin to better understand the role disruptive innovations might have in their practice. The answer to this important question often leads to one of a few possible unexpected answers:

- Provide a no-frills product without service support at a very low price point
- Deliver a stand-alone service (unbundled from the product) that has value to the market
- Provide expert advice, outstanding service, and emotional engagement wrapped around a product; in other words, engross the patient in a memorable service experience

Any of these nontraditional answers may lead audiologists to offer products, services, and experiences to an underserved segment of their market. Additionally, these changes to the traditional value proposition of hearing care professionals, which revolved around the sale of hearing aids, is forcing many in the profession to rethink how they market. The good news is that audiologists and other hearing care professionals have an opportunity to differentiate their offerings by providing unique and emotionally engaging experiences. This process starts with understanding a little something about building a brand.

BRANDING 101

Branding is such a powerful concept that we often think about the brand rather than the product itself. Companies such as Marlboro, Nike, Apple, and Campbell's Soup sell products, but their name is likely to evoke a certain feeling in the consumer. This speaks to the emotional power of a brand. The lesson for audiologists is that they must build a brand that seeks to emotionally engage their target audience. If you consider your target market to be middle- to upper-income adults older than age 60 years, your primary brand-building task is creating a reputation that emotionally resonates with this group.

A cornerstone of building your brand is something commonly referred to as "brand elements." Brands typically are made up of various elements, including the following:

- Name: The word or words used to identify a company, product, service, or concept
- Logo: The visual trademark that identifies the brand
- Tagline or catchphrase: "The Quicker Picker Upper" is associated with Bounty paper towels
- Sounds: A unique tune or set of notes can denote a brand. NBC's chimes are a famous example.

Beyond the straightforward elements of a brand, there are emotional components at the foundation of any brand. After all, for a customer's limbic system to be stimulated, there must be an emotional attachment to your brand. At the heart of this emotional response to your brand is trust. Trust in a health care provider has been defined as the patient's confidence that the provider will do what is best for the patient. Trust is thought to be optimized when health care providers are empathic, competent, and caring and have a strong ability to communicate with patients. The lesson from a branding and marketing perspective is that audiologists must strive to evoke feelings of genuine trust in their patients by infusing those traits listed above into day interactions with patients as well as other influencers in the community.

Crash Course: Building an Emotionally Compelling Brand

Get your staff together and over the course of 1 to 2 weeks, and gain an agreement on these questions: What are three words or phrases that best describe our vision of patient care? What would you want patients to say about your practice after spending an hour with you? How can we bring these elements to life in your daily practice so that patients are more likely to spread positive word of mouth about our practice?

Words and phrases such as *comprehensive, patient centered, go the extra mile,* and *honest* all come to mind when answering the first two questions. These words or phrases are your tagline and can be used in all your marketing and other customer-facing communication. The answer to the third question is your brand essence and how it is used in daily interaction with patients. This exercise is powerful when your staff is candid, authentic, and willing to put it into practice. Strive to have a unique set of behaviors that your staff engages in with patients.

YOUR BRAND AND HOW IT HAS CHANGED

The benefits of any product or service are conveyed to potential customers by its brand. Every offering, from toilet paper to luxury cars, has a brand. There is just no escaping a brand. In essence, your brand is what people think of you when the topic of hearing aids enters their mind. As you will learn, it is problematic for independent providers to associate their brand exclusively around the hearing aid itself.

The moment your product or service is branded in a consumer's mind, it begins to exist as something that can be sold, typically at a premium price point. (That is why more expensive items have a well-known brand associated with them and its generic equivalent—if there is one—is sold at a lesser price.) As this section of the chapter describes, several factors in the modern world make it extremely difficult to maintain the mystique associated with a premium brand. Let's take a look at how branding has evolved with respect to the hearing care industry.

To see just how much branding has changed in the past decade, it helps to see how the hearing care industry has changed. By most accounts, 2004 doesn't seem like a long time ago. The Internet, laptop computers, and even the smartphone were around then. Ironically, due to the rapid convergence of these technologies, we are now experiencing some monumental changes in how we acquire customers. To appreciate these changes, let's revisit the year 2004 and take a look first at the hearing care value chain. The hearing aid value chain is the process by which hearing aids are manufactured, distributed, and resold to the end user. This process is shown schematically in Figure 1–1. Manufacturers produced devices who sold them to clinical providers. These providers in turn added an essential service component and resold the devices to customers. The important point is that the end customers, the hearing-impaired patients, do not have any direct contact with the manufacturer of the device. The customers, even if they wanted to know, had no way to learn about the inner workings of the device supplier.

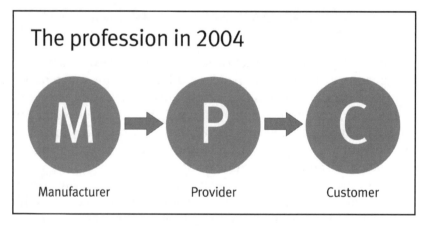

Figure 1–1. The hearing aid value chain in 2004.

Over the course of about 10 years, manufacturers have unveiled the curtain. Stated differently, the inner workings of the manufacturing and distribution process are no longer shrouded in mystery: Customers have direct access to how the hearing aid value chain is created. This idea is shown in Figure 1–2. Today, through interactive websites and consumer advocacy reviews on social media, consumers have insight into the interworkings of the manufacturing process. Customers today have the ability to learn about the various hearing aid models and components used, and they can comparison shop using websites that the hearing aid device manufacturers have created. Additionally, customers can explore alternative technology options, such as over-the-counter PSAPs by going direct to the PSAP manufacturer's website. This abundance of product information from multiple sources changes the way in which independent providers need

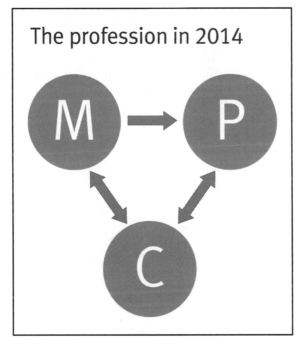

Figure 1–2. Today's more interconnected hearing aid value chain.

to brand their practice. Instead of focusing on the hearing aid as the driver of your brand, providers must now make their service and other unique offerings the center of their brand.

In the past, before consumers had access to so much information prior to making a buying decision, it was relatively easy to build a well-known brand through advertising. Branding was simply a part of your overall communications strategy. All you had to do was create a logo, image, and brand "personality" and you were able to gain traction with consumers in your market. This is shown in Figure 1–3. Prior to the information age, which arguably began around 2004, companies could methodically build their reputations and enjoy the spoils of this status for many years without the risk of a few saboteurs who may have had a negative experience, causing much harm to their brand. Today, because we live in a hyperconnected world, a few saboteurs—those few individuals who may have had a negative experience or interaction with your business are much more likely to cause irrevocable harm.

Due to the convergence of Wi-Fi, social media, websites, blogs, and smartphones, customers have the ability to do a lot more shopping around before making a purchasing decision. For this reason, it is much more difficult to build a stable brand. Today, building a reputation requires a fundamental shift in the

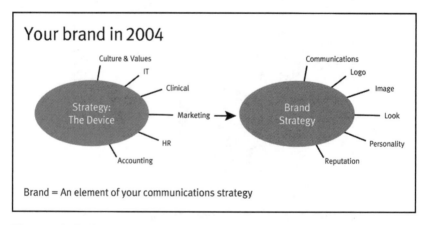

Figure 1–3. The traditional definition of a brand simply relied on solid marketing efforts centered on hearing aid technology.

way the process "branding" is perceived by a business. Rather than simply thinking of branding as a function of your marketing efforts, branding is really a fundamental part of your overall business strategy. In other words, as Figure 1–4 shows, your brand needs to be infused into all aspects of your organization, including information technology, human resources, and accounting. Furthermore, due to the commoditization of hearing aid technology, your brand needs to center on your service excellence and professionalism.

Since hearing aids technology is becoming a commodity, audiologists can no longer remain complacent. They must adapt their thinking and reconnect with the marketplace using their professionalism and service delivery expertise as center of their brand. This requires a change in the status quo: Audiologists must not only provide a higher level of emotionally engaging service but also must communicate this higher level of service to the marketplace. Before getting into the details of what a higher level of patient engagement looks like, let's review some of the basic aspects of branding.

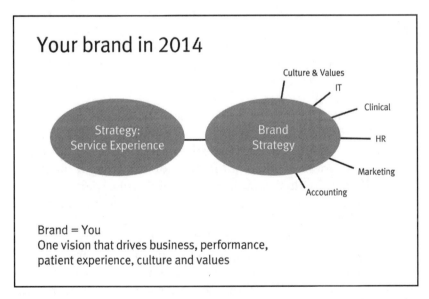

Figure 1–4. The broader definition of a brand involves all part of a business, not simply the marketing department.

THREE MAIN TASKS OF A BRAND

All businesses have a brand associated with them. Today, however, that brand and the image it conveys to customers can vacillate quickly. Gone are the days when you used advertising to build a consistent brand image that was unlikely to change. Now, your brand image is likely to change swiftly based on the rapid spread of the opinions of other people. Let's look at how brand image changes and how it affects the customer acquisition process.

Before comparing and contrasting the customer acquisition process over the past decade, however, let's review the role of branding for any business. In simple terms, there are three main tasks of branding: generate interest in your offering, build a preference for that offering, and encourage purchase of that offering. Historically, successful businesses have managed to do these three tasks by building the mystique of their brand. In other words, by having a recognizable brand, businesses were able to acquire new customers. Until recently, no matter what type of business you were in, the process of acquiring customers was in direct alignment with the perception customers had of your brand. For example, if your brand signified quality and excellent service, you were likely to attract customers who desired those traits and were willing to pay more for them. These days, companies no longer enjoy the rewards of a well-known, recognizable brand.

Now let's think back to 2004 and how customers were acquired. A person's decision to buy is affected by a mix of three related sources, which are shown in Figure 1–5. First are the prior experiences (PEs) of the individual with your business. That is, if an individual customer had a pleasant experience with a business, he or she is more likely to be a repeat purchaser. Second, marketing information (MI) is the advertising (print, TV, radio) that is used to generate interest, build preference, and encourage purchase. Finally, the opinions of other people play a role in whether someone is going to make a purchase. Before the convergence of Wi-Fi, interactive websites, and smartphones, when customers had to rely on traditional advertisements to make purchasing decisions, PEs and MI took on greater importance in the customer acquisition process. Because people did

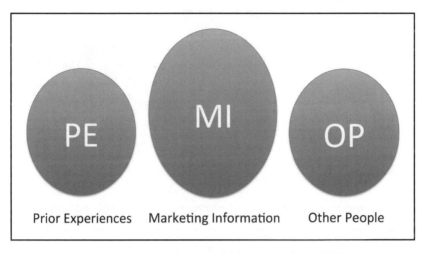

Figure 1–5. Three ways customers were acquired in 2004.

not have the means to learn about the opinions of a lot of other people prior to making a buying decision, it was difficult to change someone's beliefs or attitudes once you had established your brand perception using traditional advertising.

In 2014, just 10 short years, we live in a completely different world. Due mainly to the convergence of Wi-Fi, smartphones, interactive websites, and social media, customers can do a lot of homework, fact checking, comparison shopping, and review of other people's opinions before they even visit your practice. Of course, the three main tasks of marketing— generating interest, building preference, and encouraging purchase—have not gone away. Additionally, the three ways customers are acquired still remain, but as Figure 1–6 suggests, the opinions of other people have been amplified. Today, prior to making a purchasing decision, customers can use their smartphone or tablet PC to connect and evaluate consumer reviews at myriad websites and, after a considerable evaluation process, may finally make an appointment to see you.

For anyone who's been in business for many years, this can be a nightmare because you can never coast on past performance. Even though you may have a well-respected brand, it has become more and more difficult to enjoy the rewards of that brand image, which, as a by-product, is the ability to command higher prices.

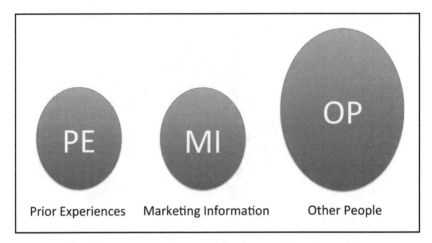

Figure 1–6. Three ways customers were acquired in 2014.

THE O-CONTINUUM

Just how important are the opinions of other people when you are making a buying decision? It depends on the product you are interested in buying. The critical question for independent hearing care providers is, to what extent do your customers depend on the opinions of other people when making a purchasing decision? To help answer that question, Simonsen and Rosen (2014) created the O-continuum. Notice in Figure 1–7 that there is an O-dependent and O-independent domain. If a business operates in the O-dependent domain, this means most of the customers are strongly influenced by the opinions of other people. Sectors of the economy that are very O-dependent include consumer electronics, nonluxury cars, and nonchain (small and independent) restaurants. O-dependent companies must ensure that they are part of the conversation when customers are interacting with other people.

On the other hand, O-independent companies operate in a completely different space on the continuum. Customers who purchase from an O-independent business typically do not seek the opinions of other people prior to making a purchase. This would include commodity items, such as those bought at a con-

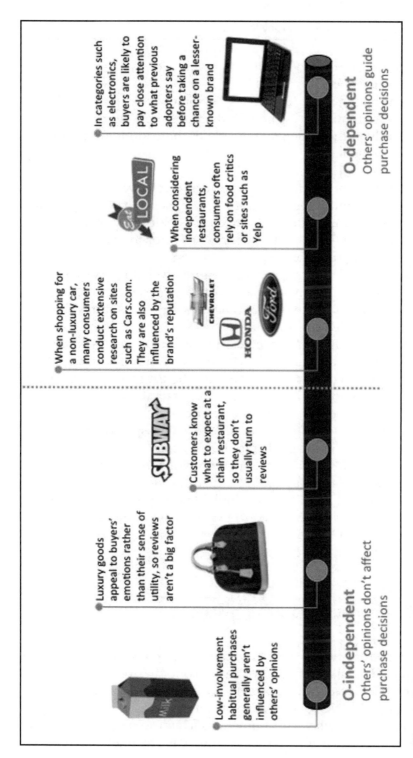

Low-involvement habitual purchases generally aren't influenced by others' opinions

Luxury goods appeal to buyers' emotions rather than their sense of utility, so reviews aren't a big factor

Customers know what to expect at a chain restaurant, so they don't usually turn to reviews

When shopping for a non-luxury car, many consumers conduct extensive research on sites such as Cars.com. They are also influenced by the brand's reputation

When considering independent restaurants, consumers often rely on food critics or sites such as Yelp

In categories such as electronics, buyers are likely to pay close attention to what previous adopters say before taking a chance on a lesser-known brand

O-independent
Others' opinions don't affect purchase decisions

O-dependent
Others' opinions guide purchase decisions

Figure 1-7. How various businesses align on the O-continuum.

15

venience store, and expensive luxury goods, including high-performance cars.

Although most businesses lie somewhere in the middle of the O-continuum, it is thought that most hearing care practices lie firmly in the O-dependent side of the continuum for the following reasons.

- Decision importance. Due to the relatively high price point and overall importance of hearing to long-term health and wellness, individuals seeking our services are inclined to do a lot of homework prior to making a purchasing decision.
- Risk and uncertainty. Again, a relatively high price point combined with stigma and the uncertainty of benefit relative to price (value) puts most practices firmly in the O-dependent camp.
- Rate of change. Since hearing aid technology is continually changing and new features are constantly hitting the market, consumers want to stay abreast of all this change. Thus, they are likely to do a lot of fact finding and studying before they visit your practice.
- Quality and differentiation. When a prospective customer might be in the market for hearing aids, chances are good they will hear a wide range opinions from other people. Because the outcomes of hearing aids are so variable and tend to differ with individual experience, prospective users are inclined to evaluate the opinions of many people via the Internet prior to making a purchasing decision.

O-Continuum Tips and Tricks

The bottom line is that you can never coast on past performance. Because they do not have economies of scale, independent businesses are especially vulnerable to a lack of brand identity. (Think about what you know about a chain business compared to what you know about and expect from a small mom-and-pop shop—you are much more likely to read reviews on Yelp before visiting a local independent restaurant than, say, buying dinner at Applebees.) Here are four specific tactics you can use to ensure you are part of the conversation when a customer is making a decision to visit your practice for services.

1. Rely on pillar-of-community marketing tactics, which we discuss later in this chapter, to build your brand. Given the importance of other people's opinions in the buying process, independents must take the time to ensure three distinct members of their community (existing patients, other small businesses/service clubs, and primary care physicians) have a firm understanding of your business's value proposition. And, they enthusiastically "toot your horn" when asked about better hearing and communication.

2. Make it easy for your customers to comparison shop. Provide a link, preferably to an independent source, where customers can do some comparison shopping from the comforts of home. This comparison shopping should not be confined to devices. Providers are encouraged to have a presence of websites that allow customers to read reviews from others on the quality of service and attention they received. For example, the Hearing Tracker website allows customers the ability to read reviews of specific hearing aid models and services provided.

3. Provide a memorable patient experience that is not centered on the device. When the device is the center of attention, it is easy for consumers to compare. However, when your core focus becomes offering aural rehabilitation and other services that lead to patient behavior changes, you have successfully moved away from the device as the center of the transaction. The likely effect of this strategy is to move you away from the far side of the O-continuum where you are vulnerable to comparison shopping.

4. Decouple fee for services from the products you dispense. Make it easier for patients to comparison shop by associating a specific price for services that may be different or unique to your practice. Take the time to devise high-value service packages unique to your practice. The convergence of social media, Wi-Fi, smartphones, and the

like require independents to rethink their marketing strategy and brand identity. It's no longer about running consistent advertising in your local newspaper. Independent practices would be wise to see where they fall on the O-continuum and build a brand using pillar-of-community marketing tactics.

"Business has only two functions—marketing and innovation."
—Peter Drucker (2000)

MARKETING 101

The primary—and many would argue the only—reason marketing exists is to create demand for your product or service. Even the coolest, most cutting-edge gadget needs to be distributed to the marketplace, and the mechanism for doing this is usually through a creative and consistent marketing campaign. Given the low market penetration rate of hearing aids and the relatively low number of individuals in the market for traditional hearing care services, it is not surprising that the most well-attended seminars at any state or national professional meeting are those that address marketing strategies. Everyone seems to be looking for a magic bullet.

Let's take a look at some of the more general aspects of marketing. Marketing is a business function that identifies consumer needs, determines target markets, and applies products and services to serve these markets. It also involves promoting such products and services within the marketplace. Marketing is integral to the success of a business, large or small, with its primary focus on quality, consumer value, and customer satisfaction.

A strategy commonly used in all commercial businesses evaluates a company's "marketing mix." The marketing mix comprises four variables known as the "four Ps" of marketing. The marketing mix blends these variables together to produce the results it wants to achieve in its specific target market. The following describes the four Ps of marketing:

■ Product. Products are the goods and services that your business provides for sale to your target market. When developing a product, you should consider quality, design, features, packaging, customer service, and any subsequent after-sales service. For hearing care, the product is not only hearing aids and other devices but also services that are delivered.

■ Place. Place refers to the distribution, location, and methods of getting the product to the customer. This includes the location of your business, shop front, distributors, logistics, and the potential use of the Internet to sell products directly to consumers.

■ Price. Price concerns the amount of money that customers must pay to purchase your products. There are a number of considerations in relation to price, including price setting, discounting, credit, and cash purchases, as well as credit collection.

■ Promotion. Promotion refers to the act of communicating the benefits and value of your product to consumers. It then involves persuading general consumers to become customers of your business using methods such as advertising, direct marketing, personal selling, and sales promotion.

The question really is, how do you deploy these 4 Ps? That's where understanding the desires and needs of the customer comes into play. Let's review an important marketing concept called the cycle of need. When you talk with professional marketers and consultants, you are likely to learn that six important things have to happen before a customer will decide to do business with you. This cycle of need is an easy way to think about how your business creates demand for its offerings within your marketplace. As Figure 1–8 shows, there are six stages to the cycle of need, and the job of marketing is to create a demand for your offerings.

Let's examine each of the six steps more carefully in general terms. One, make customers aware of your service and product offerings. Traditionally, we have used printed advertising in newspapers or the Yellow Pages, television ads, and radio spots to make people aware that our business exists. As you will learn in this chapter, there are other methods at your disposal that will make your target audience more likely to be aware of your existence.

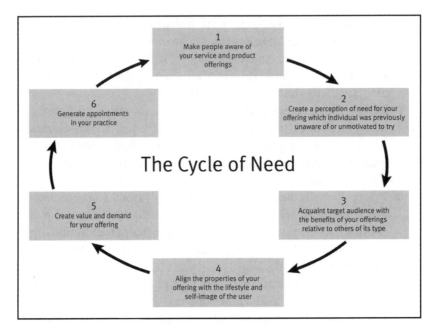

Figure 1–8. The marketing cycle of need.

Two, your business must create a demand or need for your offering that customers were previously unaware they needed or were unmotivated to try. In many industries, expensive marketing campaigns are used to create interest and demand for new products that people had no idea existed. For hearing care professionals, creating demand is more likely to focus on motivating people to get their hearing screened (see Chapter 2). Three, acquaint your target market of the benefits of your offerings relative to others of its type. Effective marketing and branding strategies are able to clearly differentiate your goods or services from the competitors. Effective marketing slogans and jingles not only help differentiate your offerings but have the potential to stick in your head like a Taylor Swift earworm.

Four, align the benefits of your offerings with the lifestyle, budget, and self-image of the customer. This means that your marketing effects are geared toward reaching a specific segment of your customer base. Five, create value in your offerings by using a call to action. This call to action can be price driven, but as you will learn in this chapter, call to actions that have an emotional appeal can be more effective. Finally, six is the act of the patient making an appointment to see you. Note that the cycle of need concept starts again when the patient is face-to-face with you in the clinic when you are advising the patient on his or her treatment options. Regardless of the exact tactics your employee with respect to marketing, the cycle of need is helpful when trying to understand how to create demand for your offerings. It's also helpful to get inside the head of potential customers to try and better understand their wants, needs, and desires.

THE NEW CONSUMER IN THE AGE OF UNCERTAINTY

The cycle of need is a generic way of looking at customer behavior, but it doesn't adequately describe how audiologists can create demand for products and services with the needs of individuals older than 60 years, which is our primary target audience. Additionally, we know that over the past decade, the American economy has undergone upheaval on a seismic scale, unlike any time since the Great Depression. There is evidence suggesting that the current economic uncertainty is the new normal and that it has begun to systematically change the buying habits and priorities of many consumers (Benett & O'Reilly, 2010). These authors present evidence gathered from more than 7,000 consumers that consumer buying habits are undergoing a shift away from gratuitous consumption to more mindful spending, which can have a significant effect on how you market. This paradigm shift in consumer behavior, which certainly could have an effect on how individuals approach the hearing aid market, can be broken down into the following four distinct ways that the "new consumer" is approaching the market.

- Embracing substance. A growing number of consumers are disenchanted with the buying transaction. They are looking for a reason to connect with a product or service. The "new consumers" are craving real, authentic experiences and they are willing to hang on to their cash until they feel a sense of engagement with a product, service, or business.

- **Rightsizing.** Many consumers feel paralyzed with the sheer number of choices for any given product. They are seeking a move toward simplification in which a trusted family member, friend, or other influencer is able to help them make an intelligent decision.
- **Growing up.** Nearly everyone has been personally touched by unemployment from the recent economic malaise or family upheaval resulting from a decade of low-intensity war in the Middle East. The result is a movement beyond immediate gratification and a trend toward establishing a sense of community with others, including businesses.
- **Seeking pleasure with a purpose.** Impulse shopping is losing its sense of appeal with the new consumer. People are still willing to spend money, but the trend is toward a more conscientious form of consumption in which shoppers do their homework and seek to connect and establish a long-term relationship with businesses that have the same set of values they possess.

THE AUDIOLOGIST'S ROLE IN THE EMERGING EXPERIENCE-BASED ECONOMY

Most audiologists would agree that the way patients interact with your practice has undergone a remarkable transition over the past 3 to 5 years. Gone are the days when you could post an occasional promotional offer in your local newspaper and generate immediate sales.

The key to overcoming the uncertainty of disruptive technology and alternative distribution models is through differentiation of your practice and brand. One way to stand out is to make the patient's interaction with your practice so memorable and enjoyable that individuals flock to your door seeking a transformative, life-changing event delivered by you. By enhancing the patient's interaction with your practice at six critical areas of interaction (Figure 1–9), you can begin to unlock the secrets of a truly transformative experience for your patient, while commanding a higher average selling price and generating more word-of-mouth referrals.

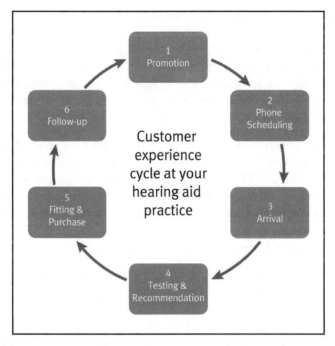

Figure 1–9. The six stages of the patient experience journey.

Marketing in the experience-based economy requires a full immersion into your local community. Let's consider the waning effectiveness of traditional marketing tactics, such as newspaper ads and direct mail. Once a staple of many practices, we can no longer rely on a consistent pull of new prospects from these traditional marketing mediums. Given these demographic and socioeconomic constraints, hearing aid dispensing practices and audiology clinics must redefine their marketing plans.

There are five distinct pillars of community marketing tactics that every practice can execute on a monthly basis. These five tactics are called the CORUS of pillar-of-community marketing. Although the core fundamentals of an effective marketing plan are unchanged (e.g., knowledge of the 4 Ps for your area, tracking return on investment, a specific allocation of resources devoted to marketing, etc.), the pillar of efforts requires a CORUS of new and emerging services.

Here is a summary of these CORUS services:

C—Captivating website. It's no longer enough to simply have a website. Your practice's website must have patient testimonial videos, downloadable educational content, and other interactive material that captivates the attention of your prospects and current patients.

O—Online reputation manager. Your website also must link current patients to your website to generate more word-of-mouth referrals. This can be done through an online reputation service, which collects patient testimonials and posts them on your website for prospects to view. You can think of an online reputation manager as an electronic version of the pencil-and-paper patient comment card.

R—Relationship and medical marketing programs. Building essential referral networks with physicians and other influencers is no longer a luxury. Physician marketing programs have been available for decades, but many of them fail because the audiologist doesn't methodically execute the program over a long period of time. Today, building relationships for physicians and other influencers requires that audiologists have a good understanding of comorbidity and disease state marketing. We cover this topic in Chapter 5.

U—Upstanding member of your community through public relations. Like relationship marketing efforts, public relations require the audiologist to have a presence in the community. Taking a few hours each month to conduct community outreach centered on the installation and use of loop systems, hearing screenings for nursing homes, or another type of service related to hearing loss is a great way to brand your practice as a pillar of your community.

S—Social media. Data suggest that more and more people older than age 70 years are using Facebook and other forms of social media to stay in touch with family and friends. Every week we hear reports from clinics that are capturing more business due to their presence on Facebook. Social media are an electronic billboard that allows you to reach an expansive number of current patients and prospects. The key to successful use of social media is your ability to seed your Facebook and Twitter feeds with fresh and informative content, and we cover this area in more detail in Chapter 6.

Crash Course: Your Clinical Skills Is Your Marketing

Advertising is just a small part of marketing. Your ability to deliver a professional, comprehensive, and memorable patient experience is part of your marketing and branding strategy. To market and distinguish products, your business culture and values are more important than ever. Marketing aesthetics are the practices, strategies, and technologies that are applied to make products more attractive. By adding storytelling, entertainment, values, culture, and arts, the products are designed to facilitate the consumer's social relationships, feelings, and identities. Joe Pine and Joseph Gilmore (2011) pioneered this concept in their book, *The Experience Economy*.

Let's continue our journey by examining the recipient of our services: the adult hearing-impaired patient. Acquired hearing loss of adult onset is the third most chronic medical condition in the United States, afflicting more than 30 million Americans, and its debilitating condition is best described as a "triple threat" for the following reasons.

- Clinically significant hearing impairment is itself a disability with several debilitating consequences. This is an indication for effective remediation in its own right.
- Hearing loss interferes with a patient's ability to be treated for other medical conditions because it hinders an individual's ability to engage with the family doctor and understand treatment advice and recommendations.
- Emerging research suggests that hearing loss may actually accelerate some disabilities such as cognitive dysfunction and vestibular impairment. The prevalence, comorbidity, and disabling effects of hearing loss underscore the

need for aggressive preventive programs that identify conditions such as hearing loss, which threaten health outcomes.

Perhaps the best way to describe the ill effects of hearing loss is that it is a hidden handicap causing its sufferers long-term emotional pain and social isolation. Although many individuals with hearing loss are described as indifferent to the negative consequences of their conditions, for those seeking remediation, quality-of-life improvements are often the result. Since an individual's reaction to hearing loss is so personal and wonderfully diverse, it is only logical for patients to seek the help of a thoughtful, caring, and nurturing professional who provides services in a comfortable environment.

To the reluctant and sometimes ambivalent hearing-impaired person, there eventually comes a time when help for his or her handicapping condition can no longer be placed on the backburner. Like any consumer shopping for the best deal, however, hearing-impaired individuals too often find the low prices of the big-box retailer alluring. Given their relentless push to drive out costs and eliminate inefficiencies, big-box retailers may be poorly equipped to meet the varied and highly personal needs of individuals with hearing loss.

DEVELOPING A MARKETING AND BRANDING STRATEGY

Big-box retailers are formidable opponents for the independent practitioner. Their high in-store foot traffic, economies of scale, and buying power allow them to excel operationally. This has proven to be a highly successful business model that has a place within the hearing care marketplace. The operational advantages of the big-box retailer, however, may also be their Achilles heel, as it is nearly impossible to deliver an extraordinary level of personalized care and service in the relentless pursuit of low-price leadership. It is the ability of the independent hearing care professional to make deep and lasting connections with patients who have long-term effects of hearing loss that differentiates an independent practice. Experts agree that there are always a substantial number of consumers in any market desiring highly personalized service, and an independent practice—one that truly understands the delicate needs of the individual with hearing loss—is the best equipped to deliver it.

As Figure 1–10 shows, businesses can create customer value and a competitive advantage along three distinct dimensions: product leadership (the best product), operational excellence (the best total cost and efficiency), or customer intimacy (the most personalized care). Research has shown that market leaders make a deliberate choice to be the best at just one of these three dimensions, while offering an acceptable level of competence along the other two dimensions. The most successful businesses make a conscious decision, after carefully assessing their marketplace, to offer unprecedented and unique value along one of these three dimensions. Regardless of your chosen discipline, customer satisfaction, word-of-mouth referrals, and profits are the by-product of the execution of this strategy. Marketing is at the heart of bringing a customer intimacy strategy to life.

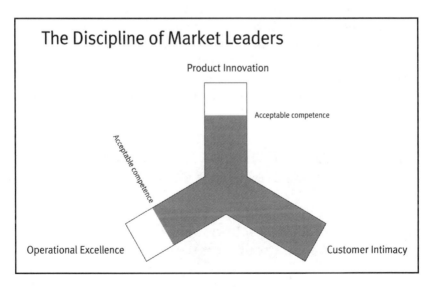

Figure 1–10. The three disciplines of market leaders.

CLINICAL ACTIVITY IS YOUR MESSAGE

"Advertising is the greatest art form of the 20th century."

"Anyone who tries to make a distinction between advertising and entertainment doesn't know much about either."

—Marshall McLuhan, Canadian philosopher of communication theory (1911–1980)

As the next section of this chapter describes, much of your brand image and marketing efforts originate from the work you do in the clinic. The challenge is to find ways, through public relations and grassroots efforts, to become known in your community for something that is valuable, unique, and different. Word-of-mouth advertising is an incredibly powerful way to attract consumers, and when you have a high-quality clinical operation that relies on established best practice and individualized care, it needs to be an integral part of your message. Indeed, the medium is the message.

Given the changing business climate, it is imperative for the independent practice to put customer intimacy at the center of its value proposition. A by-product of this strategy will be higher patient satisfaction, increased word-of-mouth referrals, and more annual revenue. To implement a customer intimacy value proposition, practices must provide a more compelling patient experience that stands out from the din of ordinary. A systematic review of several businesses—many of them outside the hearing care marketplace—reveal the following key drivers of customer intimacy.

DRIVERS OF A CUSTOMER INTIMACY MARKETING STRATEGY

Deep, Personal Connections With Patients, Community, and Influencers

Largely due to their smaller size and experienced staff, independent practices have the potential to obtain "pillar-of-community" status. *Pillar of community* simply means that other businesses and medical professionals in your area personally know about you, your practice, and the quality of care delivered. Furthermore, establishing deep, personal connections with patients means you are using techniques like solution-based interviewing to identify the unique needs of patients. Rather than building your brand around the delivery of hearing aids, practices that have achieved pillar-of-community status are known for their high level of professional engagement with patients, key influencers such as physicians, and the general community. Let's look a little more carefully at those three distinct groups.

Regardless of the size of your market, there are likely to be several other independent businesses. A pillar-of-community mind-set allows you to reach out and establish a network with all small, independent community businesses, from the local flower shop to the local barber. All independent businesses have more than a few things in common. Unlike big-box retailers, independent businesses are involved in all aspects of service delivery, from the negotiation of price with their vendors to interaction with customers to washing the floors. This level of involvement is a natural path to developing a support system with other like-minded independents. This support system is often an avenue for receiving word-of-mouth referrals because independents are naturally inclined to support their fellow independents.

One important core group of community members are primary care physicians (PCPs). Given the rise of accountable care organizations, PCPs are playing a more active role in orchestrating the care of patients. This is especially true of patients who are more likely to need the services of a hearing care professional, those who are elderly, or those with comorbid, chronic medical conditions. Independent hearing care providers have the ability to foster deep, long-lasting relationships with PCPs, and this advantage will only become more pronounced as health care policy continues to rapidly evolve.

Every business enterprise must make conscious decisions about its competitive advantage, quality of its service, and price. Big-box retailers tend to pursue a competitive advantage through scaling and buying power. In their pursuit of scale, quality of service is achieved through standardization, while buying power is used to optimize their profits. Independent practices, on the other hand, must operate differently. The natural advantage of the independent practices is their holistic approach to running their business, and the heart of a holistic approach is the ability to form deep, long-lasting relationships with your community.

For the customer intimacy leader, it is never enough to simply identify your core audience in which to create pillar-of-community status. Action must be taken. The actions, such as "lunch & learns," community seminars, and health fairs, are examples of some of the essential actions independent practices must take to achieve pillar-of-community standing. If independent practices wish to differentiate their businesses from big-box retailers, it is imperative that they do things differently. It is no longer enough to simply be an expert at dispensing hearing aids. Although that is certainly a critical task, independent practices are urged to step away from their audiometer and get into the community to work directly with the three core constituents listed above.

Crash Course: Public Relations

Public relations (PR) refers to the portion of the marketing mix that addresses and manages a company's audiences or markets directly. PR practitioners ("publicists") create, shape, and maintain relationships between business owners and their publics through strategic communications. PR firms are able to get a client's message to its intended audiences using the communication platform best suited for that particular message. This is accomplished using media, advertising, grassroots, social media, online marketing, or other tools that help tell that company's story to its targeted audiences.

Every business, no matter how big, has a story to tell, and every business contributes to its community in its own way. Small practices can partner with other businesses that complement their services (e.g., vision and audiology clinics) or organizations and associations that align with the practices' missions (e.g., American Tinnitus Association). Together, they can cross-promote and work together to contribute to their communities. Additionally, a business leader being involved and doing good in one's community sets a precedent for other businesses and puts this business leader in a positive light among his or her publics. Telling the community story through media coverage, social media, and other communication tools helps others associate good corporate citizenship with these practices' brands.

Develop and Brand Your Service Delivery Protocol

By staging the patient experience along six "touch points" (see Figure 1–9), clinicians who lead on customer intimacy are able to blend evidence-based practice guidelines with memorable signature moments, thus creating a stronger emotional bond between your practice and your patients. A significant part of using a comprehensive clinical protocol includes providing patients with customizable service offerings, such as a customized at-home demonstration of amplification devices (e.g., Unitron's Flex:trial). Let's take a look at this key driver in a little more detail.

In the typical town or city in the United States, there are several locations in which a patient can obtain hearing aids. If you are older than age 65 years, it is likely you are inundated with advertising touting the newest, most advanced amplification technology. For the unassuming consumer with hearing loss, choosing a location that will provide the best results is often left to chance. When you put yourself in the shoes of this consumer, it's not too difficult to see that all hearing aid technology looks pretty much the same. This uniformity of the hearing aid technology from the consumer's point of view is a by-product of the digital era in which we live. As consumers, we have come to expect that digital electronics will become incrementally smarter, faster, and cheaper. And from the consumer's point of view, hearing aid technology is no different.

Market leaders have recognized these circumstances for at least a decade and have made strides to differentiate their business by providing more comprehensive service. The problem, however, is that the average service provider too often relies on a fairly basic service delivery process. In short, many practices talk a good game when it comes to providing comprehensive service, but they fail to deliver on things that truly matter to many patients. According to industry survey data, most hearing aid dispensing practices do not routinely use objective measures of hearing aid benefit, speech-in-noise testing, or verification of a prescriptive fit with probe microphone measures. Furthermore, the typical practice is designed to look like any run-of-the-mill medical office, undistinguishable from the ordinary locations in which hearing aids have been dispensed for the past 50 years.

Due to the increasing competitive pressures from big-box retail chains, independent practices must rethink how they deliver services, if they expect to differentiate their offerings to the market. Gone are the days when a practitioner could simply hang a shingle, advertise digital technology, and conduct routine service delivery. Quite simply, that value proposition is as outdated as a 1994 grunge rock performance and really no different from what is offered by a big-box retail chain.

When properly executed, the selection and fitting of hearing instruments is often time-consuming and complex for the service provider but an engaging and memorable series of personal interactions for the patient. By intertwining a theme and using memorabilia and signature moments into a standardized, evidence-based process, each patient can be not only successfully helped but also emotionally touched in a profound way. The consistent use of a comprehensive service delivery process is a key driver of the customer intimacy value proposition strategy. Customer intimacy leaders in a range of health care industries have made the conscious decision to design and create truly memorable patient experiences, while simultaneously relying on evidence-based practice principles that allow patients to make informed decisions about their hearing care. Here are three best practices that are opportunities to brand your practice around the service experience, rather than the delivery of a product.

1. Develop a theme. A theme is nothing more than an organizing principle that guides behavior of you and your staff. It influences every element of the patient experience across six staging areas. An effective theme is one that is easily identified by a wide range of patients. Using the senses of sound,

sight, and touch, you can bring your theme to life. Since it is incumbent upon every practice to create its own theme, work with your entire staff to identify it. Some common themes used in medically oriented practices include, movie musicals, televisions shows from the 1950s, and old movies. Since we are in the business of improving hearing, you may want to be find a theme that has a lot of opportunities to use sound. As you may have gathered, theming is much more than redecorating your waiting room. An effective theme is interwoven throughout the patient journey along six distinct staging areas.

2. Stage memorable experiences along six staging areas. From a patient's perspective, there are six critical components to his or her interaction with a practice. They are shown in Figure 1–2. Each one of these so-called staging areas (also called "touch points") is an opportunity to contribute to a transcendent patient experience. Customer intimacy leaders are able to successfully orchestrate a memorable patient experience along these six staging areas with the use of memorabilia and signature moments. Signature moments are really nothing more than your ability to take a routine clinical procedure and, through the judicious use of memorabilia and effective communication skills, turn them into occasions that patients are more likely to talk about after leaving your office.

3. Blend evidence-based practice with personalized service. Customer intimacy leaders know that they must go the extra mile if they are to be better and different from their big-box retail chain competitors. Another underpinning of tireless, personalized service is the use of evidence-based principles that guide the patient-provider interaction. Kochkin et al. (2010) indicated that providers using a comprehensive clinical protocol, including the use of verification, validation, and speech-in-noise testing, are much more likely to create highly satisfied patients on a more consistent basis. Another recent study conducted by Ross and Stika (2011) indicated that 77% of patients were "definitely satisfied" or "satisfied" with the service received from their hearing care professional. However, this same study showed several significant gaps in the service delivery process. For example, less than

10% of patients reported that they were asked to complete a self-report of hearing aid outcome or to participate in group counseling and orientation meetings, two procedures that have been associated with higher levels of patient satisfaction. Clearly, there is an opportunity to differentiate based on personalized service delivery.

Based on the reports cited above, a comprehensive clinical protocol includes the following:

- QuickSIN to measure unaided signal-to-noise ratio (SNR) loss
- Use of solution-based interviewing questions
- Needs assessment using TELEGRAM or the Client-Oriented Scale of Improvement (COSI)
- Use of a patient journal to document outcomes over first 2 weeks of use
- Verification of match of prescriptive target using a probe microphone
- Validation of relative benefit 30 days postfitting
- Provision of aural rehabilitation and auditory training sessions in either an individual or group format

We have all come to expect that digital processing power will incrementally improve. This is truly a godsend for our hearing-impaired patients who rely on us to provide them with the most innovative technology at a fair price. The problem, however, is that all service providers have better and faster technology compared with just a few years ago—and this paradigm is not going to change anytime soon. The antidote to faster, smarter, and cheaper digital processing power is personalized service, and the only proven way to orchestrate it is to create and execute a comprehensive service delivery process based on these cornerstones.

- Personalized service
- Warm, friendly, and inviting environment
- Engaging and knowledgeable staff
- A brand centered on you—not the device

If a famous television reporter were to interview every patient you see tomorrow and ask them, "Tell me what it was like during your appointment today?" How would you want your patients to describe their experience? This chapter provides you with a basic template for orchestrating your answer to that all-important question.

Longer Than Average "Face Time" With Practice's Gatekeeper

Unlike the soul-crushing atmosphere typically found in a big-box retail location or a corporate medical practice where the provider is apt to "churn and burn" through patients, independent practices often have the luxury of spending more quality "face time" with patients. When an independent practice builds a brand that centers on the clinician and the support staff, rather than the device, patients are likely to seek you out for the personal attention and the support you provide—and this segment of the marketplace is willing to pay more for it!

Many individuals who receive medical care would agree that quality face-to-face time with the service provider is fast becoming a lost art. In a frantic rush to see as many patients as possible, medical professionals often forget that their ability to engage in an unhurried dialogue with patients is one of the cornerstones of an outstanding service delivery process. Leaders in customer intimacy know that spending a few extra minutes with each patient is more likely to result in a successful outcome and more word-of-mouth referrals. After all, no one cares how much you know until they know how much you care. And, it is the responsibility of your entire customer-facing team to enhance their "face time" with patients. This chapter is designed to get you thinking about all the whys and hows surrounding spending more quality time with patients, which is one of the five key drivers of customer intimacy. With some preparation and planning, you can put these tips into action in your own practice.

Both research and real-world experience suggest hearing aid dispensing practices that enhance their interactions with patients in three key areas are more likely to have higher levels of patient satisfaction and greater profitability. By taking the time to rethink the workflow of your practice and coach your customer-facing employees, including front office profession-als (FOPs), you will be on your way to becoming a customer intimacy leader in your marketplace. The best practices listed below are designed to help you differentiate your practice with personalized customer service.

Warm and Friendly Phone Rapport

These days, it seems like just about everyone complains about the quality of service they receive over the telephone. If you are lucky to actually talk to a live voice, the service representative is likely to be residing in a location that is several time zones away and not well versed on your own personal situation. Answering the phone effectively is a skill that can differentiate your practice. Like everything, personalized telephone service requires plan-ning, training, and managerial oversight. Since booking appoint-ments over the phone is probably the most pivotal role of the FOP, below is an outline of the process for handling phone calls.

The protocol for scheduling an appointment has been bro-ken down into five basic steps, which will cultivate a more inti-mate relationship with your patients. These steps not only are designed to increase the number of appointments that you book but also are critical to providing highly personalized customer service:

1. Greeting: sounding pleasant and upbeat when you answer the phone or personally greet a patient upon arrival in your office
2. Assessing the patient's wants and needs: the ability to dis-cover the needs of the patient without sounding pushy or aggressive
3. Advising: the ability to answer questions succinctly using nontechnical language
4. Gaining agreement: the ability to schedule an appointment in a seamless manner
5. Thanking: the act of telling someone you appreciate his or her considerations and time

The Personalized In-Person Greeting

One way to enhance your face time with patients is to adapt workflow so that FOPs spend a bit more time personally greeting patients when they arrive in your office. In an audiology practice, you often work directly with individuals who are nervous and apprehensive about their inability to hear. Of course, this is a natural by-product of hearing loss of adult onset. An important role of the FOP is to recognize some of the normal behaviors of an adult with gradual hearing loss, such as denial, avoidance, and even hostility, and have some communication strategies to put patients at ease about their appointment.

Taking the time to fine-tune the details of how the FOP should greet a patient upon arrival is critical to any office culture that wants to be a market leader in customer intimacy. When patients arrive in your office, they should be greeted as if they are well-respected Hollywood actors or members of the British royal family. In addition to proper eye contact, the FOP needs to stand up and acknowledge the patient at the check-in desk. Smiling and shaking their hand are other components of a warm greeting.

The final stages of the in-person greeting should comprise providing a warm verbal greeting, asking the patient to provide any information such as insurance card, and guiding the patient to a seat in the reception area. It also helps to advise the patients of activities they can do in the reception area and about how long they may have to wait to see the audiologist. Of course, when patients have been waiting for more than about 15 minutes, the FOP needs to personally check with the patient to see if anything is needed. In short, patients need to be greeted in your practice like you would greet a good friend you have not seen in a long time.

Lavish Amounts of Personalized Counseling

In an era of automation and artificial intelligence, there is still no substation for face-to-face human interaction. Perhaps the most competitive advantage of independent practitioners is their ability to personalize their counseling approach to meet the individual needs of the patient. Individualized counseling is typically spread over several face-to-face visits with the patient.

The relationship between quality "face time" and higher patient satisfaction is well known. MarkeTrak data suggest that clinicians spend an average of approximately 2.5 hours of collective time with each patient. This "face time" is spread over the course of three to four appointments and comprises the initial hearing evaluation/consultation, the hearing aid fitting, and one or two follow-up appointments during the 30-day evaluation period. In general terms, customer intimacy leaders would be best served to design their office so that they can spend time with patients in the following increments.

- Initial evaluation/consultation: 60 to 90 minutes
- Hearing aid fitting: 60 minutes
- Routine follow-up: 30 minutes each

Optimizing "face time" is not simply about spending more time with patients. As MarkeTrak data suggest, practices that spend too much time with patients run the risk of having below-average patient satisfaction ratings, probably because patients lose faith in your ability to solve their problem.

Like artisan farmers and craftsmen, customer intimacy leaders recognize that the "right" amount of quality time spent face-to-face with each patient will vary depending on his or her specific needs. A by-product of optimizing the quality of the face-to-face interaction is higher overall patient satisfaction and a greater number of word-of-mouth referrals. Compared with big-box retail operations that have been designed to use a cookie-cutter approach to optimize efficiency, customer intimacy leaders recognize that their true value rests with a keen ability to take the time to gain deeper understanding of the needs of each patient.

The Importance of Culture and Standards

Mastering the necessary skills required to be a market leader in the dimension of customer intimacy requires effort and commitment. Your ability to shift away from a transactional-based workflow, similar to how big-box retailers operate, to one that takes a more artisan approach involves creating an office culture committed to bringing the three best practices listed above to life. Office cultures that foster a genuine curiosity for each patient are more apt to become customer intimacy experts. Best practices surrounding the creation of a culture committed to service excellence involves the behaviors listed below. The primary role of the manager or owner is to instill these behaviors in your staff.

- Reliability—timeliness/consistency/accuracy
- Assurance—respect/credibility/confidentiality
- Knowledge—effectively answer questions about hearing aid technology and service offerings
- Empathy—transparency/clear communication/personalized service
- Responsiveness—prompt attention/flexibility/swift complaint handling

A big part of creating a culture dedicated to spending quality "face time" with patients requires independent practices to establish their own customer service standards and infuse them into their culture. Here is an example of customer service standards that customer intimacy leaders have put into practice.

- Answer the phone on or before the third ring with a consistent greeting.
- Provide each patient with a nurturing and comfortable environment.
- Personally greet each patient with a smile and handshake.
- Use solution-based interviewing techniques to gain a deep understanding of the patient's personal situation and motivations.
- Use visual aids, handouts, and your website to support your personalized approach by providing the patient with captivating educational content.
- Hiring and training should align with the behavioral style of the manager.

Another hallmark of companies that lead on the dimension of customer intimacy is the use of data to make better hiring and training decisions. Because customer intimacy leaders want to free up valuable time to spend with more patients, they must be more efficient in their hiring and training. Therefore, many of these companies use computer-based performance tools to create staff profiles, thus allowing them to work smarter, not harder, on staff development and performance gaps.

Crash Course: Word-of-Mouth Advertising

Word-of-mouth referrals have always been and probably always will be a great source of new business for audiology practices. Here are a couple of ideas from Robbie Poole of Obelis Media that might help you become a more effective word-of-mouth advertiser:

A friends-and-family rewards program is one way to encourage your patients to refer their friends and family to you. Rewarding your customers is a great way to say thank you and to make them feel appreciated for the effort they took to send a potential patient your way.

Another easy way to gain some traction with word-of-mouth advertising is to spend a few minutes each week writing handwritten thank you and birthday cards.

Use of a Value-Based Pricing Strategy

None of the drivers listed above are likely to be embraced by customers unless a value-based pricing strategy is employed. A value-based pricing strategy allows you to create service packages that place less emphasis on the commoditized device and more on the practices of professionalism and service. These services packages can become part of your marketing message. Once the independent practice has optimized its cost of goods and determined its monthly "profitability point," a value-based pricing strategy is your signal to the marketplace that your practice is different from the ordinary commodity offerings of the big-box store.

Historically, the hearing care industry has relied on margin-based pricing to determine what customers will pay. A margin-based strategy implies that the office manager negotiates the cost of goods for each device purchased from a manufacturer and then carefully calibrates the retail price that will allow the practice to cover expenses and make a marginal profit. This is a perfectly fine strategy for establishing your prices, but it may not be the best for unlocking the true value of professional services provided to patients. Now that independent providers are feeling the squeeze from big-box retailers and their incredible operational efficiency, it is time to reconsider this traditional way of pricing, which is no longer very effective. Service-based (also called value-based) pricing is an alternative to margin-based pricing. This chapter introduces readers to the concept of service-based pricing and how it can be used to signal to your market that your service offerings are unique and incomparable to those of a big-box retailer.

The key to understanding service-based pricing is thinking like a customer. Characteristics such as convenience, performance, and, above all, service determine how much customers are willing to pay for something. The more we value a certain attribute (and the harder it is to find reasonable next-best alternatives), the more we are willing to pay for it. If you pride yourself on offering premium levels of personalized service and attention, then you need to develop a pricing structure that reflects it. A service-based pricing strategy is your antidote to the buying power of large retail chains.

The key to shifting from a margin-based to a service-based pricing strategy centers on your ability to create itemized bundles of services that accurately reflect your unique value proposition. If you have made the conscious decision to lead on the dimension of customer intimacy, then these itemized bundles need to signal to the market that your practice offers unsurpassed "high-touch" service and professionalism, in addition to innovation products. Here are the five essentials of implementing a service-based pricing strategy.

1. Determine your competitive advantage. In relation to your direct competitors, identify the things you do better or differently and cannot be easily duplicated by others in your market. Customer intimacy leaders typically hold a decisive competitive advantage around the quality of "face time"

spent with patients and the overall professionalism of their comprehensive service delivery process. An independent practice's competitive advantage oftentimes can be very unique, so take some time to identify it.

2. Optimize your cost-of-goods (COGs) and fee-for-service rates. With the help of your accountant or "numbers person," strive to optimize the dollar value you pay manufacturers for product. Unlike big-box stores and retail chains, independent practices lack economies of scale, and that's okay. You may still have some real opportunities to lower your cost of goods by committing more business to fewer manufacturers and negotiating better prices with them. In addition to a thorough analysis of COGs, identify your breakeven point. Finally, strive to simplify by tiering all products you dispense into three or four price points.

3. Create a list of value-added features. Most practices stop at point 2 above, and that is fine if you are using a margin-based strategy. However, you may be missing some real opportunities to add patient value and increase your margins. By creating a list of all the additional items patients might be willing to pay more for or need, you are taking a critical step in creating service packages that reflect your competitive advantage in your marketplace. Here is an example of such a list.

- Remote control
- Companion microphone
- Wireless accessories
- Dry & Store Global II unit
- Additional warranty
- Comprehensive aural rehab services
- Additional batteries
- Unlimited service visits

4. Determine your minimum service bundle offering. Sometimes known as your "line in the sand," this is the first big step toward establishing service-based price bundles. Rather than making the device the center of your pricing strategy, this step allows you to place service and professionalism at the center of the patient-provider interaction. Importantly,

this is your opportunity to ensure that your service bundles reflect your competitive advantage. You can complete this step by asking yourself, "What is the minimum level of service and technology that I am willing to offer patients in my marketplace?" Of course, your answer to this question is unique to the mission and vision of your independent practice. An example of one practice's minimum service bundle looks like this.

- Diagnostic evaluation (unbundled and billed to insurance, if applicable)
- Pair of devices (entry-level technology)
- One year of follow-up office visits
- Group hearing aid orientation classes
- One-year warranty/Loss & Damage Insurance (L&D)

Notice that the service components (office time and group orientation classes) are bundled with a pair of devices. The basic idea here is that you are packaging items that you know to be effective for the typical patient—that is, "face time" with you, an aural rehab support group, and a bilateral fitting of an entry-level product.

5. Create three to four service bundles. Once you have created your "value" service bundle at a relatively low price point, the next step is to scale up to an additional two or three service bundles. The main idea here is to add more technology, additional service, and other perks that patients may want or need. See Table 1–1 for an example of three service bundles from one practice. Independent practices are encouraged to be on the constant lookout for novel and exciting items they can add to the premium service bundle. Notice that there are just three bundles, and as the price increases, both the product and the service become more sophisticated. Another important part to devising service packages is creating catchy names for them. An eye-popping or descriptive name can be used in your branding and marketing message.

Economists like to say that prices are signals to the market wrapped in an incentive to buy. By creating service packages, you are likely to keep the choices for patients

Table 1–1. Service Bundles

Level 1: Economy Service Package	Level 2: Mid-Level Service Package	Level 3: Premium Service Package
2 hearing aids— entry-level technology	2 devices—mid-level technology	2 devices— premium-level technology
1-year warranty	2-year warranty and supply of batteries	3-year warranty and supply of batteries
1-year comprehensive care plan	2-year comprehensive care plan—unlimited office visits	3-year comprehensive care plan—unlimited office visits
	1 wireless accessory	2 wireless accessories
	Dry and store unit	Dry and store unit
$	$$	$$$

at a manageable level while itemizing specific elements of your professional service. Through creative marketing of a service package, you are more likely to provide the much-needed incentive to buy. Customer intimacy leaders in all businesses recognize the urgent need to use price as a signal to the market that your offer is remarkable and distinct from your competitors. In our industry, this can be done by creating itemized bundles that wrap professionalism and service around innovative products.

To differentiate your audiology practice, you can tailor these five drivers of customer intimacy into the culture of the business and employ them as part of your marketing strategy. Granted, there are many complexities associated with bringing all of these components to life in a busy practice, but to compete in this new age, it is essential—you cannot stand pat and expect to survive. No two practices are alike, and it is a long, tough journey, but at the heart of the customer intimacy leader is the ability to move forward by doing the following:

- Define your vision. What do you want your practice to look like in 2 to 3 years? How will your practice be different from a big-box retailer?
- Create alignment with staff and business partners. What essential role does everyone in your practice play and are they aligned with your vision? What business partners are needed to foster a deeper relationship with patients?
- Execution. What do you need to do every day to set your practice apart? How do you build a brand that centers on professionalism and service quality, rather than technology?

As Peter Drucker (2000) said, "One or two priorities is effective management, more than two is a circus." To help you identify your priorities as a customer intimacy leader, complete this assessment. Place a checkmark in the box for each statement below if it is true of your practice. Add up the number of checked boxes. If the number is less than six, you need to work on your customer intimacy and pillar-of-community status.

- ☐ I have a written marketing plan that includes community-based outreach programs (e.g., local public relations).
- ☐ At least 10 other local businesses in my area know me by name or face.
- ☐ I receive at least five referrals per month from PCPs.
- ☐ My practice has a theme that is uniquely recognizable to many in my community.
- ☐ I routinely* conduct a comprehensive communication needs assessment using solution-based questions and standardized tools, such as the COSI or TELEGRAM.
- ☐ I routinely* verify prescriptive targets with real ear measures (REM) and validate using a standardized self-report on each patient fitted with hearing aids.
- ☐ Patients often don't comply, but I offer two or more types of aural rehabilitation or auditory training programs in my practice.

☐ I use a computer-based tool to identify learning and behavioral styles for hiring and training purposes.

Routinely is defined as 80% or more of new patients.

> "All established businesses are standing on ground that is crumbling beneath their feet."
> —Joseph Schumpeter, Harvard Economist and Nobel Laureate, 1883–1950

Faster, smarter, cheaper technology and the ability to instantaneously communicate with anyone around the world have indeed changed the way in which any company builds its brand. Rather than throwing in the towel, audiologists are encouraged to stake their future on building a brand focused on service delivery, not product dispensing. Audiologists must adapt to these changing times so that their profession does not disintegrate like those of the copper and blacksmith. To avoid the fate of those professions, audiologists must center their actions on unique services that differentiate them in the marketplace. Branding and marketing are the vehicles that communicate this reality to the marketplace.

This chapter provided an introduction to pillar-of-community marketing and how a brand can be built around you, the professional. In today's era of economic uncertainty, pillar-of-community status and a brand centered on your professionalism are the cornerstone of a sustainable practice. The foundation of a brand built around you involves providing patients with an emotionally compelling service experience, dispensing innovative products, delivering personal service, and being known as a technological leader. In essence, a blend of emotional engagement with customers using scientific principles in the clinical decision-making process is likely to put you on the path to obtaining the elusive status of pillar of community.

Pillar-of-community status, which is summarized in Figure 1–11, is likely to draw the attention of influencers in your geographic location, as well as get the attention of your competitors as well as patients in the market for your services. Each of the proceeding chapters addresses a different aspect of marketing in an audiology practice.

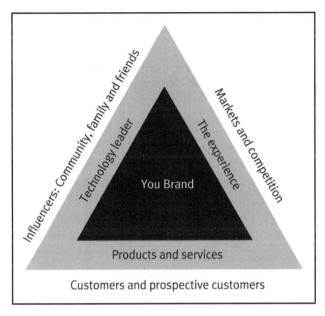

Figure 1–11. Brand: you.

REFERENCES

Bennett, A., & O'Reilly, A. (2010). *Consumed: Rethinking business in the era of mindful spending*. New York, NY: Palgrave MacMillan.

Christensen, C. (2003). *The innovators dilemma*. New York, NY: Harper's Business.

Drucker, P. (2000). *The effective executive: The definitive guide to getting the right things done*. New York, NY: HarperCollins.

Kochkin, S. (2009). MarkeTrak VIII: 25-year trends in the hearing health market. *The Hearing Review*, *16*(11), 12–31.

Kochkin, S., Beck, D. L., Christensen, L. A., Compton-Conley, C., Kricos, P. B., Fligor, B. J., . . . Turner, R. G. (2010). MarkeTrak VIII: The impact of the hearing healthcare professional on hearing aid user success. *The Hearing Review*, *17*(4), 12–34.

Pine, J., & Gilmore, J. (2011). *The experience economy*. Cambridge, MA: HBS Press.

Ross, M., & Stika, C. (2011). *Hearing aid services and satisfaction: The consumer viewpoint*. Retrieved January 3, 2015, from http://www.hearingresearch.org/ross/hearing_aid_use/hearing_aid_services_and_satisfaction_the_consumer_viewpoint.php

Simonson, I., & Rosen, E. (2014). *Absolute value: What really influences customers in the age of (nearly) perfect information*. New York, NY: Harper Business.

Taylor, B. (2009). Survey of current business practices reveals opportunities for improvement. *The Hearing Journal, 62*(9), 25–31.

2

USING MARKETING TO SHAPE PEOPLE'S ATTITUDES TO HEARING CARE

Curtis J. Alcock

Marketing is ultimately an exercise in shaping people's attitudes. Get it wrong, and at best people ignore us; at worst, they seek to avoid what we have to offer. Get it right, and people will follow whatever action we are recommending to them. So understanding how attitudes work and how we shape them is integral to developing effective marketing strategies for hearing health care. This chapter provides guidance and insight on how consumer attitudes form their buying decisions and how hearing care professionals can shape these attitudes in a positive manner.

ATTITUDES: OUR GUIDEBOOK TO LIFE

Attitudes are like having mental guidebooks for everything we encounter in life. They tell us what to pay special attention to, what to avoid or approach, where to spend our resources, and how to behave. We don't have attitudes for everything, mainly just those things that are relevant or important to us. The more positive our attitude is toward something, the more likely we are to approach it. The more negative our attitude, the more likely we'll be to avoid it. Attitudes enable us to make rapid decisions that keep us from harm's way and gravitate toward those things that are in our best interests. If we're not really sure about something, or it doesn't really matter one way or another, our attitude will be neutral.

We are not born with our attitudes; we form them over the course of our lives using information we pick up along the way —so the things that we see, hear, do, and feel all play a crucial role in how our individual attitudes are shaped. Marketing is therefore about making sure our audience has access to the right kind of information—through the things that they see, hear, do, and feel—so they are more likely to form a positive attitude toward what we have to say.

We can think of an individual's attitude as a lump of clay. When the attitude is neutral, it's like wet clay: very impressionable, easily shaped, and inclined to take on the form of its immediate environment (e.g., peer groups). But once an attitude has been "firmed up," it becomes like fired clay, tending to retain its shape despite its surroundings and capable of rebuffing even the most vigorous of attacks on its integrity. So in marketing terms, it's far easier to influence someone who has a neutral attitude than someone who's already made up their mind—providing we can make our message relevant enough for them to pay attention to it.

One interesting aspect of attitudes is that they are often formulated "on the fly" in response to the demands of a situation. Imagine you were asked your opinion on something you've given very little thought toward up until that point—what do you do? You can either plead ignorance, or you can ask yourself whether you have enough information available to provide a suitable answer.

If you choose to answer the question, you'll likely use a combination of strategies as you formulate your answer. You'll check your memories to see what you know, giving precedence to the information that springs most easily to mind. You'll consider what other people may have said about the subject, giving special attention to people you respect or who seem to know a lot more about the subject than you do. You'll weigh up the pros and the cons by contrasting them with related topics. You may ask yourself how you feel about the subject ("follow your heart"), whether it makes you feel good or bad. You'll examine your actions past and present to see if they offer any guidance as what your attitude toward it might be.

This process of attitude formation can make us open or vulnerable to persuasion techniques, and research into attitudes has shown that even the manner in which people are asked about their attitude can alter what they report their attitude to be.

For example, if we were to ask people, "Do you normally recycle?" and then in a separate study ask them about their attitude toward the environment, they are more likely to report having a more positive attitude if they answered yes to the first. But ask them, "Have you ever dropped litter?" and they will later report having a more negative attitude toward the environment. Even the order in which multiple-choice answers are provided can change the outcome of what someone reports his or her attitude to be.

This gives us an insight into just how flexible attitudes can be and why context is so important when shaping people's attitudes toward hearing care, whether it's through our marketing or in our counseling. Imagine two different adverts. The first introduces a new hearing system as a tool to ease conversation in background noise. The second presents the same hearing system but as a new treatment for hearing impairment. Notice how our attitude toward the technology changes? In the first, it is seen as a tool to overcome a difficult situation that "everyone knows" can be a challenge. In the second, it is something that separates "hearing-impaired" people from "everyone else."

If we happened to notice someone using the hearing system, what judgements would we make about them based on the advert we had seen? Which one would we feel more comfortable responding to? Notice how the first advert has relevance to a wider audience?

RELEVANCY IS KEY

The more relevant or important something is to us, the more effort we'll put into formulating our attitude toward it. Imagine you were being asked about plans to build a new road. If the road was being built in another part of the country, then chances are the subject is not particularly relevant or important to you because it doesn't directly affect you. You are less likely to make the effort to research the pros and cons of building the road, because the benefit of such an effort wouldn't outweigh the cost of the effort involved. Your "opinion" may simply be a recitation of something you'd heard on the news. But if that road was to be built through your own backyard, then it does directly affect you. It's going to be in your best interests to make every effort to gather as much information as you can before you give your response.

Psychologists call this "low involvement" when a subject is of less relevance or importance to us and "high involvement" when it is more relevant or important. The greater our involvement, the greater the effort we'll put into it formulating our attitude. So whether or not our audience considers hearing care to be personally relevant to them will directly influence how they form their attitude, which in turn will determine their response to our marketing.

We can think of attitude formation like preparing a meal. If we don't feel like putting an effort into it, we may simply pick up a "ready-made" meal or visit a fast-food outlet; everything's already done for us. On the other hand, if the meal is for a special occasion—or we're trying to impress someone—we may choose to put additional effort into preparing something special. Rather than picking up something "off the shelf," we prepare everything directly from the raw ingredients.

This is what happens when we formulate our attitudes. So if hearing care is not particularly important to us as a consumer, we'll pick up a "ready-made" attitude where all the work has been done for us already. We don't have to think too deeply about the issues; we simply follow popular opinion or look for something that makes us feel good. Examples of "ready-made" attitudes are shown in Table 2–1.

Table 2–1. Examples of Ready Made Attitudes

Ready-Made Attitude	Negative Hearing Care Example	Positive Hearing Care Example
Follow expert opinion	"My doctor says my hearing's OK."	"Audiologists say everyone should have their hearing checked regularly."
Following the crowd	"Most people don't get their hearing checked unless they're deaf. Neither will I."	"Most people have their eyes and teeth checked regularly; surely it's the same for hearing."
Follow your peers	"People my age don't usually get their hearing checked."	"Anyone who wants to be at their best will get their hearing checked regularly."
Follow your feelings	"Seeing pictures of old age makes me feel uncomfortable. Hearing technology is probably bad for me."	"Seeing successful, attractive people makes me happy. That means hearing technology is probably good for me."
Follow the stereotype	"People who are older, deafer, and more desperate than me use hearing technology."	"People who love their hearing use hearing technology."
Follow the memorable	"That advert jokes about people who mishear. I don't want to be an object of ridicule. I'll avoid."	"If you ask to repeat, check your hearing's complete."

Ready-made attitudes tap into powerful mental shortcuts known as "heuristics" that every human being is vulnerable to. By contrast, the more relevant hearing care is to us as consumers, the more prepared we'll be to put the effort in to ensure we "make the right decision." We'll do our research, we'll gather information, and we'll construct an attitude from scratch based on our thoughts, feelings, and actions.

There's an important principle at work here: The better the quality of the raw ingredients, the better the meal. If people are using ingredients that are well past their "best before" date, we'd expect the meal to repulse them. It's the same with attitudes: If people are formulating their attitude toward hearing technology using information that is out of date or based on ideas they find repulsive, the resulting attitude is going to put them off. Marketing offers a powerful means to provide the public with correct, up-to-date information.

If someone comes to us with a negative attitude toward hearing technology, we can safely assume it's because they are using information or ideas that are either repulsive or out of date. For example, see Table 2–2.

Hearing health care marketing must therefore implement a two-pronged strategy. First, we must provide the general public with our own, specially prepared ready-made attitudes that promote appropriate behavior toward their hearing without inadvertently repulsing them. Second, we must ensure that the "raw ingredients" we provide people with for their thoughts, feelings, and actions are not based on outdated information or repulsive ideas.

IGNORE, AVOID, APPROACH?

Earlier, we saw how attitudes can be neutral, positive, or negative. A positive attitude will promote an approach response, a negative attitude will encourage avoidance, and a neutral attitude will generally result in "doing nothing."

Table 2–2. Attitudes Toward Hearing Technology

Information or Idea	Attitude Type
Hearing aids are for old people	Ready made: "Follow the stereotype."
Hearing aids whistle all the time	Raw ingredient: "Memory of my mother's hearing aid."

This ignore-avoid-approach behavior is intrinsic to every living thing. At its most primitive level, it's about survival. Attitudes are essentially a way of tapping into this natural drive we all have. The better we understand how this drive works, the better equipped we'll be to shape our audience's attitudes through our marketing.

How do people know what to avoid and what to approach? Through a combination of nature and nurture, biology and learning. Humans, like every living organism, are biologically wired to approach things that are in their best interest and to avoid things likely to be harmful. Some of these things we recognize instinctively: We see the bared teeth, the ears thrust forward, the hackles raised, and we know the dog means business. Its body language acts as a signal to us that we immediately pick up on. But see that same dog as a puppy, and even a small child will instinctively want to reach out to touch it: The rounder face, the proportionately larger eyes, and the way it tilts its head to one side all invite us to approach. In both cases, we're recognizing the signals the dog is sending us.

Think too how we instinctively recognize the signals given off by our own kind. A crawling infant will watch its mother's face to see whether it's safe to move in one direction or another. If she smiles, the infant will mirror the smile, which in turn will make the infant feel "safe" in proceeding. If she frowns, the baby will hesitate and avoid that direction.

As we make our way through life, we gain experience in learning what the people important to us or our wider social group wants us to avoid or approach. Sometimes this is implied, with our behavior "rewarded" by their attention and acceptance or "punished" by their ignorance or rejection. At other times, the wishes of the group are clearly stated in the form of rules or expectations. We recognize these signals and respond accordingly, knowing that it is normally in our best interests to maintain the acceptance of the wider group; there's strength in numbers, and excluding ourselves puts us at risk.

Sometimes there are no signals for us to pick up on, or the signals we receive are misleading. Think of the person who smiles to our face but betrays us behind our back. Here we must learn from experience what to approach and what to avoid. But whether we have signals to pick up on, or it is a response

Table 2–3. Avoid or Approach?

Avoid . . .	Approach . . .
Loss, or the expectation of loss	Gain, or the expectation of gain
Isolation from our social groups	Acceptance by our social groups
Threats to self, both physical and self-image	Self-consistency

learned through experience, our drive to avoid or approach always follows the same set of underlying rules, as in Table 2–3.

We examine these rules in more detail shortly, especially as they relate to hearing care, but for now we can summarize them as follows: We avoid the things that weaken us, and we approach the things that empower us.

We're constantly looking for signals from the things we encounter in life to tell us which category they fall into: Do they weaken us or empower us? Should we approach or avoid? Marketing is about sending the right signals to our audience to evoke the response we intend them to have: If we want them to approach something, we must demonstrate that it empowers them. If we want them to avoid something, we must show that it weakens them.

AVOIDING LOSS, APPROACHING GAIN

As human beings, we do everything we can to avoid losing what we already have. What we currently possess is our norm; it's safe, an extension of ourselves, and a baseline against which we measure subsequent experiences. Our aversion to loss is so strong that we'll even avoid the *risk* of loss or the *perception* of loss. It's the reason we take out insurance, why we check we've locked our doors at night, why there's a public outcry if privileges are taken away, and why we're attracted to time-limited special offers.

We get attached to the things we currently possess—or perceive ourselves to possess—and these form a status quo for us in our minds that we seek to maintain. Imagine you have a concert ticket to a band or sports game you wish to see. You've been looking forward to going for many months; you may even have stood for several hours or more in a queue just to get them.

A few days before the concert, you learn that someone else, who was standing in the same queue as you, had been unsuccessful in getting a ticket because they had sold out by the time that person reached the ticket desk. You both know how much the tickets are really worth, and you both really want them. The other person offers to buy yours: What would you be willing to sell it for? The same as what you paid for it? More? If so, how much more?

Experiments such as this one consistently demonstrate that people who own something, even if they haven't paid for it themselves, become reluctant to let go of what they already have. When monetary value is placed on it, it becomes clear that people value what they already have disproportionately higher than something they would *like* to have. But sometimes the true value to us only becomes evident when there is a very real threat we might lose it.

LOSS OF HEALTH

This desire to avoid loss plays a central role in how people deal with their health. If we are offered a screening test to see if we have a condition, we will avoid or approach that test depending on whether we see the potential outcome as a threat to what we already have.

Remember that the purpose of a screening test is to detect something we wouldn't otherwise know about. So we compare the possibility that we have the condition to our current status quo.

If we are happy with our current status quo ("I am in good health"), we will naturally be reticent about discovering we have a condition that upsets that status quo, because it means losing what we believe ourselves to have ("I have lost my status of good health"). Our reticence will be exaggerated if we were to learn we had a condition that we must simply "live with." How much better if we'd been blissfully unaware! Our reticence will be exaggerated further still if we have to change our lives as a result of knowing we have the condition, especially if those changes affect other people's perception of us.

As an example, consider people taking a test that told them they had a contagious disease for which there was no cure and that nothing could be done about it. They would be "sentenced to" live in isolation and announce their presence to others by means of ringing a bell, as those with leprosy did in times past. If you believed yourself to be in good health, would you take such a test if it was offered to you? Even if it was a free test? Or would you continue to assume everything was normal, unless something indicated to you otherwise that caused you to question your good health? Taking such a test *increases* our risk of loss, so we're inclined to avoid it.

Let's take the same example, but let's change one thing. This time we learn that early detection of this condition greatly increases the likelihood of curing it. Curing it would mean that you wouldn't have to live in isolation, and you wouldn't be stigmatized by a ringing bell. Now your decision to have the test would *reduce* your risk of losing what you already have, so we'd be inclined to approach it.

If you learned that the condition was at its *most* curable in the earlier stages, when it was most difficult for you to notice it yourself, you would be even more comfortable with taking the test sooner because any delay in doing so would increase your risk of loss. In our earlier example, the absence of any noticeable symptoms was a deciding factor in *not* taking the test; now that same absence of noticeable symptoms is an indication that the condition is still curable, if indeed you have it. So *taking* the test, when there are symptoms to notice, now becomes far less risky than *not* taking the test—because the longer you leave it, the more you increase your risk of "noticing something"—and the more you notice it, the less curable it becomes.

Health psychology tells us that people's desire to adopt a health behavior such as having a screening test is dependent on three main factors:

Factor 1: How serious the condition is if left undetected and untreated

Factor 2: How high the likelihood is that a person has the condition

Factor 3: How curable the condition is if detected

So a fatal condition accompanied by suffering that affects the majority of the population, but can be cured completely if detected early enough, will have the strongest motivating influence on someone taking a screening test—because the risk from "doing nothing" is extremely high. Whereas a rare but nonfatal condition, causing minimal disruption to daily life and that cannot be cured even if detected, will have a weak influence on motivating someone to take a screening test. The risk of doing nothing is extremely low.

So where does hearing loss fall within this scale of risk? Can we predict how motivated the average person will be to respond to a recommendation to have his or her hearing tested?

Factor 1: The Seriousness of Hearing Loss

Seriousness is normally thought of in terms of whether a condition is fatal, how much suffering it causes, and how much it disrupts a person's life. In the developed world, hearing loss is generally nonfatal and is not accompanied by pain (although some conditions will cause both pain and hearing loss). At milder levels, a reduction in hearing causes very little perceivable disruption to a person's life.

First, people only hear what they hear, not what they're missing, so they're often blissfully unaware of any disruption. Second, hearing works in seamless combination with our vision, cognition, and interaction with others. If hearing is not "pulling its weight," these systems will pick up the slack and create the impression that all is well. Third, changes in hearing generally happen gradually, so people unconsciously adjust and accommodate; any resultant changes in lifestyle are frequently equated with waning interest or advancing age, rather than diminished hearing.

For hearing loss to be considered disruptive, the role that hearing itself plays in a person's life has to be considered important in the first place; otherwise, losing it is "no big deal." Many people do not appreciate just how important their hearing is, which is completely understandable when you consider it is active 24 hours of the day, 7 days a week, with no means to evaluate the difference of living without it. Eyesight and breathing, on the other hand, can be switched off and on at will so people get a better idea of the role it plays for them.

Taking together the nonfatality, the absence of obvious suffering, and the lack of perceived disruption means that hearing loss as a condition would not be considered particularly serious by most people, so why would someone bother having his or her hearing screened? If it's not that serious, it really doesn't matter if they have a hearing loss or not, does it? It is a huge obstacle for any marketing message.

Hearing care professionals often try to rectify this by emphasizing how serious hearing loss is, with messages and news stories that follow the pattern: "Hearing loss increases the risk of *[insert secondary condition]*." Past examples have included depression, anxiety, falling, memory loss, tinnitus, and dementia.

But notice the problem with such messages? They increase the risk associated with *having* hearing loss, regardless of whether or not you address the hearing problem. Having your hearing tested doesn't decrease your risk of these secondary conditions. All it does is confirm you are more at risk from these things.

Such marketing messages generally backfire for two reasons. One, if people don't have the secondary condition ("I don't suffer from depression"), they may take that as proof that they don't have a hearing loss either. Why, then, would they need to take the test? Two, some may be afraid that if they learn they have hearing loss, they somehow make themselves susceptible to the secondary condition as if "tempting fate." Taking the test now has even greater consequences.

So our messages must be presented in such a way that the risk of doing *nothing* is always greater than the risk of discovering the condition. Our marketing must therefore focus our audience's attention on the seriousness of unaddressed hearing problems, rather than hearing loss itself. Just remember that any message insinuating that a secondary condition can be dealt with by addressing a hearing loss must have the evidence to back it.

Factor 2: The Likelihood of Hearing Loss

Hearing loss tends to be "someone else's problem": people who are "older than me," "deafer than me," "more desperate than me." We notice when someone doesn't hear us, but we assume that when *we* don't hear, it's because of the situation: It's the background noise, or other people mumbling, or we were distracted.

Even people with the "world's best hearing" will encounter situations where they can't hear as well as they expect to. If their hearing were to change gradually, how would they recognize that anything had changed? They would still be encountering those same situations where listening is more of challenge, just as when they had the world's best hearing. Why, then, would they suppose it was because they were "suffering from hearing loss"? So the likelihood that "we personally" have a loss of hearing is assumed to be low.

Statistics often reinforce this notion. When people learn that 1 in X number of people have a hearing loss, and only a minority use hearing technology, they learn that the majority of people do *not* have a hearing loss, so the odds are in their favor that neither do they. If it's unlikely they have a hearing loss, why bother with the effort of having their hearing checked?

So our messages must be presented in a way that are as relevant and universal as possible. They must create the assumption in people's minds that they are at risk *unless* proven otherwise by means of routine hearing checks, in the same way that we are at risk of gum disease *unless* we are having regular dental checkups.

Factor 3: The Curability of Hearing Loss

In most cases, hearing loss cannot be cured, and as many hearing care professionals point out, even the available treatment (i.e., hearing aids) do not correct hearing loss. "They are only an aid," we tell them. So the main intervention we are offering doesn't cure hearing loss; it doesn't even correct it! It only *helps*.

People are then told they have to "get used to wearing them" and that they must impose listening strategies on others: "Get them to face you when they are talking. Tell people to slow down when they're speaking." We can be so focused on fostering realistic expectations that the overall effect suggests a largely ineffective intervention that will interfere with normal life.

To discover that you have a hearing loss, then, means you will have to live with the condition for the rest of your life, and you'll have to wear a device that announces your impairment to the rest of the world. The risk of finding out you have the condition is therefore significantly riskier than not knowing. At least "not knowing" means you can assume other factors are responsible for the difficulties you are facing, such as the situational ones we all encounter from time to time—until, of course, your difficulties reach a threshold hard to ignore. Meanwhile, why risk a hearing check and upsetting the status quo?

Thus, our messages must provide our audience with a solution that either cures or reduces the condition we are checking for, if we want people to approach hearing care. But to say we can cure hearing loss would obviously be incorrect and misleading. We must therefore encourage people to have their hearing checked by finding something that we really *can* cure, or at least greatly reduce, through (early) detection.

THE HEARING CHECK AND LOSS AVERSION

When the hearing test is presented as a means to detect a nonserious, low-probability, incurable condition, people's natural aversion to loss will encourage them to avoid it. But as we saw earlier, if people are avoiding something, it suggests the signals they are picking up from us are wrong. If we want them to approach the hearing test, it must be seen as empowering them to do so. Somehow we must convey in our marketing that having your hearing checked *reduces* your risk of loss, rather than confirms it. But we cannot even hope to do so if we are telling them our purpose is to detect a hearing loss; the clue is in the name.

When faced with the prospect of a loss, people typically employ a loss-coping mechanism designed to minimize the impact of that loss. The first stage in this process is to assume that everything is normal or will return to normal. The second stage is to try and identify the cause of the loss on the basis that if we can find it, we can root it out, thus preventing or minimizing further loss. If we're unable to remove the loss, the third stage is to begin exploring ways in which we might do things differently to suppress or minimize the hearing loss. The fourth stage begins when we've exhausted all our possibilities, and we resort to evaluating the implications the loss will have for us. The fifth and final stage, should we get there, is to accept the loss and begin rebuilding our lives around the absence of whatever it is we have lost.

This loss-coping mechanism is best known as the grieving process: anger, denial, bargaining, depression, and acceptance. While it is most often associated with bereavement, the application of the grieving process is far wider, applying to everything from losing our keys, to losing a job, to losing our hearing, as Table 2–4 suggests.

The grieving process takes time. If we tell people that having a hearing test is to discover they've lost something important to them, how do we think they will respond? Will they willingly approach us, eager to discover they've lost it? And if they are told they've lost their hearing, do we believe they will bypass the first four stages of the grieving process and skip straight to acceptance?

You can immediately see the problem we have: The idea of hearing loss is *inherently* aversive, which makes it a hard thing to market. It can only ever trigger an avoid response. Unless we can get people through all five stages in our marketing messages, we are going to be waiting a very long time until that person responds. It is likely to be a significant factor in the time it takes someone between onset of hearing loss and taking action.

But every month or year that people take to work through the grieving process is another month or year of changes they have to make just to cope with the reduced auditory stimulus:

Table 2–4. The Loss Coping Mechanism

Stage of Loss—Coping	Loss of Keys	Loss of Hearing
Denial: "Assume all is normal"	Check where we normally keep them. Repeat, assuming you missed them. Check other pockets, in case misplaced.	Background noise must be higher. People's distinction is becoming sloppier.
Anger: "Fix what's to blame"	Ask if anyone's picked them up or seen them. Blame yourself for not being more careful.	Accuse family of mumbling. Tell them to speak more clearly. Blame yourself for not protecting your hearing.
Bargaining: "What can I do to get it back"	Retrace steps to identify where you last had them.	Have ears checked for wax.
Depression: "What are the implications"	"Can't get to work, will risk my job, risk unemployment, won't be able to pay my bills . . ."	"I'll have to wear hearing aids, people will see me as old, I'll have to learn sign language and lipreading, I won't be able to enjoy social situations anymore . . ."
Acceptance: "Time to rebuild"	Contact a locksmith.	Get my hearing checked.

changes in their brain, in their behavior, and in their relationships. The longer someone takes to approach hearing care, the more ingrained those changes become, making our intervention progressively less effective. We therefore have an ethical responsibility to facilitate earlier intervention.

How, then, should we deal with the grieving process in our marketing to minimize the time between onset and action? Simple. Don't trigger it in the first place. Any message we present must enable someone to reduce (rather than accept) his or her risk of loss by responding to it.

PREVENTABLE LOSSES
THROUGH HEARING CARE

Another way to view loss aversion is to see it as "status quo maintenance": People act in ways that are consistent with how they see themselves and how they want to be seen. When we see hearing in terms of status quo maintenance, we discover that the ability to hear is core to so many aspects of a person's life. Table 2–5 lists some of the most important ones.

Hearing connects our brains "in real time" to the world around us, to other people, and to the opportunities of life. That connection must remain strong and constant, either through natural ability or with hearing technology, to maintain our optimal performance. If the connection is allowed to fade, then we fade. Because changes in hearing happen gradually, we rarely notice it ourselves, which means that the only way to be certain we're not fading away is through regular hearing checks.

Hearing checks are therefore a crucial part of status quo maintenance. They prevent loss of that status through early identification of undetected risks to "who we are, what we are, and what we can be."

Table 2–5. Functionality Provided by the Sense of Hearing

Self-consistency	The ability to take hold of opportunities as and when they happen
Self-awareness	
Self-assurance	
Sharpness of mind	Effectiveness at work
The ability to lay down new memories	Ability for others to depend on us
Attention and concentration	Confidence
Mental and physical energy	Independence
Awareness and safety	Involvement
Interaction with others	Music and humor
The ability to respond in the right way at the right time	Quality of life

Let's see what we've done here:

1. We've made the risk of "doing nothing" greater than the risk of discovering a problem. Doing nothing means you risk unknowingly losing how you see yourself and how you want others to see you.
2. We've presented hearing technology as equivalent to naturally good hearing. We've done this not by saying it cures or corrects hearing loss (which would be incorrect) but because natural and technologically enhanced hearing both maintain the brain's connection. Now the intervention is seen to symbolize hearing (approach), rather than hearing loss (avoid).
3. We've demonstrated that hearing itself is important—so the possibility of an undetected, unaddressed reduction in hearing will be perceived as serious enough to warrant action.
4. We've increased the likelihood in people's minds that the problem highlighted in our message affects them too, by demonstrating that "not being aware of the problem" is itself a symptom of the problem. But we've also shown them that by having their hearing checked, they are reducing the likelihood of there being a problem because now that problem can be "cured."
5. We've avoided triggering the grieving process because our focus has sidestepped "hearing loss" and focused instead on hearing, a much more life-affirming subject.

We can now see that the problem we're inviting people to address with a hearing check, or by using hearing technology, is not really hearing loss at all; it's mishearing.

If we're mishearing, we're distorting our reality, recall, and relationships—something most people would be keen to avoid. When we're *not* mishearing, we maintain our opportunities in life, our social acceptance, and our self-consistency—something we'd be keen to approach.

A simple hearing check reduces our risk of mishearing through detecting it, and our intervention, hearing technology, can "cure" mishearing for the majority of people. We now have an approachable message, as seen in Table 2–6.

Table 2–6. Examples of Messages for Hearing Checks

General message	"Routine hearing checks throughout life reduce your risk of mishearing."
For audiences likely to be concerned about their hearing	"If you've not had your hearing checked in the past 2 years, you are increasing your risk of (unknowingly) mishearing."
For audiences who believe they have good hearing	"By having your hearing checked routinely, you'll be confident you're not mishearing."

AVOID ISOLATION, APPROACH ACCEPTANCE

As social animals, we have an inbuilt desire to be accepted by our social groups. It's the reason peer pressure is so powerful, why we engage in gossip, and why it's important to be liked or be needed by the group. Each of us belongs to multiple social groups, and this in part defines how we see ourselves and our relationship to others. We may define ourselves by our family, our profession, our language, our race, the team we support, the phone we use. A group of students visiting another university may identify themselves in terms of their own university. That same group visiting a retirement home may identify themselves in terms of their youth.

We tend to focus on the differences between our own group and other groups, particularly if it is beneficial to our own group's success: We highlight our own strengths and point out the others' weaknesses. It's as if we have a primeval drive to mark out our territory, but instead of using boundary stones, we use names or badges to separate the "them" from the "us." We're the good guys, they're the bad. We're the freedom fighters, they're the terrorists. We're the chosen ones, they're the unclean. We fly the flag, we wear the clothing, we display the badge. Those who aren't for us are against us.

Good marketing taps into this drive: Those who use our product are "in," gaining special status or desirable attributes in the eyes of others. Ownership becomes their key to all the attributes associated with that product, and as long as those attributes are desirable, we will have a proposition that people want to approach.

To use this principle to make the marketing of hearing technology approachable, we must convey that ownership is a person's key to desirable attributes, and it must endow upon him or her a status that others wish for themselves. Traditionally, the marketing of hearing care has done the complete opposite.

GROUPS IN HEARING CARE

Most of the individuals we will be marketing to have been born with good hearing and experienced this for most of their lives. They would therefore not consider themselves part of either the "deaf" or "hearing-impaired" social groups; they are part of the "people with normal hearing" group.

Let's put ourselves in their shoes. If our hearing changes, it triggers an incongruity. Our family notice we're mishearing and so will no longer consider us to be part of their social group of "people with normal hearing." But if we are no longer part of that group—a group we've belonged to all our life—what group do we belong to? While our family would have little hesitation assigning us to the deaf or hearing-impaired group, we don't believe we belong there. One, when we look at what type of people are in that group, we see people who are "older than me," "deafer than me," "more desperate than me." Two, we remind ourselves of all the occasions when we hear everything we're supposed to hear, and this confirms our right to continue belonging to the "people with normal hearing" group.

Nobody likes to be isolated from their group, so we learn to nod in the right place and avoid situations where our hearing will let us down, so that we maintain our place in the "people with normal hearing" group with the rest of our friends and family. We know that if we have to use hearing aids, we'll be different. Often hearing care professionals exacerbate this by highlighting "normal" hearing on an audiogram, implying that everything else is "abnormal."

Hearing care marketing must be careful never to force people to move out of their social groups or suggest in any way that someone doesn't belong where he or she wants to belong. Doing so automatically invites resistance because it is fighting against human nature. Good marketing, on the other hand, taps into human behavior. So hearing care marketing must demonstrate that using hearing technology *maintains your belonging* to your social group.

REDEFINING THE SOCIAL GROUPS

We therefore need to redefine our social groups, so that the desirable group includes both "people with normal hearing" *and* "people who use hearing technology." We must therefore look at what these two subgroups have in common that unites them: that they both hear as others expect them.

MINIMUM EXPECTED LEVEL

There is an unwritten contract among people who primarily communicate using an oral language: that we will hear each other accurately, first time. Imagine giving people an instruction or sharing a secret with them and never being certain if they've heard and understood correctly. Imagine the chaos it could cause in government, business, or education or health.

Two-way communication requires a shared effort, and when someone isn't maintaining his or her side of the contract, it increases our own effort. If we have to repeat or reword what we have said, it requires additional effort to compensate for what the other party was lacking, which is why, when we are tired or stressed and have less effort to give, it becomes easier just to say, "It doesn't matter."

It works the other way round too, so that if people mumble or don't make themselves clear, it frustrates us because we have to increase our effort in listening, using additional mental processes to "fill in the gaps" just to follow along. Hearing ability, therefore, plays the primary role in this unwritten contract. While it may never have been formally defined, there is clearly a minimum level of hearing that is automatically expected of us to maintain our side of the contract. When we can't hear, it sets the stage for friction unless we can demonstrate a valid reason for not being able to do so (e.g., we are profoundly deaf).

Seen through this perspective, using hearing technology enables us to continue to maintain our side of the contract. In doing so, we remain integrated into the social group of "those who hear as expected." By contrast, those who *don't* hear as expected, but *could* be using hearing technology, have chosen to exclude themselves from the group. Suddenly, there becomes a strong reason to have our hearing checked regularly to ensure we are always hearing as expected and to avoid any delay in using hearing technology should we fall below that minimum expected level.

In doing so, the marketing of hearing care shifts away from "identifying, calling out, and stigmatizing those who are different for being hearing impaired," and our calls to action cease to be perceived as "a life-changing decision to wear a mark of that difference." Instead, our marketing becomes about empowering people to continue to be all that they can be, both as an individual and through their continuing connectivity with "people who hear as expected." Our marketing begins to tap into human nature by shifting away from sending avoid signals ("Leave your group!") to sending approach signals ("Stay in the group").

AVOID THREATS TO SELF, MAINTAIN SELF-CONSISTENCY

People avoid threats to themselves, both physical and to their self-image. We have already seen examples of this when we considered how people have a bias to avoid loss or the risk of loss, but the implications for hearing care go even deeper.

The greatest threat that faces us all as human beings is the annihilation of our own existence. Advancing age is a reminder that we all face the certainty of death, the point when everything we have accumulated in life—our experiences, memories, expertise, possessions, or relationships—will come to an abrupt end. For most people, anything that reminds them of this inevitability will naturally be avoided, which includes any stereotype relating to old age.

One of the paradoxes of aging is that when we are younger, we are happy to stereotype older people, possibly in an attempt to distance and protect ourselves from the prospect of death. Yet as we become older ourselves, we resist any attempt to pigeonhole us into the same old-person stereotype. Even in "old age," we find ourselves quicker to identify with younger stereotypes than with those for older people, and in fact, research has found this strategy to have positive health benefits, both mentally and physically. Remind older people of the elderly stereotype and you impair their health and performance: Their memory performance suffers, their stress increases, their confidence in their own ability diminishes, and you even reduce their will to live.

The overall effect of the elderly stereotype is therefore to weaken a person, and as we saw at the beginning of this chapter, people avoid things that weaken them. That includes any marketing that uses such a stereotype. People find it hard to identify with "being old"; it simply isn't consistent with their lifelong experience. They compare themselves to the stereotype for the older adult—someone who is "doddering but dear," "incompetent socially, cognitively, and physically"—and see it as foreign to their own experience and achievements.

Unlike entering adulthood, where there is a clear boundary separating us from childhood such as the legal age to vote, "old age" is a moving target as we try to push it further away from us. So people must look for other outward signs to determine whether a person, including themselves, belongs to such a social group. It may be a physical attribute such as an increase in wrinkles or white hair, or it may be a prop such as a walking frame or dentures.

Whether such props become associated with the stereotype for the elderly depends on whether it is exclusively used by such a demographic or whether it is portrayed as being exclusively used by them. The way that hearing technology is presented in our marketing is therefore a key determinant in whether it becomes symbolic of old age. If hearing aids are seen as symbolic of old age, then people will avoid them because they would be seen as an initiation into the very demographic they have successfully resisted up until now.

Entry into old age brings with it a whole host of issues that someone must now deal with, including acceptance of their own mortality and a perceived loss of social, cognitive, and physical competence. Until people are "ready" to accept the psychological baggage that comes with crossing such a boundary, they will avoid hearing aids. Our marketing must therefore be careful to avoid creating or reinforcing such deterring stereotypes. At best, they delay the time when someone seeks professional advice. At worst, they put someone off hearing technology altogether.

CREATING ASSOCIATIONS

When we present two things together in close proximity, either in time or in space, we form an association between those two objects in the minds of our audience. Repeatedly showing them together strengthens this bond so they become "permanently" linked in people's memory. Think how Pavlov's dogs heard the bell ring and immediately began to salivate because a ringing bell had been repeatedly presented together with their food. Presenting the one triggered the other.

This principle of deliberately and repeatedly associating things together can be seen throughout the world of marketing to powerful effect. Attractive people are shown drinking our favorite beverage. Powerful sports stars are shown wearing our favorite brand of sportswear. People enjoying life are seen driving our favorite car or using our favorite electronic device. The result of creating such associations is that our audience begins to unconsciously assign the attributes of the one to the other.

If those attributes are consistent with how they (want to) see ourselves and how they want others to see them, they become more inclined to approach the product, service, or brand we are offering.

When we market hearing health care, then, we must always be conscious of the links we are creating in the memories of our audience. They will use these links when they are forming their attitudes toward hearing care. If we have repeatedly shown them images of elderly people or retired couples, this is what will spring to mind when people think of what we do. If that's not consistent with how our audience wants to see themselves, they will avoid us. And as we saw earlier, even older people seek to avoid having the attributes of "old age" applied to them. Therefore, instead we must create associations through our marketing that are consistent with how people want to see themselves and be seen by others. If we know that even older people find it easier to associate with a youthful identity, then we won't be far off the mark if we portray such ideals in our marketing.

By repeatedly and consistently depicting people who are in the prime of their life, then linking social, cognitive, and physical competence of these people to their ability to "hear as expected," we begin to build positive associations for the users of hearing care. Want to be seen as reliable? Hear as expected. Want to be exciting and in the "now"? Hear as expected. Want to be a good friend? Hear as expected. Figures 2–1 through 2–3 are examples of advertising messages that attempt to do three things: provide a relevant call to action, create positive associations, and avoid threats to the self. Readers are encouraged to compare this type of advertising message to traditional device-centric, price-driven ad campaigns that have been the staple of hearing care marketing for decades.

Our product is no longer about "getting old." As these examples in Figures 2–1 to 2–3 suggest, it's about empowerment—about being all you can be. As we saw at the beginning of this chapter, people are more likely to approach the things that empower them. Hearing as expected enables each of us, no matter what our age, to act in ways that are consistent with how we want to be and to preserve the attributes of youthfulness. This is what people should be seeing in our marketing.

Figure 2–1. Example of marketing campaign using positive cues to action. Republished with permission of the Academy of Doctors of Audiology.

Figure 2–2. Example of marketing campaign using positive cues to action. Republished with permission of the Academy of Doctors of Audiology.

Figure 2–3. Example of marketing campaign using positive cues to action. Republished with permission of the Academy of Doctors of Audiology.

SUMMARY

In this chapter, we have looked at how marketing plays a crucial role in shaping people's attitudes toward hearing care and hearing technology. Our marketing provides an essential source of information that helps people decide initially whether hearing care is relevant to them and, second, whether they should be avoiding or approaching us. If responding to our message somehow weakens them or suggests they might be something they do not want to be, they will avoid us. But if our message empowers them, by allowing them to act in a way that's consistent with how they want to see themselves and be seen by others, they are more likely to approach us.

Marketing that focuses on the idea of having a condition weakens people by highlighting a permanent loss people cannot reduce and by threatening to separate them from "being normal." But marketing that focuses on "hearing as expected," whether through natural hearing or by using hearing technology, empowers our audience to "be all they can be" and maintain attributes associated with youthfulness and competence.

We need to be aware that we have two types of audiences: those who consider hearing care relevant and those who don't. How these two audiences form their attitude will be different. The less relevant hearing care is to people, the more they will rely on mental shortcuts such as following the crowd or following the opinion of experts. We must therefore ensure that we provide the public with "quick and easy" messages that help move them toward seeing hearing care as personally relevant, such as the idea of having their hearing checked regularly, just as they do their eyes and teeth. Once hearing care becomes relevant, people will put more effort into working out their attitude. For these individuals, we must ensure they have access to up-to-date information that avoids stereotypes and negative associations.

3

A PRACTICAL GUIDE TO A MARKETING STRATEGY AND PLAN

Karen Ann Jacobs

An effective marketing plan is the heart of a sustainable audiology practice. Yet many private practitioners venture into the competitive, complex world of business without this powerful weapon. Although simple in outline, a marketing plan cannot be developed without thoughtful assessment, reflection, measurement, and management. An effective marketing concept implies that all activities of a practice are driven by a desire to satisfy the consumers' needs or wants. The marketing plan is essential to ensure that concept is realized and, to that end, profitable. The aim of this chapter is to provide the reader with some practical guidance on the creation and implementation of a marketing plan. For some, this objective may seem too simplistic, but over the past few years, several industry surveys have confirmed that approximately half of all audiology practices in the United States do not have a formal marketing plan. If you believe the adage "failing to plan is planning to fail," then many practices are poised to struggle as competition gets even tougher.

> Companies without an effective marketing planning system tend to suffer more serious commercial organizational consequences when environmental and competitive conditions become hostile and unstable. (McDonald, 2007)

Advertising may be part of marketing. Selling may be part of marketing. But advertising and selling are not the whole of marketing. Marketing is the act of influencing consumer choice by demonstrating the value of a product or service. In a competitive world where there is overlap in the job descriptions of commercial hearing aid dealers, physicians, technicians, and audiologists, marketing is an exercise that educates consumers to your unique qualifications as a hearing and balance expert and influences them to purchase products or services from you over someone else. While marketing is not just selling or advertising, it should take cues from purchasing patterns and consumer needs so that sales of product or service become a consequence of your marketing efforts.

> Marketing is everything you do to promote your business, from the moment you conceive of it to the point at which customers buy your product or service and begin to patronize your business on a regular basis. (Levinson, 1984)

In today's competitive business climate, personal marketing will not be enough to sustain, let alone grow, your business. You will need a well-thought-out, step-by-step guide to send a consistent message to the public. This is the objective of your marketing plan. Writing an effective marketing plan will take effort, education, and honesty. The results will need to be monitored and tracked. The process will provide an opportunity to truly define who you are as a business and what you hope to be in the future.

Time is often the most valuable commodity for a business owner. It repeatedly seems there are not enough hours in the day to manage the patient load, the staff, and the business, not to mention a life outside of work. But the benefits of spending a portion of your valuable time developing the market plan will provide lasting benefits, including the following:

- Better coordinated marketing activities
- Less wasted time and money on things that don't work
- Improved communication resulting in a more directed, motivated staff
- Provides a framework for continuous review of efficacy
- A means to track progress and identify early signs of regression
- Improves preparedness for change
- Minimizes irrational or reactive responses to unexpected events
- Reduces vulnerability
- Increases profitability

As you sit down to write your marketing plan, feel consolation in knowing your market plan will help you identify actions that bring rewards, allowing you to eliminate the unnecessary and providing you with more time to enjoy life.

Marketing is continually going on around us. It is what made us pick out the breakfast cereal or decide to stop for the $5 foot-long sub for lunch. Regardless of practice setting, be prepared to market on a daily basis. Market your practice on a personal level to promote a positive image of oneself and our profession. Take opportunities to increase awareness of who you are, what you do, and how uniquely qualified you are to do it. Prepare a 10-second "elevator speech" to inform and educate the public in answer to the inevitable question, "What do you do for a living?" Simply imagine being stuck in an elevator with an inquisitive stranger, like the one shown in Figure 3–1. Consider volunteering a couple of hours with a school science class or community service group such as Quota Clubs or Lions Clubs and share your expertise on hearing and balance. Provide education on hearing conservation at gun clubs or as a guest presenter for a local OSHA program. Audiology has become a recognized profession in part due to the personal marketing efforts of our colleagues over the years.

Before you can create your marketing plan, it is important to develop a marketing strategy. The marketing strategy is determined by your overall business goals. It includes a definition of your business, a description of your products and services,

Figure 3–1. The elevator speech. Cartoon created by Janet Mankel, republished with permission.

a profile of your target patient or consumer, and a comparison between your practice and the competition. It should reflect how you want your business to be seen by the consumer. The marketing strategy answers the following questions: Who are my consumers, where do they come from, what do I provide to them, and what makes me uniquely qualified to provide that service or product?

The marketing strategy is essential to determining the effectiveness and relevance of your marketing plan. The marketing plan will identify the specific actions you are going to carry out to achieve the goals defined in the marketing strategy; it is your road map.

A *marketing strategy* is an overall approach to designing products to meet customer needs, letting customers know that these offerings are available, and giving them reason to purchase them. A *marketing plan* provides concrete details for implementing a marketing strategy, with specifics about budgeting and time frame, as well as indicators for gauging the success of different marketing. (Gartenstein, 2014)

DEVELOP THE MISSION

Writing a marketing mission statement may not necessarily be the first thing you tackle when it comes to writing your marketing plan. Many business advisors argue that you can't plan where you are going if you don't know where you are and should; therefore, develop a marketing strategy prior to writing a mission statement. Others argue that the mission statement sets the tone for who you want to be and identifies what you want to accomplish and should therefore be the first step in writing a marketing plan.

Regardless of when you formulate this statement, it should be included in your plan. The mission statement reflects the ultimate desire or ultimate outcome of your marketing plan. It should embody the vision and values of your practice as identified in your business plan. Not all marketing mission statements will be identical because each company is unique to itself. Depending on the complexity of the business, many practices will have multiple mission or purpose statements. A mission statement should include the following key attributes:

- The role or contribution statement: What do you want to do?
- The business definition: Define benefits you provide and needs you satisfy.
- The distinctive competencies: What resources, services, skills, and products do you offer that are unique to your business?
- Indications for the future: What the practice will do, won't do, or might do.

Mission Statement

BEST Audiology will increase sales and ultimately profitability by educating consumers about the benefits of our holistic, highly skilled approach to minimizing the negative effects of tinnitus and hearing loss through the use of scientific knowledge, state-of-the-art technology, and incomparable service.

DEVELOP THE MARKETING STRATEGY

The initial step when developing your marketing strategy is identifying your product. As mentioned previously, you cannot have a marketing plan without identifying what you intend to "sell." Your business is probably not the only audiology practice in your town. That doesn't mean your practices are identical, but it does mean you have to think about how you are different from other businesses engaged in the same thing and why customers should visit you, rather than your competitor. For example, you may be the only practice in the area providing tinnitus or vestibular assessment. Perhaps you specialize in pediatric assessment or aural rehabilitation counseling. You may be the only practice offering specialized tests like otoacoustic emissions (OAE) or auditory brainstem response (ABR). Call out products that are exclusive to your practice or have a unique appeal to a specific population. Doing so will give you the competitive edge to bring in niche populations. Pediatric patients or patients with tinnitus, for example, may be exclusive markets for your practice. You may be the only practice in your area that provides vestibular or cochlear implant services. To stand out from similar competition and appeal to the consumer, you must have something or do something that differentiates you from the practice down the street.

When defining your products, be specific in your description. For example, identifying one of your offered services as a "hearing test" does not set you apart from the hearing test being provided in the "big box" store down the road. It is more accurate to identify the service as a "diagnostic audiometric or hearing evaluation" center of excellence. This more accurate product title is now marketable because it sets your practice apart. It will differentiate you from the commercial hearing aid dealer who is providing the free "hearing test" or the "hearing screening." It adds value for the patient because it describes a higher level of assessment. Remember, part of your marketing goal is to educate the public. If you or your staff tell patients that you provide "hearing tests" as opposed to "diagnostic hearing evaluations," the lines between what *you* do compared with what *they* do become blurred in the public eye.

> When asked to identify "the hearing expert," most consumers do not know which professional holds that distinction. (Foltner & Mansfield, 2006)

We may have all heard the old selling adage "a good product sells itself." This statement illustrates the influence that a product has on a sale. But what constitutes a product? A product is what we sell to stay in business. Most audiologists offer products that consist of a combination of goods and services. These are the *tangible* and *intangible* products. Tangible products such as hearing aids, tinnitus maskers, or cochlear implants are physical, touchable items. Their value is often based on visual comparisons and features. Certainly, the tangible goods are important. They must be reliable and appropriate as well as offering something the patient is interested in obtaining and using.

> A sale is the purchase of a service or product to gratify a want, fueled often by the erroneous belief that it will give the buyer what they need. Therefore . . . sell people what they want, but give them what they need, so they'll be around long enough to get them where they really want to go. (Goulston, 2007)

The intangible products you provide may be more difficult to identify. Services like "evening hours" may provide the intangible product of "convenience" for the working adult. Having a technician available for cleaning and repairs allows the patients to keep their hearing aids working and in their ears. The intangible products are "resolution" to their problem and "support."

Intangible products may also include *you*. Your expertise, your years of experience, your skill, and your compassion are unique to your practice. These intangibles are important for obtaining the desired outcome of patient success or satisfaction. Intangible products may include your community ties and altruistic activities. Belonging to service organizations can be good illustrators of the intangible product of compassion. Your ties to community illustrate the unspoken, intangible product of stability and commitment. To a consumer, it may also provide a sense of familiarity and connection. Seeing your name or company name associated with good works allows potential consumers to feel like they know you. Some of those potential consumers may also serve with you on local organizations or clubs. Their personal connection to you increases the "word-of-mouth" marketing that brings business to your door.

Another intangible product you may offer is assurance. Policies like "satisfaction guaranteed" or "trial periods" may be used to add strength of the claim that your practice is better than the competition. Advertising your years of experience or your years in business may also provide assurance. The patient assumes that because the business has survived for a number of years, it must be viable. The longer you have been in business, the greater the assurance. This assurance is a vote of confidence. It validates that you can be trusted to provide the solution they want just as you have done for all the patients who have supported your practice over the many years you have been in business.

Include in your marketing strategy a statement identifying the products (physical goods and services) that will be offered and how they will benefit the patient. Here is an example of how a practice can differentiate when devising its marketing strategy.

Marketing Strategy

BEST Audiology will offer a holistic approach to providing improved communication ability to our patients. We recognize that this will take a combination of:

- Physical goods, including hearing aids, batteries, cleaning supplies, assistive listening devices, LACE Aural Rehabilitation home and online programs, and access to the resource library, offering an opportunity

for patients to check out on loan assistive listening products
- Products, informative books, and videos dealing with hearing and hearing loss
- Services, including patient education, diagnostic audiometric assessment, OAE, ABR, video-nystagmography (VNG) , tinnitus treatment, aural rehabilitation services, counseling, outcome measures, user satisfaction surveys, follow-up, repair, assistive listening device (ALD) demonstration, access to community resources, and cleaning and maintenance services
- Staff: reception, insurance/billing specialist, technician, and adult and pediatric audiologists
- Community involvement: participation in local service organizations and clubs, as well as financial support to the local Hearing Loss Association of America (HLAA) chapter and Quota Club to bring awareness of the detrimental effects of hearing loss to the consumer
- Professionalism: adherence to a code of conduct that ensures ethical behavior and places the needs of the patient as the primary focus of service, communication with other health care professionals to ensure holistic wellness, and continued education to ensure knowledge of current treatment options

We use a diverse line of physical goods to offer a competitive pricing range, cosmetic appeal, versatile features, and performance options. We focus on identifying and addressing patient expectations for those variables. BEST Audiology provides counseling and support services to validate patient success, including LACE training, group aural rehabilitation class, and home study aural rehabilitation exercises. Product marketing will focus on BEST Audiology's ability to provide "Problem Solution" and our commitment to improving the lives of the people in our community. Advertising will focus on the value of our intangible products and services, as opposed to brand name or pricing of the tangible goods.

The next step to creating your marketing strategy is identifying your consumer. Knowing what you sell will help you identify to whom you intend to sell your product, where they live, and how you intend to reach them. This is known as your target market. The target market is made up of several factors: your consumer, the geographical area, and the demographic composition. Who will want or use your products? Where do they live? What will drive them to seek out your practice?

Consumer Target Market

Your target consumer is the description of the person or entity to whom you will market your product. You may have multiple consumer target markets depending on the diversity of your products. The consumer target may or may not be the end user of your products. For example, you may identify local pediatricians as a consumer market for your pediatric audiometric testing services. A second consumer target market for that same product may be parents of children in need of service. Identify all consumer target markets for your products. Choose a manageable number of these markets for your marketing plan. Focus on consumer target markets that have the greatest potential for sales or that represent a niche market.

Geographical Target Market

Part of that identification process should include a profile of the market demographic. Identify the geographical area where your market lives and works. Are there natural barriers that inhibit easy access? How far will the typical consumer travel for services? From where do your current patients come? In what geographical areas have previous marketing efforts been more or less effective? You may gather information by investigating the travel patterns of your existing patients or contact an area marketing company to provide you with measured local data. If you have a highly unique practice, you may consider a much larger geographical market.

Identification of the physical geographical area will be important when considering your advertising options. Your geographical target market may be influenced by the existing advertising boundaries. Cable companies often divide their coverage areas into smaller advertising areas. Local newspapers typically have specific distribution areas. Your geographic market may be influenced by these existing advertising boundaries. Identify advertising mediums available in your target area.

In your geographical definition, you will also want to identify all the locations that provide similar services. Knowing your approximation to the competitor will help you develop your marketing message.

Demographic Target Market

Have an idea of the financial resources available to your target consumer. This information will be important when you decide the focus of your marketing plan. Keep in mind that you may have enough demographic diversity to warrant multiple target markets. Identify each target market for use with your marketing plan. Knowing the median income level and retail sales per capita will help you identify the presence of sufficient market potential in which to "sell" your products. The U.S. Census Bureau can help provide this information at no cost through its website (http://www.census.gov).

Another demographic provided by the census department is the median age of your marketing area. This information is highly important for correctly identifying the message and medium for your marketing efforts. If you are a pediatric specialist in an area whose median age is 75 years, your message might be placed in a local newspaper and geared toward the grandparent who is seeking help for his or her grandchild. If your median age is 35 years, your market may be the younger, adult parent. Placing an ad in the newspaper will not likely find this market. The information-gathering techniques used by these two groups will vary greatly. Choosing the correct message and the most likely mode of information gathering will make a difference to the success of your marketing efforts.

The census and demographic information needs to be reviewed annually along with your marketing plan. In some areas, predominantly older adults give way to younger first-time homeowners. Recognizing changes in demographic patterns allow for changes in the marketing plan, ultimately keeping services and products current to the needs and expectations of the patient.

The demographic and census information may also assist in identifying the market area's purchasing potential. This information helps ensure that the target market population has the financial resources to obtain your products. Population size, average household income, home value, debt ratio, and average retail sales data are key indicators for a successful practice. An example of the target market is as follows.

Target Market

The BEST Audiology Company is centrally located in a geographical target market area approximately 30 miles in diameter encompassing the more affluent northern Richmond County and the eastern half of York County. The practice is accessible within a 30-minute drive, which is consistent with 90% of the current patient demographic data. Two cable television carriers, six primary radio stations, one major newspaper, and four smaller local newspapers service the area. The geographical market area has approximately 350,000 adult residences.

The average household income in the target market area is $63,000 with a per-capita income average of $36,500. The annual per-capita sales average is $21,943. The target market is educated, with 32% of the population having a minimum of a bachelor's degree. This is higher than the national average of 22%. Over 60% of the target area population is currently employed. Homes in the market area have a median value of $140,000, which is slightly higher than the state median value of $115,000 and are primarily owner occupied with a rate of 76%. The target market area is educated, employed, and vested in the community, as evident by the high percentage of home-ownership. The market has renewable income and higher retail-sales-per-capita figures compared with state averages. These are good indicators of an appropriate target market and purchasing potential.

Demographic data show that approximately 35,000 (10%) of the residents are older than age 75 years, and there are approximately 116,000 between the ages 45 and 74 years. Applying the National Institute of Deaf and Other Communication Disorders (NIDCD) statistics for hearing loss (47% older than 75 years, 30% between ages 65 and 74 years, and 18% between ages 45 and 64 years) shows a target population of 45,450 potential consumers for audiometric services and products.

After your target audience has been identified, it is important to pinpoint your referral sources. Identify within your geographical target market possible referral sources. These are other professionals or businesses that may be willing to send patients to you for specific services. These sources may be colleagues who are in need of support services that they do not provide. It may be a local service club that support causes such as hearing loss (Lions or Quota Clubs) or provide support for people with tinnitus or hearing or balance deficits (American Tinnitus Association (ATA) or HLAA chapter or other health support groups). Physicians in your area who treat comorbid diseases such as diabetes, high blood pressure, and cancer or who treat geriatric patients may also be great referral sources for your practice. General practitioners, oncologists, internists, cardiologists, endocrinologists, and ear, nose, and throat (ENT) physicians are a few specialists who see patients who will, by nature of their diseases, need audiology services. Including them in your target market will prompt you to add directives to your marketing plan that will foster a symbiotic relationship with these providers. Here is an example.

Referral Sources

In the geographical target market, there are eight internal medicine physicians and three geriatric general practice physicians, four endocrinologists, four cardiologists, and two Podiatrists who provide service to the adult diabetic population. There are two oncology physicians not exclusively tied to the two local hospital systems (dispensing audiology services are present in both hospital systems). There is one nondispensing ENT physician in the marketing area. He does have audiology support for testing but does not offer any tangible goods. The target area also has two active Lions Clubs, a local HLAA chapter, and a Quota Club.

Another essential component to developing your marketing plan and strategy is to identify your competition. In today's market, there is potential competition from a multitude of provider types—Internet sales, mail-order sales, durable medical sales, big-box stores, hospitals, university clinics, insurance companies, physician practices, manufacturers, chain stores, and private practices. Knowing why a patient chooses a competitor over your practice may give insight into what appeals to the target market. The rational for completing a competitor analysis is also to help identify open market niches and points of differentiation on which to capitalize in the marketing campaign. Is there a marketing segment that is being underserved? Is there a service that is being offered by a competitor that you could include or improve? Other key items of interest may include hours of operation, staff education, practice accessibility, good or bad reputation, visibility in the community or local organizations and clubs, public appearances, multiple languages, goodwill actions, price, and value. The more you know about your competition, the more focused your marketing plan can be.

In many instances, you will need to apply some assumptions you have made about the value of each differential. For example, if your competitor offers evening hours, you may assume they are trying to appeal to the working adult who does not want to take time away from the job. Now you must put a value on that variable. How important is the potential evening business? Does the variable create a possible niche market? Can that segment of the market generate enough income to offset the costs associated with adding the service such as additional staff, overtime, and time commitment? If you offer the service, will you be able to gain part of the target market? Is there really a market for evening hours? To help answer this question or other service option questions, you may want to survey your current patients or perhaps survey potential patients through a direct mailing or email survey. An example of a competition analysis is the following.

Competition Analysis

Competition for hearing aid sales within the target market includes two commercial hearing aid dealer offices. Location "A" is approximately ½ mile west and on the same road as my practice. Location "B" is also on the same road and is approximately 3 miles from my location. One big-box competitor, "C," is located 8 miles south of this practice. There are two ENT offices that employ audiologists. Practice "D" is located 6 miles south of this location and employs one full-time audiologist and one part-time audiologist. Practice "E" is located 8 miles southwest of this location and employs two full-time dispensing audiologists. Commercial dealer office "A" represents a national chain offering service in hundreds of locations across the United States, appealing to patients who travel or reside in another state for a portion of the year. They do, however, have difficulty retaining staff. Because of their national ownership, they do not have strong community ties. Commercial site "B" has a reputation for aggressive sales pitch and poor patient follow-up. They advertise heavily in the city newspaper but not in the local community paper. Site "B" does not have audiology staff or support. They do offer on-site service to four senior living communities within the target market area. Big-box location "C" does not offer audiology services or participate with insurance coverage, has limited visibility, and has a physical plant that is crowded, noisy, and highly retail oriented. They do offer low cost. Audiology practice "D" provides hearing aid sales and audiological services in support of three ENT physicians. They offer below-market pricing for hearing instruments and direct referrals from the ENT. These factors are offset by poor visibility and no direct access to audiological services without going through the ENT. They also have limited patient access hours as they must support ENT referrals for testing. Location "E" is primarily a pediatric ENT with audiology support. Although they are a dispensing practice and will occasionally fit adults, we do not share the same target market.

IDENTIFY YOUR UNIQUENESS

Key discriminating features or KDFs (also called the unique selling proposition [USP]) as described by McDonald (2007) are the characteristics and properties of a purchase that patients regard as decisive when making a distinction between alternative offers. As mentioned previously, to the patient, there seem to be endless choices when it comes to buying a hearing aid. The key to who will get the business will be directly related to the KDF. Some of the KDFs will be positive, such as "our staff holds the highest credentials in the area." Some KDFs will be negative. For example, "our business is not as easily accessible as the other practices in town." Some of the KDFs will be under your control and others will not. Identification is valuable for the positive as well as the negative. To help decide the impact of the KDFs and to identify those target markets most affected by the KDFs, a more thorough analysis is suggested.

Using a SWOT analysis can help focus your thoughts and add a value to the abstract differences identified. Albert S. Humphrey originated the SWOT analysis in the 1960s but it is still a very useful tool in the development of your marketing strategy today. The SWOT acronym stands for strengths, weaknesses, opportunities, and threats. The strengths and weaknesses of your practice represent the internal factors. They are areas in which you have control. Conversely, the threats and opportunities represent the external factors. They are areas in which you will have little control. Here in an example of change in the competitive landscape that can be viewed as both an opportunity and a threat.

Threats and Opportunities

A Costco opens across the street from you. This is a possible threat. The store will bring in a lot more traffic to your area. The increased visibility of your practice may be an opportunity because more people will see your business when they travel to the store.

You have no control over the location and building of the new store. You have no control over the level of traffic volume. You do have some potential to turn this threat into an opportunity. By maximizing your practice's visibility and marketing your unique services, promoting ease of access and expertise, the threat is now an opportunity to increase your business.

The SWOT analysis will help you identify, develop, and define the objectives you will use in your marketing plan. It will help you identify the best strengths to use in order to exploit opportunities, while minimizing the threats and weaknesses.

Strengths:

- What advantages does your practice have? Easy access? Good visibility?
- What do you do better than anyone else? Staff? Practice as a whole?
- What unique resources can you draw upon that others can't?
- What do people in your market see as your strengths?
- Why do your patients purchase from you?
- What are your practice's KDFs (USP)?

Remember to ask your current patients why they purchased from you. You can do this in a survey or perhaps develop a patient advisory panel. Staff can be particularly insightful with this process as well. They often hear the comments made by our patients as to what they did or did not like about the tangible and intangible offerings.

Weaknesses:

- What could you improve?
- What should you avoid?
- What are people in your market likely to see as weaknesses?
- What do competitors do better?
- What factors cause you to lose sales?

Some weaknesses you will not be able to address, but you may be able to minimize their effects. For example: The street sign frontage of your practice is small due to the city ordinance. This is a weakness you may not be able to change. But perhaps you can minimize the negative by having a sign with bright, eye-catching letters or placing a florescent light in the window.

Try to look at your practice through the eyes of your patients and competitors. This means walking through your office as if you were a patient and noticing the way you are greeted at the door, the décor, and the ease of access. Don't make excuses for what you see. This is likely the most difficult portion of the SWOT because you must remain unbiased by your belief and assumptions. This is an information-gathering activity, and realistic assessment will lead to a better outcome.

Opportunities:

- What good opportunities can you spot?
- What interesting trends are you aware of?
- What changes in technology are changing the market?
- Do you expect any change in staff, location, product, or pricing?
- Is there any change in the competition foreseen?

A useful approach when looking at opportunities is to look at your strengths and ask yourself whether these open up any opportunities. Alternatively, look at your weaknesses and ask yourself whether you could open up opportunities by eliminating them. As an example: You are the only dispensing audiologist in your area who does not work with an ENT. Your strength is that you are the only practice that sees patients without having a referral through the ENT. The weakness has been that most of the primary physicians are unaware that you take direct referrals. The opportunity is to market to the primary physicians and internists, informing them of your services and educating them to the reduced patient costs, expedient service, and thoroughness of your evaluations.

Threats:

- What obstacles do you face?
- What are your competitors doing?
- Is changing insurance policies threatening your reimbursement?
- Do you have bad debt or cash flow problems?
- Could any of your weaknesses seriously threaten your business?

No practice is without threats. Many of these are external and may be out of your control. For example: There is a new Costco opening up down the street. Perhaps a large portion of your business revenue comes from an insurance company that just excluded hearing aid sales and services as a covered benefit. You do not have any control over these events, but by completing your SWOT analysis thoroughly, you may be able to identify these possible threats and minimize them before they adversely affect your business. See Table 3–1 for an example of a SWOT analysis. For example: Knowing that 50% of your business comes from one source should prompt you to look for alternative referral avenues. The Costco down the street brings a lot of new potential customers to your area. Good sign frontage and proper marketing focused on your value should put you in a position to win those patients who are looking for a solution to their communication deficit as opposed to buying a hearing aid.

Be prepared to capitalize on your practice strength and opportunities, while mitigating the threats against your weaknesses. As an example: You have had a commercial hearing aid

Table 3–1. SWOT Analysis Example

Strengths	Weakness
30 years of experience as an audiologist	Small practice with limited marketing budget and time
Opportunities	Threats
No other independent audiology practices in area: Become the premier provider of comprehensive hearing solutions	Big-box retail and an abundance of hearing aid dealers

dealer just a few doors down from your practice. This may be a threat because it is competition. When the company unexpectedly closed, hundreds of patients were left without a service provider. What was initially a threat is now an opportunity. An excellent opportunity for growth has come from this previous threat. Marketing your business as a location that welcomes patients for services regardless of where the hearing aid was purchased may allow you to capitalize on an opportunity.

Consider opportunities to create a highly distinctive practice, whether that results through adding specialized staff or through creation of a unique physical plant. Highly distinctive practices attract more patients from a larger demographic area and may be able to demand higher compensation than the area prices may indicate. Take, for instance, the Mayo Clinic; its unique holistic approach to diagnostic and treatment services and its specialized staff bring in patients from around the world. Because of this appeal, the Mayo Clinic may be able to set fees higher than those being asked by other hospitals in the area. Keep in mind that there must be a balance between differentiation of your practice and the cost of providing that differentiation.

"If all you're trying to do is essentially the same thing as your rivals, then it's unlikely that you'll be very successful."

—Michael Porter (1980)

IDENTIFY YOUR MESSAGE

Your marketing message should be more than a slogan. It should identify who you are and the niche you serve. It should represent the image of your service, your expertise, and your value. Your marketing message will be perpetuated in your advertising, practice environment, location, products, technology level, community involvement, public presentations, customer services, staff, and you.

To create a successful marketing message, McCarthy (1964) introduced the idea of having the right "mix" of information in the marketing message. This became known as the four Ps of marketing. He identified four components of a marketing message that could be manipulated to influence a consumer to purchase a product:

1. Right product—it has physical appeal, has the right features
2. Right price—where the patient feels the benefits outweigh the cost
3. Right place—from a location that is convenient to the patient
4. Right promotion—the target market must be aware of the available solution to the problem

Lauterhorn (1990) updated the four Ps to express the marketing mix from the consumer's point of view and created the four Cs:

1. Customer solution (product)
2. Customer cost (price)
3. Customer convenience (place)
4. Customer communication (promotion)

Customer Solution (Product)

The product being sold does not have to be focused on tangible products. In truth, patients don't want to buy a hearing aid, a cochlear implant, or a tinnitus masker. They don't care (or shouldn't care) about the manufacturer. What they want is a "fix" to their problem. Traynor (2014) identifies a marketing message designed to provide consumers with an intangible product —the product being sold is the ease of communication, ability to talk on the telephone, or relief from tinnitus. It is the "solution." By adopting a marketing message that focuses on the intangible product, the tangible product may adapt and change without appearing to the patient that he or she is investing in an instrument that is merely the "flavor of the month." It allows for techniques to change, equipment to be updated, and physical goods to come and go without having to change or rewrite your marketing message. It also reinforces the message that the audiologists and the services they provide have value. Without *you*, there is no solution or desirable product.

Marketing the intangibles can be challenging, especially when the desired product is made up of many intangible services. It is important to offer quantifiable evidence of the benefit you and your practice provide. Using patient surveys to illustrate satisfaction ratings can be a helpful tool. Use patient testimonials to lend credibility to the stated value of your product.

According to Marston (2007), the "boomer" generation relies heavily on the experiences of their peers when making a decision to purchase. Using survey and testimonial information in your marketing message qualifies and quantifies the benefits you provide. It differentiates you from the competition, and it will create an emotional connection between your practice and your patients. Being able to state "98% of our patients would recommend us to a friend" says a lot to that potential customer. It is also provides that all-important reassurance that your product is the right choice to obtain their desired outcomes.

Customer Cost (Price)

To some patients, the intangible product will be of little interest. They are likely looking for the tangible, the price. Patients have identified the tangible item they want, and they want it for the least amount of money as possible. There are many colleagues who still market the tangible—the hearing aid. Unfortunately, with only a handful of major hearing aid manufacturers to choose from, odds are high that your competitor is selling the same durable goods as your practice. When making the tangible goods the focus of your marketing message, you are, in a sense, advertising for the competition. This strategy also places the equipment or technology as the solution to the patient's communication difficulty. By removing the importance of the audiologist, the field is leveled when it comes to patients' question of which provider is most suitable to sell them what they really want, which is the solution to their problem.

Practices or businesses that only promote "brand X" or special discount pricing have not marketed the intangible. Their business will be easily compared to any practice whose marketing message is centered on cost. This type of situation leads to pricing wars. Without the intangible to set them apart from their competition, they will lose business unless they lower their pricing. In a world with manufacturers selling at huge volume discounts to big-box providers, this is a war that is likely to be lost if the marketing mix is not diversified to include the intangible products.

A better way to approach the customer cost is to focus on what the untreated condition costs in lost enjoyment of life or lost performance at work. An untreated hearing or balance disorder keeps patients from communicating with friends and family. It can reduce their ability to drive or walk, restricting them to smaller and smaller social settings. Kochkin (2005) also identified that unaided hearing loss can cost $1,000 in personal income for every 10% decrease in sensitivity compared to patients who use amplification. Cost can also be discussed in terms of time. Having a practice that has easy access, ease of appointment scheduling, and a physical plant conducive to testing and treating can save the patient waiting time and the time needed to seek out multiple providers and multiple locations (nonaudiology for screening, primary for referral, ENT for access to audiology, or private audiology for diagnostic testing).

Customer Convenience (Place)

The physical plant is also important when looking at patient convenience and accessibility. The patient may value having plentiful parking close to the door, easy access to the office, comfortable waiting areas, convenient hours of operation, and private areas for testing, consultation, and treatment.

When selling the intangible, keep in mind that the perception of value generally relates to the experience of the patient. When you go to a restaurant, you buy food—a tangible good—but you may also pay for the ambiance and service, for a total experience. The same is true for your practice. From the moment the patients pick up the phone to make an appointment, they are developing their experience. When they walk into your office, consider what they see. Make the practice a physical representation of what you want to project. A modern décor may depict state-of-the-art, modern technology. A décor with cozy chairs and soft lighting may feel very welcoming and comfortable. What does it say if the patient is sitting on an aluminum chair between the bulk toothpaste aisle and checkout counter? Staff will often set the tone for the patient experience. The desired ambience and experience should be communicated to staff to ensure the patient experience meets the practice vision. When the tangible goods are not unique, it is the experience that becomes paramount.

Customer Communication (Promotion)

The marketing message will need to appeal to the target market and be identifiable through avenues that put the message in front of the patient. How are you going to reach that new patient? What is your appeal? Take into consideration the demographic information obtained during the market assessment. For example, let's assume the average household income in your target market is $25,000 and a mean age of 75 years, and your identified strengths are convenient location and patient financing. Your marketing message may be "we provide affordable solutions right in your neighborhood." The promotion may reach the greatest number of potential patients through the community newsletter. Consider a target market that has a mean age of 50 years and an average home value of $300,000. Your competitor markets outstanding service, which means it is no longer a distinction. Your differential strengths were identified as state-of-the-art equipment and extended hours of service. Your marketing message may be "modern solutions for busy adults." Your promotion avenue may be a presentation on hearing loss at the local chamber of commerce meeting or other venue that gives you access to working adults.

Your marketing message must be consistent and ongoing. Take, for example, the story of a small airline company that suffered from a decline in business despite improvements in flight accessibility, lower prices, and friendlier service. They had not thought to improve the cleanliness of their terminals or airplane interiors. To the consumer, the image of shabby chairs and dirty floors meant poor aircraft maintenance and, therefore, unsafe flying conditions. The customers ranked safety above price and chose to purchase service from another airline. The airline's marketing image was inconsistent with the physical image. To the consumer, perception is reality. Is your practice reflecting your marketing message? If your message is "modern solutions for busy adults," the office facility needs to support the image you are trying to create. Your marketing plan will define ways to confirm that the customer communication or promotion is effective.

The marketing message may be different for each target market you have identified. Each target market may have different purchasing patterns that will be a factor in your marketing strategy and marketing plan. Identify where each segment goes for information. If, for example, you plan to market to baby boomers, investigate market trends through local marketing companies or through online survey results. Your research may uncover facts such as these:

- Boomers spend 16 h/wk watching television.
- Boomers spend 19 h/wk surfing the Internet.
- Boomer females are number one users of Facebook.
- Eighty-two percent of boomers use the Internet for health questions.

■ Seventy-six percent use the Internet prior to making a major purchase.

Knowing the habits of your target market allows you to customize a message and place it in marketing mediums that are currently being used by those you want to contact.

For instance, let's say you have identified a marketing segment as "hearing-impaired baby boomers":

> Based on the consumer patterns identified above, you conclude that the marketing message will be focused on issues that concern working adults such as convenient lunchtime and evening hours, importance of hearing on overall health, and your years of experience. The medium will be Internet based, using Facebook and the company website. They will highlight information on years in service and extended hours of service. Information will be provided on comorbid diseases with high hearing loss correlations, articles on effects of untreated hearing loss, electronic brochures on how to talk about hearing loss with family and friends, and testimonials from satisfied patients.

Development of your strategy is key to your success. You must know the habits of your target market and be able to customize a message that influences them to choose *you*. Your strategy will be visible in what you say, where you say it, and to whom you say it. It will drive your company goals, objectives, tactics, and actions.

"The company without a strategy is willing to try anything!"
—Michael Porter (1980)

Crash Course: Nine Steps to Marketing in an Independent Practice

1. Assessment: Consult business plans, patient satisfaction surveys, volume reports, community surveys, and any other information you can gather. Consider market dynamics such as seasonality, shifting alliances between physician groups, and other "political" issues.

2. Comparative analysis: Study your competitors, considering their historical advertising levels, any new product launches that may be forthcoming, and the overall competitive nature of your market. Develop your own "unique selling proposition." What makes you different from your competition?

3. Define your vision and strategy: Where do you want your program or organization to be in 3 to 5 years? How can marketing help realize this vision? Make a list of all the tools at your disposal and determine what options will work best for your product, marketplace, and expected budget. Among other tools, consider the following:

   - Direct marketing to your existing database—Use letters, fliers, brochures, postcards.
   - Advertising—Consider print, broadcast, outdoor, special publications such as chamber of commerce directories, and sports programs.
   - Free media—Write articles for news media; make your practice known as the expert.
   - Public relations—Consider sponsorships that "fit" with your service; hold events, tours, and open houses.
   - Website/emerging media—It's not just for young professionals anymore; fast-growing segments of the elderly and minority populations are using the Internet to gather information on their health care options. See Chapter 6 for more information on how to use social media.

4. Build support and enthusiasm: Locate your champions in the organization. Find a local public relations expert who will help support your marketing efforts by helping you by locating speaking engagements, newspaper interviews, and quotes for newsletters and media releases from you.

5. Segment your market: Consider target audiences and think outside the box. How will you cater to the 65 years of age and older crowd? What will they find appealing about your practice?

6. Budget: Now that you have the tools you need and have determined the best way to reach your target audiences, build your budget to support the marketing plan. Focus on the top group or groups to make sure your plans have the greatest impact. Determine what you can do in-house and what you need to outsource.

7. Build your creative product: Turn your ideas into the creative product that will support your plan. Keep referring to your vision and strategy to ensure that the creative concepts support your ultimate objectives. When outsourcing, give your agency as much information as you can gather. Always share your vision.

8. Kick it off right: Tell physicians, your staff, and other stakeholders. They are often your best marketing support. Conversely, if they don't "live the message," your marketing efforts will be for naught.

9. Measure and evaluate: Whenever possible, include a call to action that can be quantified. Track new patients, calls for information, physician referrals, website hits, patient/procedure volumes, or other data meaningful to your practice.

DEVELOP THE MARKETING PLAN

A primary step in the development of your marketing plan is to identify specific goals that you want your marketing efforts to achieve. As Frey (2003) said, "A wish is a goal that hasn't been written down." Marketing goals will reflect the "wish" that you have for your marketing efforts. They will be general statements that reflect the intentions of the marketing strategy. They will use the practices' strengths and opportunities identified in the SWOT analysis to promote your agenda. For example, you may identify that you want to increase your profits, reach a new consumer demographic, or educate potential referral locations. These general goals will serve as platforms on which to build objectives and actions.

Depending on the diversity and resources of your company, you may identify numerous goals. Although each goal is valuable, having too many active goals will likely be unmanageable and diffuse focus. Try to focus on no more than five goals at a time. After a goal has been accomplished, a new goal may be added. Although you will flesh out your goals with objectives and actions, keep a simple copy of your top goals in an obvious location so you will be able to see them throughout the day. Consider posting them in a lunchroom or staff meeting room. Having your goals visible will:

- Motivate you and staff to continue to take action
- Provide a filter for other opportunities and keep you focused
- Help you or staff to overcome resistance
- Help make you and staff conscious of progress

Identify Your Assumptions

When determining your marketing goals, you will need to apply some assumptions you have made concerning the marketing climate. Assumptions may be based on knowledge of an upcoming event (i.e., Costco is going to open a store within a mile of your practice). It may be based on historical patterns (i.e., in January, 50% of the over 70 population goes to Florida for 4 months). It may be based on an economical event (i.e., the stock market is overdue to have a corrective drop). These assumptions should be stated and considered when determining the likelihood of success of your goals.

Identify Your Objectives

Objectives will differ from goals in that the goal will encompass a broader vision of what you wish to accomplish, whereas the objectives will define a means to an end. Each of the goals you have identified will be further defined by a series of objectives. Objectives are precise statements that are typically tangible and measurable. They are meant to be realistic targets for attaining the goal. Marketing objectives should be about the products you sell (tangible and intangible). They should not be confused with pricing objectives or advertising objectives.

Many reference materials talk about writing "SMART objectives." This refers to an acronym built around five characteristics of an efficient objective: specific, measurable, achievable, relevant, and timely.

This acronym is quite useful with respect to creating and implementing a marketing plan for your practice. By sticking to a SMART marketing plan, you are more likely to achieve the financial goals of your practice. Let's take a closer look at how you can bring these essential traits to life as you create and implement your marketing plan.

Be Specific

The characteristic answers the question, "What exactly, in numbers, are we going to do?" Identify a percentage of change or number of patients to be affected. Be precise with the criterion for accomplishment.

Bad example: Increase the number of new patients seen.

Good example: BEST Audiology will increase annual new patient appointments by 10% compared to previous year totals, beginning in January 2015.

Be Measurable

When we say that an objective must be measurable, we mean there is a stringent need to have the possibility to measure, to track the action(s) associated with the given objective. We must set up a distinct system or establish clear procedures of how the actions will be monitored, measured, and recorded. If an objective and the actions pertaining to it cannot be quantified, it is probably not an objective and should be reconsidered.

Bad example: We will have good patient satisfaction.

Good example: We will maintain a monthly average score of 4.5/5.0 on a completed and collected Hearing Satisfaction Survey provided to patients following initial and annual appointments.

Be Achievable

Think your objective through. Be honest and realistic. An objective that is too grandiose or lofty many not be attainable. On the other hand, an objective that is not lofty enough will not provide sufficient change. Objectives should be designed to inspire advancement and may even be difficult as long as they're realistic and not futile. You should ask yourself if you can get it done in the proposed time frame, in the current economic climate, with the resources that are available or obtainable.

Bad example: BEST Audiology will become the recognized leader in hearing health care.

Good example: Ten percent of the target market will be able to identify three services provided by BEST Audiology as measured by a random marketing survey to be administered by John's Marketing Company.

Be Relevant

Being "relevant" means establishing appropriate objectives for a specific staff member or department. The objective must be in line with what the job or position is capable of attaining.

Bad example: The receptionist will help increase the number of hearing aids sold.

Good example: The receptionist will be responsible to fill 80% of available appointment times each week through the use of a call list, tested not sold list, or cancellation list.

Be Timely

Your objectives must have a clear, realistic timeframe of when it will start and/or when it will end. Without having a defined timeframe, there will be no urgency to attain that objective.

Without a start and finish, a goal can lay in limbo. It will not be a motivational tool to prompt you or staff to "get busy," nor will there be a sense of accomplishment when it is attained.

Bad example: We will increase sales in the future.

Good example: BEST Audiology will increase annual gross sales in dollars, compared to the previous year, by 10% over the next 12 months beginning on January 1, 2015.

Identify Your Tactics

Your tactics will be the strategic methods used to promote your products to your target market. The tactics you choose should support your overall marketing strategy and your overall business philosophy. These tactics are the broad activities or tasks that you will undertake to accomplish the objective. Use action words like *educate, inform, sell,* or *guarantee.* Identify in your tactic the target market (identified in the marketing strategy) and the medium (consider the marketing mix).

The marketing medium is the tactic that will serve as the vehicle you use to deliver your message. There will be many mediums to choose from, all of various costs and visibility. It is beneficial to determine what resources are at your disposal. Examples of internal and external tactic include the following:

Internal: staff, patients, existing marketing materials, financial, location, and physical plant

External: referral sources, media, other related organizations, events

Often your marketing message will be promoted through multiple mediums. The key is to identify a combination that will meet your budget, reflect your values, and persuade consumers to become your patients.

Bad example: Use a newspaper advertisement to promote a youth hearing conservation program.

Good example: Contact local schools and hunting safety programs with flyers promoting BEST Audiology's youth hearing conservation program.

Identify Your Actions

Once individual marketing tactics have been flushed out and formulated, specific actions for each tactic need to be created. In the example below, note how the goal, assumptions, and objectives flow into a specific tactic with several actions. The actions are particular behaviors that are executed by you and your staff, which can usually be tracked and improved.

Goal: Increase hearing aid satisfaction.

Assumption: Satisfied hearing aid users will help increase our sales through positive word-of-mouth promotion.

Assumption: Aural rehabilitation training increases user satisfaction with their hearing aids.

Objective: Increase participation in the Aural Rehabilitation Workshop (ARW) by adding three new attendees each month for the next 12 months beginning on January 1, 2015.

Tactic: Use direct mail, personal contact, and affiliation with key referral sources to promote the ARW offered at a monthly evening program at BEST Audiology. The target market is all patients experiencing communication difficulties despite hearing aid use regardless of where they received their amplification and their significant others.

Action: John's marketing company will develop an informational direct mail piece to be distributed quarterly to the target market of adults older than 70 years in the target market area.

Action: BEST Audiology's front deck staff will call patients who scored 2 or lower on the Hearing Satisfaction Survey at their annual evaluation and invite them to participate in the ARW.

Action: BEST Audiology will contact the local HLAA chapter monthly, in person or by written communication, to inform/remind leaders of the ARW and provide copies of the informational direct mail piece for dissemination to their club members.

Action: Front desk staff will keep a count of ARW attendees monthly and compare numbers to those obtained the year prior.

You will note that the goal is general, the assumptions identify key beliefs, the objective is specific, the tactic defines who will be targeted and how they will be contacted, and the actions define who will "own" the action and how it will be measured.

Identify Your Budget

The goal of your marketing budget is to control expenses and project your revenues. It also provides a sense of stability that keeps you from being reactive to an unforeseen change or events. Having a marketing budget also makes it easy to resist an impulse marketing activity. A realistic budget establishes a standard of performance for your actions and communicates those standards to others responsible for implementing your marketing plan.

Having data from your prior marketing activities and knowing the cost/benefit of previous campaigns will provide you with a realistic starting point for your budget development. Consider your marketing plan objectives, sales history, and prior activities (successful and unsuccessful). Consider a change in your budget due to an opportunity identified in your annual SWOT analysis. Prioritize your spending to match your priorities identified in your goals and your marketing message.

There are several approaches to creating a marketing budget. Examples of these approaches may include basing your budget on per-unit sales, seasonal activities, cash flow, or percentages of projected or past gross sales. Select a budget methodology that will work best for your business. You may want to select your method based on how you track your sales and revenues or on industry standards. One of the best ways to create your budget is to build off of your previous year's performance. Look at trends and expectations from each marketing activity and modify these numbers based on your expectations for the upcoming year. Apply assumptions about market changes, trends, and the economic forecast. If you do not have previous marketing data or budget information available, talk with a noncompetitive colleague or review previous sales records and try to glean information about when sales were made in relation to the marketing activities. You may also put greater reliance on industry information, which will require more research to determine your budget. See Table 3–2 for an example of a simple marketing budget. Note how activities have been assigned to specific months, along with an approximate dollar amount for each activity.

New practices or practices with no history of marketing efforts should realistically budget at 10% to 12% of the estimated annual gross. Most marketing experts suggest that an established small business should budget 7% to 10% of its gross revenues for marketing. Beyond this rule of thumb, marketing costs will vary depending on these factors:

- How aggressively the competition is marketing and what is required to offset their marketing efforts
- The age of the practice. Existing practices have a history in the community and will not need to allocate funds for initial market exposure.
- Introduction of a new location
- Introduction of a new feature to an existing practice (staff, service, technology)
- Improve the practice image because of an incident or outcome that portrayed the practice in a negative way

It is important to recognize that some of the marketing expense is covered in the practice budget. For example, business cards and letterhead may appear in your office supplies when in fact they are marketing tools. Another example may be contributions. These may be marketing activities (especially if

Table 3–2. Sample Budgeting Plan

Marketing Activity	January	February	March	April	May	June	6 Months	Notes
Direct mail			3,000				3,000	For the educational programs
Newspaper		Free		Free		Free	0	Use press releases
TV spot development				3,500			3,500	Local marketing company
TV-run program				1,500	1,500	1,500	4,500	Run 2- to 3-month series
Radio spot				500	1,000	1,000	2,500	Includes setup and talent
Website development	1,500						1,500	Onetime expense to upgrade
Email campaign			500		500		1,000	Development and drop
SEO optimizing	1,000	1,000	1,000	1,000	1,000	1,000	6,000	Pay per click may be less
Social media	50	50	50	50	50	50	300	Staff charge 1 h/wk

Marketing Activity	January	February	March	April	May	June	6 Months	Notes
Coffee hour chat	100	100	100	100	100	100	600	Refreshments
Physician referral program			100		100		200	Materials and staff time
Patient referral program	60	20	40	70	100	80	370	Based on number of referrals
Newsletter		3,000			3,000		6,000	10,000-color piece 4× year
Educational seminar			200			200	400	Materials and refreshments
Phonebook	500	500	500	500	500	500	3,000	Down from previous year $988/mo
Local magazine ad			500			500	1,000	Targeted exposure
Local school publications	250						250	2× year in event calendar
Total costs	3,460	4,670	5,990	7,220	7,850	4,930	34,120	

Notes. All figures are in American dollars ($).

you generate a press release) but will be accounted for in the general budget. Be aware of these expenses and make a decision about where you will account for them. Identify all cost-related marketing efforts and determine what the activity is, when will it occur, and how much will be budgeted.

Keep detailed files describing the cost, distribution area, lead time, market penetration, and return on investment. Prepare a profit and loss statement for all marketing efforts and determine the value of that activity. Not all marketing activities will be assessable by connected sales or profits but may be a valuable activity to promote good will. When assigning a value to the activity, include the intangible. Marketing activities may include the following:

- Advertising—TV, radio, billboards, newspaper, direct mail, email
- Press releases, new equipment, new office, new staff, noteworthy activity, education
- Signage, Yellow Pages
- Educational programs, "ask the expert," lunch & learn, guest speaker, newsletter
- Marketing materials to referring sources, brochures, free batteries, screening packets
- Customer appreciation activities, picnic, referral program, birthday cards, mugs, and so on
- Web-based media, Facebook, Twitter, website, landing pages
- Memberships in community professional and social organizations or charitable donations
- Marketing activities your staff has engaged in, such as representing you in a local service club or health fairs

Tracking

The final part of the marketing plan is probably the most important—tracking. Tracking will allow you to identify which of your marketing activities, messages, and mediums are most successful

(Table 3–3). Many of the electronic record software systems even prompt you and staff to identify how your patients found their way into your office. The information will help identify areas of the target market that are not being moved to action and areas where a change in the marketing mix may be necessary. The data may also be used to develop a profit and loss statement for each marketing activity. Keep in mind that "profit and loss" may apply to your time, effort, visibility, and community standing and not just income.

Make sure that each action item in your marketing plan has an "owner." This person will be responsible for the action's implementation and tracking outcome. It is good practice to have staff provide information about the outcomes of their action items during staff meetings. Not only will this provide an opportunity for all staff members to hear what is working and what is not working, but it can also be a team-building exercise when staff strives to support an objective that they have helped define. Make accountability part of staff key performance indicators (KPIs) to help keep staff motivated and cooperative with implementation and monitoring.

Your marketing plan is not a passive document. It will change and grow as opportunities arise and objectives expand. To be successful, be sure to have the following in place:

- Qualified goals
- Compatibility of professional and personal goals
- Limited number of manageable goals
- Synergistic, executable marketing objectives, tactics, and actions
- Adequate resources in staff, time, and money
- Definition of how you will track outcomes
- Contingency plans for unexpected threats
- Staff involvement and commitment to follow the plan

Although developing a marketing plan is a proactive exercise that should eliminate the need to be reactive to changes, it cannot safeguard you from unexpected threats. Your marketing plan must be flexible enough to adapt if new threats become evident, threats that may affect your bottom line such as a change in the

Table 3–3. An Example of a Tracking Form

Week			Recall Program	Call Center Call	Reactivation	Promotional Offer	Print Ad	Flyer Insert	Direct Mail	Radio	Television Station
Date	Caller's Name	Phone									

Promotions Currently:	Directories:
Open House (O)	Yellow Book Central (C)
Bring a Friend (B)	Yellow Book North (N)
Upgrade Program (U)	Web (W)

Directory	Street Signage	Friend—Who	Physician Office—ID	Insurance Referral	Reason for Call	Comments	Appt. Scheduled	By

Seen on Facebook Tally:

economy, staff changes, personal emergencies, and unforeseen problems with the physical plan or suppliers. Add objectives and action items when they support both the goal and the budget. See Appendix 3–A for a sample marketing plan for BEST Audiology Practice.

"The future depends on what we do in the present."

—Mohandas Gandhi

REFERENCES

Foltner, K., & Mansfield, B. (2006). Branding audiology: It's a budding opportunity. *Hearing Journal, 59*(5), 41–44.

Frey, D. (2003). *The small business marketing bible.* Minneapolis, MN: Nasus Publishing.

Gartenstein, D. (2014). *Marketing strategy vs. marketing plan.* Retrieved June 10, 2014, from http://www.ehow.com/info_8054569_marketing -strategy-vs-marketing-plan.html

Goulston, M. (2007). Archived blog submission July 15, 2007. Usable insights. Retrieved August 28, 2014, from http://markgoulston.com/ sell-them-what-they-want-2/

Kochkin, S. (2005). *MarkeTrak VII: The impact of untreated hearing loss on household income.* Retrieved June 8, 2014, from http://www .betterhearing.org/pdfs/MarkeTrak7_Kochkin_August2005.pdf

Lauterhorn, B. (1990). *New marketing litany: Four Ps passé: C-words take over.* Retrieved June 1, 2014, from https://readtiger.com/wkp/ en/Marketing_mix#Lauterborn.27s_four_Cs

Marston, C. (2007). *Motivating the "what's in it for me?" workforce manage across the generational divide and increase profits.* Hoboken, NJ: John Wiley.

McCarthy, E. (1964). *Basic marketing: A managerial approach* (pp. 45–55, 167–206, 607). Homewood, IL: Irwin.

McDonald, M. (2007). *Marketing plans: How to prepare them, how to use them* (6th ed., pp. 29–61, 184–327). Amsterdam, the Netherlands: Elsevier/Butterworth-Heinemann.

Porter, M. E. (1980). *Competitive Strategy.* New York, NY: Free Press.

Traynor, R. (2014). Fundamentals of marketing the audiology practice. In R. Glaser & R. Traynor (Eds.), *Strategic practice management: Business and procedural considerations* (2nd ed., pp. 119–160). San Diego, CA: Plural.

APPENDIX 3–A
SAMPLE MARKETING PLAN

MARKETING MISSION

The Purpose for Your Marketing Efforts

BEST Audiology will increase sales and ultimately profitability by educating consumers about the benefits of our holistic, highly skilled approach to minimizing the negative effects of tinnitus and hearing loss through the use of scientific knowledge, state-of-the-art technology, and incomparable service.

MARKETING STRATEGY

Product Identification

BEST Audiology will offer a holistic approach to providing improved communication ability to our patients. We recognize that this will take a combination of the following:

- Physical goods, including hearing aids, batteries, cleaning supplies, assistive listening devices, LACE Aural Rehabilitation home and online programs, and access to the resource library offering an opportunity for patients to check out on loan assistive listening products, informative books, and videos dealing with hearing and hearing loss
- Services, including patient education, diagnostic audiometric assessment, OAE, ABR, ENG, tinnitus treatment, aural rehabilitation services, counseling, outcome measures,

user satisfaction surveys, follow-up, repair, ALD demonstration, access to community resources, cleaning, and maintenance services

■ Staff: reception, insurance/billing specialist, technician, and adult and pediatric audiologists

■ Community involvement: participation in local service organizations and clubs, financial support to local the HLAA chapter and Quota Club to bring awareness of the detrimental effects of hearing loss to the consumer

■ Professionalism: adherence to a code of conduct that ensures ethical behavior and places the needs of the patient as the primary focus of service, communication with other health care professionals to ensure holistic wellness, and continued education to ensure knowledge of current treatment options

BEST Audiology uses a diverse line of physical goods to offer a competitive pricing range, cosmetic appeal, versatile features, and performance options. We focus on identifying and addressing patient expectations for those variables. BEST Audiology provides counseling and support services to validate patient success, including LACE training, group aural rehabilitation class, and home study aural rehabilitation exercises. Product marketing will focus on BEST Audiology's ability to provide "Problem Solution" and our commitment to improving the lives of the people in our community. Advertising will focus on the value of our intangible products and services, as opposed to brand name or pricing of the tangible goods.

Geographic Description

The BEST Audiology Company is centrally located in a geographical target market area approximately 30 miles in diameter encompassing the more affluent northern Richmond County and the eastern half of York County. The practice is accessible within a 30-minute drive, which is consistent with 90% of the current patient demographic data. Two cable television carriers, six primary contemporary or talk radio stations, one major newspaper, and four smaller local newspapers service the area. The geographical market area has approximately 350,000 adult residences.

Demographic Description

The average household income in the target market area is $63,000 with a per-capita income average of $36,500. The annual per-capita sales average is $21,943. The target market is educated, with 32% of the population having a minimum of a bachelor's degree. This is higher than the national average of 22%. Over 60% of the target area population is currently employed, but the percentage of residents older than 50 years is 43%. Homes in the market area have a median value of $140,000, which is slightly higher than the state median value of $115,000 and are primarily owner occupied with a rate of 76%. The target market area is educated, employed, and vested in the community as evident by the high percentage of homeownership. The market has renewable income and higher retail-sales-per-capita figures compared to state averages. These are good indicators of an appropriate target market and purchasing potential.

Demographic data show that approximately 35,000 (10%) of the residents are older than 75 years, and there are approximately 116,000 between the ages of 45 and 74 years. Applying the NICDC statistics for hearing loss (47% older than 75 years, 30% between ages 65 and 74 years, and 18% between ages 45 and 64 years) shows a target population of 45,450 potential consumers for audiometric services and products. In the geographical target market, there are eight internal medicine physicians and three geriatric general practice physicians, four endocrinologists, four cardiologists, and two podiatrists who provide service to the adult diabetic population. There are two oncology physicians not exclusively tied to the two local hospital systems (dispensing audiology services are present in both hospital systems). There is one nondispensing ENT physician in the marketing area. He does have audiology support for testing but does not offer any tangible goods. The target area also has two active Lions Clubs, a local HLAA chapter, and a Quota Club.

Definition of Competition

Competition for hearing aid sales within the target market includes two commercial hearing aid dealer offices. Location "A" is approximately ½ mile west and on the same road as my practice. Location "B" is also on the same road and is approximately 3 miles from my location. One big-box competitor, "C," is located 8 miles south of this practice. There are two ENT offices that employ audiologists. Practice "D" is located 6 miles south of this location and employs one full-time audiologist and one part-time audiologist. Practice "E" is located 8 miles southwest of this location and employs two full-time dispensing audiologists. Commercial dealer office "A" represents a national chain offering service in hundreds of locations across the United States, appealing to patients who travel or reside in another state for a portion of the year. They do, however, have difficulty retaining staff. Because of their national ownership, they do not have strong community ties. Commercial site "B" has a reputation for aggressive sales pitch and poor patient follow-up. They advertise heavily in the city newspaper but not in the local community paper. Site "B" does not have audiology staff or support. They do offer on-site service to four senior living communities within the target market area. Big-box location "C" does not offer audiology services or participate with insurance coverage, has limited visibility, and has a physical plant that is crowded, noisy, and highly retail oriented. They do offer low cost. Audiology practice "D" provides hearing aid sales and audiological services in support of three ENT physicians. They offer below-market pricing for hearing instruments and direct referrals from the ENT. These factors are offset by poor visibility and no direct access to audiological services without going through the ENT. They also have limited patient access hours as they must support ENT referrals for testing. Location "E" is primarily a pediatric ENT with audiology support. Although they are a dispensing practice and will occasionally fit adults, we do not share the same target market.

SWOT ANALYSIS

Strength

BEST Audiology product differentiation strategy is the result of a strong market orientation, commitment to high-quality products, and customized personal care. The product line includes multiple manufacturers to provide consumers with a broad range of pricing, technology level, features, and styles. Two of the top competitor offices offer only one manufacturer, limiting patient options. BEST Audiology also has very little staff turnover. This provides a reliable, consistent, recognizable, and trusted staff recognition for the patient. This has been ranked as an important factor through the annual patient survey. The experienced staff promotes camaraderie with coworkers and clients, fostering trusted communication and intuitive responses to patient needs. Long-term relationships with primary health centers in the area have been cultivated over the long term, helping to ensure consistent, cooperative communication between service providers.

Weakness

BEST Audiology has been unable to obtain maximum manufacturer volume discounts due to multiple providers of goods. This reduces the competitiveness of our pricing structure when comparing similar products. Because we do not work with private label products, patients are able to shop around and compare our pricing to the competition. BEST Audiology does not have an ENT physician in the area that does not dispense hearing aids. This makes it very difficult to have appropriate medical resources for referral and be assured that the referral will return to BEST for hearing aid sale.

Opportunities

BEST has had an increase in referrals from competitive practices because the chain stores do not have product flexibility or pricing flexibility. BEST has also been able to appeal to the consumer's need to support local business. With the fewer locally owned practices, national chain stores have reduced the number of competitors meeting this criterion. More patients have been price shopping, but BEST is often able to show the benefit of value-added services. Many of the chain stores have lost audiology support after 1 to 2 years. This has caused a decline in repeat business. Many of these patients are now looking for new providers.

Threats

Every ENT in the area has a dispensing audiologist on staff. Big-chain companies have been active in the area and purchased several of our competitors. This has increased the amount and frequency of large advertisement campaigns, including direct mail, television ads, newspaper ads, and inserts. Pricing has been a focal point of their campaigns, resulting in more patients asking for price comparisons.

Marketing Message

BEST Audiology will market to a broad patient base specializing in adult hearing aid fitting. We will identify three separate targeted marketing groups—senior adults, working adults, and children of senior adults. The market message will focus on the following:

1. High patient satisfaction
2. The value of professional staff and services
3. Convenient hours and easy access
4. Benefits of supporting local business

MARKETING PLAN

Based on business goals, marketing mission, and marketing strategy.

Goal: Increase annual hearing aid gross sales from $ to $$.

Assumption: BEST's convenient hours and exemplary professional services increase the likelihood of patient satisfaction over our competitors.

Assumption: BEST's satisfied hearing aid users will help increase our sales through positive word-of-mouth promotion and repeat sales.

Assumption: Aural rehabilitation training increases user satisfaction with their hearing aids.

Objective: Increase participation in the Aural Rehabilitation Workshop (ARW) by adding three new attendees each month for the next 12 months beginning on January 1, 2015.

Tactic: Use direct mail, personal contact, and affiliation with key referral sources to promote the ARW offered at a monthly evening program at ABC Audiology. The target market is all patients experiencing communication difficulties despite hearing aid use regardless of where they received their amplification and their significant others.

Action: John's marketing company will develop an informational direct mail piece to be distributed quarterly to the target market of adults older than 70 years in the target market area.

Action: BEST's front desk staff will call patients who scored 2 or lower on the Hearing Satisfaction Survey at their annual evaluation and invite them to participate in the ARW.

Action: Audiology will contact the local HLAA chapter monthly, in person or by written communication, to inform/remind leaders of the ARW and provide copies of the informational direct mail piece for dissemination to their club members.

Action: Front desk staff will keep a count of ARW attendees monthly and compare numbers to those obtained the year prior.

Objective: Increase the annual number of word-of-mouth referrals as identified by a new patient listing a "referred by" name on the initial intake sheet, from 113 identified in 2014 to 150 in January 2016, beginning January 1, 2015.

Tactic: Use multimedia avenues and staff call-to-action to describe and promote the patient referral program (PRP) to existing patients, significant other support persons, family, and friends.

Action: Have John's marketing company develop a standard column for inclusion in the newsletters, describing the PRP program prior to the January publication.

Action: Audiology and staff will remind patients of the PRP and ask them to make a referral if they have been satisfied with BEST services. This will be tracked by initialed designation on the patient visit checklist. This will be tracked for KPI goals.

Action: BEST front desk staff will illicit response for "referred by" on the new patient intake form. This will be tracked for KPI goals.

Action: Front desk staff will post information and benefits of PRP on Facebook once a month for 12 months beginning in January 2015.

4

MARKETING IN A MODERN PRACTICE: A REAL-WORLD PERSPECTIVE

Geoffrey Cooling

The world is changing and constantly evolving. The world of innovation and technology is changing at a frightening rate. Things that were unimaginable even 10 years ago are commonplace today. The Internet has made many things possible, and the explosion of its uptake is truly awe inspiring. The Internet has brought many challenges to many industries. To be more correct, the openness of the Internet and its use by consumers have brought about many of these challenges.

Consumers have changed and changed radically. They are more demanding and have more knowledge. These two considerations when aligned can make it difficult for any business. It has been labeled the age of the consumer for good reason. The power within a transaction has moved toward the purchaser.

We have been seeing this happen in our profession for about the past 5 years. It is only accelerating, and like Pandora's box, there is no going back.

Within our industry, the challenges that are arising are new business models, Internet provision, low-margin and high-volume providers, and so on. I will not depress you by going on. However, I believe in the traditional service delivery model, I believe it has a future, and I believe it is the best model for patients. The traditional model, however, needs to look at how best it can convince patients that this is so. I hope to explore this question and others in this chapter. The purpose of this chapter is to provide you with a real-world example of how your daily routine in the clinic builds your brand perception. Everything you do is part of your marketing efforts.

Everything within this chapter stems from a hard-won lesson. I hope to tell you what I have discovered in order that you don't have to make the mistakes I have made. In doing this, I hope to pass on knowledge, will probably make you laugh, sometimes make you go through a Homer Simpson-esque DOH! moment, and try to cover everything that I think will help you to secure your businesses future. Before we move into the daily activities in a best clinical practice and how they are reflective of your entire marketing strategy, let's examine the essential aspects of a marketing plan and budget.

YOUR MARKETING BUDGET

I think, though, that it is important for me to qualify what I believe is marketing. I think that all activities that speak to a prospective patient and all activities that speak to an actual patient, already logged into your database, fall under the term *marketing*. So included in my budget is planned communications and activities around patients. I set my marketing budget at 12% of my expected revenue and then break it down into a monthly amount. Some people seem surprised at that figure, and I know according to industry benchmark surveys, it seems very high. I think that 12% is ideal for me; it gives me the marketing power and activities that I need to drive enquiries and sales.

It is important that you remember your existing patients. A sale in our profession is never finished; it continues long past the purchase, and you really need to know and understand that. The courting process is continual. With this in mind, I plan marketing activities like free giveaways throughout the year. Things like batteries for birthdays, drying tubs and tablets for the summer, and free wax filters. All of these things are effective in my marketing strategy, but they cost me money. I budget for them in my marketing plan.

MARKETING PLAN

A 12-month marketing plan outlines your activity for the coming year. Assess your performance last year and plan out marketing activities that will help you deliver this year. I look at performance for last year and compare to the marketing activities I have undertaken.

I then compare that data against my revenue data. I can then plan to spend on marketing that I know that works when I know I am going to need it. That is a marketing plan in synopsis. In order to draw up one, you need data that assist you to do so. We will talk about that later; let's focus on your marketing plan first.

Your marketing plan needs to contain at its highest level campaigns that you plan to run. You identify campaigns that will bring people to your location. You must think about the calls to actions for those campaigns and the value proposition. You then detail how you will deliver those campaigns and cost them. A proven strategy is to plan four major quarterly advertising campaigns; these can be your headline promotions.

But it doesn't end there. In between those campaigns, you need continuous activity. Activity that will continue to drive appointments and enquiries. The marketing plan needs to cover all channels, including online channels and traditional marketing channels. Our demographic—which is mainly individuals older than 65 years—more than any other demographic is cautious; they need confidence to make a purchase decision.

A consistent campaign cannot be overstated. My practice purchases a yearly place setting in three local newspapers. That placement is on the same page in the same place every 2 weeks without fail. Because we are buying in advance, we get fantastic rates. We also schedule insert advertising in these papers and reserve it loosely with them. This allows us to purchase advertising from these newspapers at exceptionally reasonable rates.

We have standard advertisements that we cycle during the year. During an insert period for a major campaign, we use advertisements designed to support the campaign. Because we are regular purchasers of ad space, we also get free editorials or better termed advertorials during these periods. All of this activity is heavily supported with content marketing and website marketing.

We agree to our activity loosely in advance with these newspapers. It gives us really strong buying power, and it also helps us with our relationship with those papers. The staff there will, and does, go the extra mile for us because we are established customers. While traditional marketing is waning for return on investment, this type of consistent marketing activity is essential for our practice.

Traditional advertising builds and enforces brand awareness, and more important, it builds confidence. Confidence that can be used every quarter when we run an ad that is attempting to generate office traffic in our marketing footprint. The return on investment on this activity can be patchy; however, our practice has data to show that this type of activity is still cost-effective over the long run.

We know from our reports that 30% of our revenue comes from walk-in traffic. We are situated on High Street, which is the British equivalent of any busy shopping area in North America, and we are most definitely deployed to take full advantage of that fact. In other words, our shop fronts scream for attention. We are doing as much as possible to attract walk-in traffic. More than likely, these walk-ins have seen us in the local paper, and they have noticed our adverts whether they were cognizant of them or not. Then, on the fateful day they happened to be on High Street, they noticed the shop and thought to themselves, "I must go and have a chat with those people."

So a clear and written marketing plan based on a strategy that has been discerned from historical data is imperative. It will allow you some comfort and faith that your practice isn't going to collapse. It will deliver to you the ability to demand best rates for marketing based on planned activities. Most important, it will help quell that gnawing voice in your head that the end is nigh every time you have a slow week.

MARKETING CALENDAR

Yes, I can hear you from here, a marketing plan and a calendar? I feel your pain; don't forget, I have been through this. A marketing calendar allows you to put your marketing plan into action. You can clearly mark out on a calendar exactly what activity you are undertaking and when you are undertaking it. You can set reminders for those activities and the planning functions pertaining to those activities.

Believe me, if you are running a practice that's as busy as mine, you need this calendar. I have problems remembering what day it is most days; I set reminders for everything. My phone is going to melt down or explode one of these days. The marketing calendar lets you clearly lay out the marketing plan in chronological order.

It also gives you the facility to let certain events become part of your marketing plan. Think about World Diabetes Day, World Heart Health Day, World Alzheimer's Day, and Hearing Awareness Week. All of these are real activities that you can fit into your calendar. Recording them allows you the opportunity to write articles and run advertisements that keep you current in the mind of the customer.

Because they are wider health campaigns, they also give you the opportunity to be put in front of people who may never have thought to see you. All of this provided by a calendar? How cool is that? I know you are busy, I get it; I'm busy too, but you need to do this stuff so you can keep busy seeing more patients and generating revenue. Tools like plans and calendars actually take the pressure off.

After the initial expenditure of time and effort to come up with plans and calendars, you can then auto pilot them with tools such as Outlook or Google calendar. I get a reminder

4 weeks before Hearing Awareness Week that it is happening. I then begin to write an article that will take advantage of that search term. I also design adverts that will cater to it. Voilà, you got enquiries and appointments.

TRADITIONAL MEDIA

Businesses of all sizes within our profession are looking at strategies to maximize opportunities and decrease risk. More and more businesses find themselves with decreasing returns—in particular, on traditional marketing tactics and the prevailing sense of downward pressures on margins and profitability. This is compounded by new entrants to the market and changing habits of our demographic. Our demographic is more educated, more demanding, and more aware of their choices available today than ever before.

Traditional news media marketing can still deliver some results. However, in order for that to happen, how you present your advertisements has needed to change. Size of adverts needs to be large, and the call to action needs to be strong. Quite often, the return is increased if the advert is undertaken on a newspaper insert rather than an advert in the paper. Traditional advertisements clamor for attention, unless they are half or full page. Even then they may be easily ignored unless they are colorful, with a really strong call to action.

Newspaper Inserts

Newspaper inserts are a leaflet inserted between the pages of a newspaper. There are endless amounts of sizes and types of leaflets that can be printed. We find these leaflets give us the single best return on investment. They consistently come in below the 12% ceiling I set for marketing costs as a percentage of returns.

The key is to use them to support major campaigns with really strong calls to action. I believe they work because more people see them. It is easy to ignore traditional newspaper adverts; I manage to read the Sunday paper from cover to cover every week without consciously seeing one advert. However, when something drops out of the paper, I always pick it up and look at it.

With this fact in mind, you need to carefully design your insert. Color, imagery, and headline are imperative. We always go with a strong large headline that immediately states what the offer is about. We include imagery that immediately lets people know that the leaflet is about hearing. We always use the brand colors of the practice because they are a pleasing if different combination.

Using this strategy, you can be surer that your advertisement is getting viewed by readers. You can be surer that your money is not wasted. This strategy has paid off for me. I am sure that you are more than aware that half- and full-page advertisements are quite expensive, particularly if you are doing an advertisement in a large or national newspaper. While it certainly seems that return on investment on traditional marketing appears to be almost nonexistent, I feel that traditional marketing is still valid, certainly under the conditions I have discussed.

ONLINE MARKETING

Online marketing has come strongly to the fore in recent years. Your website has truly become your shop window to the world. Conditions have changed, though; a website is not enough. Your website needs to be supported by a consistent online strategy. This strategy needs to include social media elements, content marketing strategy, and more than a tip of the head to search engine optimization (SEO) principles. A key part of any online marketing strategy has become Google Authorship. In online marketing terms, we have to realize that Google is the 500-pound gorilla in the corner.

Don't believe for a minute that an online marketing strategy is a future need. You are fooling yourself; you needed it about 2 years ago. The funny thing is, though, because of the lack of consistent online strategy within our profession, many audiologists think online marketing is ineffective. Let's dive into the online marketing world and what you need to do.

An Online Marketing Strategy for Audiology

Step 1

Put a blog on your website. I really love WordPress for this. It is a fantastic content management system that is easy to use. There are also reams and reams of instruction about how to post out there. WordPress has a massive community who is only too willing to help newbies. There is also a massive amount of free themes and plug-ins that extend the ease and power of Word-Press. Once your blog is set up and looks the way you want it to, go to Step 2.

Step 2

This is a key step, an imperative step; don't miss out on this one. Set up Google Authorship for yourself. Simply set up a Google+ account and then link it to your website and your blog. Don't panic: There are plug-ins on the WordPress side that will help. The website will either need a line of code or possibly a plug-in depending on what content management system is being used to power your website.

Step 3

Set up social media profiles for your business on Facebook, Google+, Twitter, and any other network you feel inclined to use. Make sure these profiles are presented well with your logo, key information details, and any tagline that you particularly like. Keep it consistent across networks; these are your business profiles and demand consistent branding. You should and most likely will engage with people on these networks. However, they are primarily to be used to support your content and your website.

Google+ in particular will give you real benefits in search engine returns if you use it properly. Google is the predominant search engine in the world. It will probably remain so for some time and, therefore, we cannot ignore it. It makes sense that its social network is key in any content marketing strategy.

Step 4

Back to your blog for this one; ensure that your blog is connected to all of your social media accounts. Publicize, a feature on WordPress, will automatically post details of your latest blog post to your social media accounts if you set it up. This is an imperative; it will support your blog posts and allow them the opportunity to appear on the search returns.

Step 5

Time to begin posting content: The content needs to be good, informative, something that somebody wants to read. It needs to be written in your own voice, the voice you use when you speak to patients. Allow your personality to shine through, your compassion, your sense of empathy, your knowledge. If you do it right and keep true to yourself and your brand, you will be doing it well.

Consider both your business brand and your personal brand. Consider what they are, what you feel they are. (If you are unsure about your personal brand, go back and read Chapter 1 for some pointers.) Write those points down, the bullet points of your brand. Keep them to one side because we will come back to them. To write a blog post, you need to consider who you are writing that post for. Think about their personality; really consider who they are and what their issues are. What information do they want, and how do they want it displayed? If you do this, really do it; you can then write powerful content that will touch the people you wish to touch.

Step 6

You can hire someone to do Steps 1 to 5 with insight and guidance from you.

Content Marketing

What you say in an article, blog post, or advertorial is critical. This is the "content" of content marketing, which has come to the fore in the past few years. It has been accepted as a key part of any online strategy for some time. Content will be the main driver of your online strategy as we move through the next decade. Without it, your strategy is doomed to failure. Content marketing is based on good educational articles—articles that cater to the questions your target market is asking. While the physical mechanics of this are relatively complex, the core of it is as simple as that. Let's get into some of the details of online marketing.

Targeting Search

It used to be easier to target searches. Google once made that information freely available. Unfortunately, it's not quite as easy to get the information any longer. If you have an AdWords account with Google, you can still look at keywords, their value, and their search relevance. This is not the whole story, though. While keywords are an important factor, people rarely search keywords alone.

You need to consider how people will phrase a search using the keywords that matter. So they won't just search for hearing aids, they might search for hearing aids prices. Or modern hearing aids or Unitron hearing aids and so on. You also need to understand that they may also localize the search term.

If you think about it clearly, it makes perfect sense. You are in Detroit, or London, or Berlin and you need a plumber. Do you search for Plumber or plumber in Detroit, or London, or Berlin? What you are targeting is called long-tail key phrases, not just keywords. Targeting search is about the following:

1. Identify keywords and phrases around your industry.
2. Localize the data in order that you can target real prospects.
3. Deploy a SEO strategy designed to leverage those localized terms.
4. Design and deploy content through your online marketing channel to leverage the data.
5. Leverage that content through multiple online channels, Twitter, Facebook, and Google+, in order to create solid backlinks that drive your organic search returns.

Keywords

As I said, finding the keywords is not quite as easy as it once was. The information about those keywords, their relevance, and their search prevalence are exceptionally difficult to get a hold of. I happen to have a list of keywords and their search prevalence from 2013 (Table 4–1). We can use it to extrapolate what keywords are still important.

Although this is old information, it still has real value. Although there will be new keyword searches, particularly in relation to the release of new products, we can keep abreast of them and are probably in the best position to ascertain or guess how popular they might be. In particular, I am thinking about something like the Made For iPhone hearing aids.

Table 4–1. Keywords of 2013

Keyword	Searches	Keyword	Searches
hearing	6,120,000	cost hearing aids	40,500
aids aid	4,090,000	hearing aids cost	40,500
aids hearing	823,000	cost of hearing aid	40,500
which hearing aids	823,000	hearing aid cost	40,500
about hearing aids	823,000	cost of a hearing aid	40,500
aids for hearing	823,000	cost hearing aid	40,500
where to get hearing aids	823,000	aid batteries	40,500
what is hearing aids	823,000	price hearing aids	40,500
what is a hearing aids	823,000	hearing aids price	40,500
hearing aids hearing aids	823,000	price of hearing aids	40,500

continues

Table 4–1. *continued*

Keyword	Searches	Keyword	Searches
for hearing aids	823,000	prices of hearing aids	40,500
hearing aids	823,000	prices for hearing aids	40,500
what are hearing aids	823,000	prices hearing aids	40,500
aid hearing	823,000	hearing aids prices	40,500
which hearing aid	823,000	prices on hearing aids	40,500
the hearing aid	823,000	hearing batteries	40,500
what is hearing aid	823,000	best hearing	40,500
hearing aid in	823,000	beltone	40,500
hearing aid	823,000	hearing aid batteries	33,100
what is an hearing aid	823,000	aids reviews	33,100
what is a hearing aid	823,000	hearing aid battery	33,100
a hearing aid	823,000	hearing aid costs	33,100
compare prices	673,000	hearing aids costs	33,100
hearing loss	450,000	digital hearing	27,100
hearing impaired	368,000	hearing aid reviews	27,100
hearing devices	368,000	hearing aid review	27,100
hearingaids	368,000	reviews on hearing aids	27,100
hearing aid devices	301,000	reviews hearing aids	27,100
hearingaid	246,000	reviews of hearing aids	27,100

Table 4–1. *continued*

Keyword	Searches	Keyword	Searches
phonak	165,000	hearing aids reviews	27,100
oticon	165,000	review of hearing aids	22,200
hearing device	135,000	hearing aids review	22,200
re sound	135,000	in ear hearing aids	22,200
hearing aid device	110,000	in the ear hearing aids	22,200
test hearing	110,000	ear hearing aids	22,200
where can i get a hearing test	110,000	ear hearing aid	22,200
how to test hearing	110,000	phonak hearing	22,200
where to get a hearing test	110,000	phonak aids	18,100
www hearing test	110,000	phonak hearing aids	18,100
hearing test	110,000	hearing aids phonak	18,100
the hearing test	110,000	digital aids	18,100
what is a hearing test	110,000	hearing aid center	18,100
hearing problems	74,000	all about hearing	18,100
hearing store	60,500	hearing health	18,100
price of hearing aid	40,500	digital hearing aids	18,100
price hearing aid	40,500	hearing aids digital	18,100
hearing aid price	40,500	test hearing online	18,100
cost of hearing aids	40,500	online hearing test	18,100
phonak hearing aid	18,100	hearing test online	18,100
hearing test on line	14,800	hearing aid phonak	18,100

It is quite obvious that they are going to be exceptionally popular. Therefore, search phrases around that search phrase will be popular. We just need to consider what those long-tail keyword phrases will be for the locations we wish to target.

The meat of your content strategy will be based on the keywords in the table. They are mostly strong everyday general keywords, keywords that will be searched as long as people have hearing problems. Our job is to review these words, try to ascertain the information that searchers are looking for, and write articles that meet those needs.

Localizing

You need to localize your targeting. Google is making a lot of changes in the background in relation to localizing of search returns. It assesses where the searcher is and supplies returns relevant to that location.

You can localize some of your articles and page titles. This will help a great deal, but a Google Business Places entry will really help. Set one up and connect it back to your website. On your website, set up a page for each branch and clinic that you own or run. Call that page "Our Hearing Aid Center in Location." Write about the clinic, write about the staff, and write about the services available there. With these simple pages, you are already targeting local searches with an SEO strategy. Cool or what?

Anchor Text Backlinks

Anchor text is the visible characters and words that hyperlinks display when linking to another document or location on the Web. In other words, if I wrote, "Our hearing aids are the most modern hearing aids available from each manufacturer." Then hyperlink the phrase "most modern hearing aids available" to point at my hearing aid product page, it is more likely to keep searchers at my website, rather than browse a competitor's webpage.

I would be using anchor text to tell the search engines that my products were the most modern hearing aids available. Search engines use this text to help determine the subject matter of the linked-to document. In the example above, the links would tell the search engine that when users search for modern hearing aids, my product page might be a good place to start.

In this way, we weave a web of supporting documents on the Internet that are designed to support your shop window to the world. Two things, though: Use it sparingly, and when you are using it, change the anchor link text across different documents—in other words, most modern hearing aids in one post and then Unitron hearing aids, or ReSound, or Widex, whatever the manufacturer you use, in another post.

The second thing is that it is more powerful when the backlink comes from a website other than your own. But don't let that stop you using them; if used intelligently, sparingly, and in context, they give you real benefit. This strategy can be used to highlight terms of reference for all of your articles or website pages.

Say, for instance, you offer tinnitus therapy; you have a page that outlines your tinnitus therapy on your website. Somewhere on that page is the phrase using only the newest tinnitus relief technology. A new product pertaining to tinnitus therapy is released, and you write an article about it and its introduction to your practice.

In that article, somewhere you write about your tinnitus relief therapy protocol or service, linking some of that phrase back to your tinnitus therapy page. On your tinnitus therapy page, you hyperlink the phrase *newest tinnitus relief technology* to the article about the new product. Voilà, you are now using anchor text to set the terms of reference for both pages, and they are mutually supporting.

As I have said, I caution you on its use; don't go mad. If you have one or two backlinks to your site in an article, make sure you have several to somewhere else like Wikipedia. If you are using WordPress, you can accomplish this easily with a plug-in like Zemanta. It will analyze what you are writing and offer backlinks.

Writing Articles

I find writing relatively easy and satisfying; I know that not everybody does. I think that the articles will come easier to you if you have a list of article ideas laid out. Again, we need to understand that we are writing these articles for others, not for ourselves. You need to visualize who you are writing the article for. Really understand who they are, their general education level, their pains, and what information they are looking for. A young man recently said to me when I was designing an advertisement, "Stop thinking like an audiologist; think like a patient." It was an excellent piece of advice then, and I am now happily passing it on to you. If you don't like writing or don't have the time, don't worry. There are services available that will do this for a fee.

Visualizing the Prospect

Visualize your prospects: How old are they, what difficulties do they have, what concerns do they have, and what answers do they want? How might they ask the questions? If you do this well, it will allow you to write an article that appeals to them and meets their needs. If you think you know your prospect, you can comfortably write copy that interests them.

This is key: You need to remember that you aren't writing for yourself or your colleagues. So if you are writing about the prevalence of skin cancer on ears, you don't say, "So I noticed a minor mottled brown lesion on the anterior fold of the anti-helix." Try "I noticed that there was a suspicious brown-colored sore on the upper part of his ear that I wasn't happy about."

Considering the questions they may ask allows you to write headlines or article titles that fit that search term. Consider search terms like the following: How does hearing loss happen? What is hearing loss? How do hearing aids work? Why do I have problems hearing in noise?

These search terms and more are out there waiting to be targeted. After you have visualized your prospect and decided what question you want to answer, you then write a headline or title based on that question. Something like, "Problems hearing in noise? Here's why!" "How hearing aids work, knowledge you need to make the best decision!"

Cringe-worthy titles, aren't they? But you cannot believe how they will motivate people to click on the link when they come up on the search returns. Title or headline writing is an art form; there are some really good examples out there that may help. Try searching 100 examples of fantastic headlines and see what comes up.

The Body

Here we look at the body of the article, the story you will tell. That is exactly what it is, a story, and it should be told in just that fashion. It should have a beginning, middle, and an end. In the beginning paragraph, you should touch on your conclusion or your evidence. This will keep the readers interested. Then you should work through the article until the conclusion.

Only then should you review it to see if it actually makes sense and also for opportunities for keywords and anchor text backlinks. Don't stuff the text; place the words and the backlinks where they make sense but only where they don't disrupt the flow and look natural. I often write a blog post for *Celtic* magazine and completely miss keyword opportunities. I only pick them up in the review before publishing and entering them.

I also regularly make a mess of spelling or occasionally miss out a word on the first draft. The spell checker doesn't always pick this up, particularly if it's something like *where* or *were* or *there* and *their*.

This post always has to be seen as an extension of your brand, so spelling and grammatical mistakes don't bode well. The conclusion of the article is all important. How you sign off says something about you as a person and, by extension, your business. I don't sign off Celtic posts, but I do sign off "Just Stuff" posts. I always sign off "Regards Geoff"; I always have, no matter what I am signing off. Many people have said to me that it makes them feel that I am informal and probably approachable.

A lot is perceived from a simple signoff; that is the beauty of the written word. We can invest real emotion, real passion and portray it to the reader. The reader can get a sense of who you are and what you stand for by reading some of your articles. Consider this carefully when you are writing and when you are coming up with your signoff.

The Formula

There is a formula for good copy, and it's not a big secret. It's commonly termed *AIDA*, which stands for attention, interest, desire, and action. Let's look at that formula in a little bit of detail.

Attention

This is your title or subject line. It needs to grab their attention immediately and hold it. I will tell you a little secret that someone told me. Your prospects, the people who you are trying to attract, don't care about you; they care about themselves. Sad, but very true. Don't think it's a statement on humankind; it is simple truth. They don't know you, they haven't met you, and they don't care.

What they do care about is themselves and their problems. That is, what is motivating them to research? That is their spur to action. To grab their attention, any headline needs to cater to that simple fact. Your title, your headline, your call to action, and your subject line need to be about them and their problems.

So to give you a few ideas, let's look at their problems. We all know them; we hear them every day. TV, the phone, social isolation, frustration, speech intelligibility in noise. Let's also look at the information that they generally tend to look for: They want to know about hearing loss, the types, how it occurs, and what can be done about it.

They want to know about treatments, about hearing aids, about how they work, their features, their costs, their benefits, and how they will help them communicate and thrive in their daily lives. They want to know about the tests, what they can expect, and what they will reveal. These are all their wants, their pains, and their problems.

To grab their attention, you need to cater to them. Think about a particular need and focus on a headline that frames that need in terms that will grab their attention. Here are some examples of attention-grabbing headlines that have worked for me:

- "Sick of fighting over the TV volume, here's why it happens and what YOU can do to fix it"
- "Tired of saying WHAT? Frustrated at being left behind in the conversation?"
- "Worried about your hearing health? Afraid YOU don't hear the important stuff?"
- "So what exactly is a hearing test? Simple, easy and we don't bite, we swear"
- "So you're buying hearing aids? Info & tips that will allow you make good decisions"
- "Sick of the tech jargon? The simple guide to what hearing aid features do"

In the preceding, we have addressed many of the concerns of hearing aid purchasers. We have keyed into their emotional issues with some of them. We have attacked their knowledge needs with others. All headlines are about them and their needs.

None are about us and our needs. That is the way to grab their attention: cater to their problems, their needs. In this way, you have a higher chance of getting their attention, getting their click, getting their call.

Interest

After the headline, you need to encourage their interest. So flesh out the details somewhat; in some posts, you may be discussing the prevalence of something or other. In others, you may be fleshing out tech details or processes. In nearly all interest parts, you will be delivering facts and figures relevant to them and the article.

Desire

In this portion of the article, you need to encourage desire. Build desire for a product or a service. Build desire to know more, to get more information. Whatever the article, whatever the subject, you should always build desire—desire for a product or service that you supply. Any article that you write that hasn't taken the opportunity to raise desire is wasted.

Action

After you have grabbed their attention, widened their interest, and built desire, you need to give them a clear action to undertake. It needs to be clear and unequivocal; spell it out and then spell out what will happen after they take that action. I am afraid you cannot underestimate people. The general public is stupid; it hurts me to say it, but they are.

Give them a clear action to take. With luck, they will take whatever that action is, and you will have converted a viewer to a lead. That is what we are trying to do at this stage. It is a step-by-step process, viewer to lead, lead to consultation, consultation to sale. Don't forget this: You are courting the prospect, and there needs to be a flow that leads to a conclusion.

Perhaps the first step is a hyperlink at the bottom of the article that brings readers to a different article. An article that moves them along on the process that you have set. Then at the end of that article is a clear hyperlink to another step of the process. If you can get them moving along that process, you can then encourage them to contact you. Because that is what we all want, for them to contact us. It is only then that they become an inquiry.

Article Titles

In the online world, the title of the article or page can and should be very different from the headline. The title of the article is the phrase that will be used for the hyperlink. Think carefully about this title; it needs to be used for SEO purposes, so you will use keywords that are important to you in this title.

They, of course, have to remain in context to the content on that page. So if we were doing a TV volume post, I would title the page "hearing loss and problems with the TV volume." In this way, I am going after keywords that matter to us and are in context to the content.

Page titles or article titles, sometimes more correctly called URL titles, are important. You need to get them right, so the search engine brings the prospect to your website.

Meta Descriptions

Meta descriptions are the descriptive snippets that appear under the search return. This is where you make sure your headline goes, because this snippet is your opportunity to grab readers' attention. This snippet is what will make them click on you before they click on anyone else.

In every content management system, there is a facility to put a URL title and a meta description. Use them and use them well, because if you do so, you will see a jump in click-through rates to your site. Think about the paragraph from earlier about headlines and grabbing their attention.

There is no point being at the top of all the search returns if no one is clicking through (known as CTR for click-through rate) to your site. Believe me, this is a hard-won lesson, and I am speaking from experience. We identified this as a problem on our site. It was my idiotic mistake due to a slipup through haste when I was setting up certain posts. We fixed it, and we are seeing our CTR jumping because of it.

Believe me when I say this: Everything in this chapter stems from a hard-won lesson. I would like to ensure that you do not make the mistakes that I have.

YOUR BRAND

Building a brand is an imperative for any business; the building of the right brand will help to drive your business to the heights of success. What is a brand, though?

A brand is a "name, term, design, symbol, or any other feature that identifies one seller's goods or service as distinct from those of other sellers. A brand may identify one item, a family of items, or all items of that seller. If used for the firm as a whole, the preferred term is trade name." You can find this definition of a brand on Wikipedia. Wikipedia itself has become a one-word brand, recognizable internationally.

That definition is exceptionally narrow and does not reflect how the concept of brand has evolved. When I speak about the branding of an audiology practice, I am not really referring to its name becoming a household name or a world-recognized brand. What I am speaking of is the perception that your practice portrays to its customers and indeed its prospective customers in your local marketplace, which is sometimes called a footprint.

You need to understand explicitly that you indeed have a brand, and every element of your practice speaks to that brand. What elements in your practice speak to your brand? Every element of your practice speaks to your brand. I read a really excellent article about defining brand recently by a guy named Shep Hyken. Like me, he is convinced that your customers set the definition of your brand. He asked, "What do you want to be known for? If there were one word or short phrase you wanted to be known for, what would it be? In essence that word is what you should strive to engender in your patient's perception."

Your understanding of brand and how it affects your practice is imperative. You really need to believe that strategies to generate a brand must cover every part of your practice. Brand should be a consummate part of your thinking when it comes to all facets of your practice, not just your health care marketing. You also need to clearly understand that every facet of your practice should be viewed through the marketing prism. In effect, every part of your practice, from how the phone is answered to how problem patients are handled, is part of both your brand and your ongoing health care marketing strategy.

Every customer-facing touch point in your business should be clearly designed with this in mind, because everything affects your patient's perception, everything! Table 4–2 is an outline of elements of any brand. Get the attributes listed in Table 4–2 aligned, and you are more likely to have a consistent brand message.

The Elements of Your Brand

Have you ever paid six thousand of your favorite currency, be that euro, sterling, or dollars, for a product or service that you do not understand? I would say the answer is probably no, but many of our patients do every day. Yes, they may do some research on the Internet. Yes, they may even recognize one or two of the

Table 4–2. Essential Brand Elements in an
Audiology Practice

Cleanliness of your shop front
Signage that you use
The smell when they walk through the door
Cleanliness of the carpet
Type of furniture
The freshness of your walls
Type of décor
Magazine quality
Friendliness of your staff
How your phone is answered
The appearance of you and your staff
Personal greeting used by staff

manufacturers' names, but they don't understand the product at all. They do not have the knowledge to undertake true comparisons when making purchase decisions, so we in fact make those decisions for them.

What a clinic really "sells" at the beginning of the relationship is trust. This trust is engendered through many strategies in a clinical process, but perception of efficacy is the highest contributor gaining the agreement from a patient to do business with us. The patient's perception of our practice drives his or her willingness to become a loyal customer of our business. If you look deeper, you will see that what we, in fact, engage in is an experience. If you understand that patients are more likely to buy or accept our recommendation when we engage them in a memorable experience, you can take steps in your practice that will attract patients to your clinic.

I do not mean, nor would I advocate, smoke-and-mirrors theatrics. What I mean is real efforts to enhance somebody's experience with your practice. You will also need to understand that the experience does not end after the sale; to deliver ongoing value to your business, a patient's experience within your practice needs to be continuous.

That experience is your *brand*.

It is our patients who actually define of our brand. We can encourage or steer their thoughts, their perceptions. We can and do influence the perception of our patients every time we interact with them. There is a large crossover between the strategies you have established to retain patients and the perception of your brand. They are both comprehensive affairs with similarities. The strategies you undertake to encourage patient retention and customer referral are, in fact, exactly the strategies that will encourage a favorable brand perception. Let me explain.

There are two critical aspects to maintaining a steady flow of office traffic: (1) retaining your current patients who have previously purchased from you and (2) receiving referrals from highly satisfied and loyal patients. Patient retention tends to be seen as a long-term return concept, but customer referral pays off immediately. The efforts that you put into ongoing patient retention can immediately affect your bottom line through customer referral. To achieve sufficient patient retention and customer referral, you need to implement comprehensive strategies, which create loyal patients who willingly promote your practice to others. If they are ecstatic about you and your practice, that feeds the perception of your brand.

In order for customer referral to happen, you need to make your patients evangelists for your brand; happy customers are just not enough. A happy customer may tell a few people how good you are, but evangelists will become active advocates for your business, publicizing your brand far and wide. As we are all aware, word-of-mouth business is often the best business, simply because most of the impediments that traditionally exist to a transaction have been removed prior to your consultation.

The strategies that you put in place to bolster your patient retention are also designed to increase customer satisfaction and will lead to evangelist customers. A more common term for these patients is *relationship customers*; relationship customers love your practice. They are the people that you want to be setting the terms of your brand. Most patients have no brand awareness when it comes to hearing care; their loyalty or otherwise is based on the perceptions of your practice.

Before we go further, let's look at why we lose patients. We all know that some die, we all know that some are unhappy for whatever reason, we all know some may move away. Although some patients leave a practice because they die, others move away, and some leave because they can just never be satisfied, most leave because of a perceived attitude of indifference.

Feeling ignored when entering the office, being rushed through an appointment, leaving without having questions answered, or not having a problem solved in a timely manner may be sufficient to cause a patient to search for a new practice. Since the routes traditionally used appear to have become ineffectual and the cost incurred of acquiring a new patient has similarly increased, the retaining of a current patient is critical to the profitability of a practice. It has become critical to maintain a relationship with a patient for as long as possible and to design strategies to service this need.

Developing a long-term relationship with a patient may be the best way to maximize not only patient retention but also patient satisfaction. Patient satisfaction is the route to evangelism; evangelism is exactly what you need to build your brand. There is some evidence that an overwhelming majority of consumers make important purchasing decisions based on relationships, and we have no reason to believe that our industry is any different. Relationship buyers are customers who love your products and services. They build a relationship with your employees, and they think of your company as the primary supplier of their needs within your category.

They do not want to be bothered to have to shop around every time they make a new purchase. They look for quality, good service, helpfulness, friendship, and information. If you supply these things, they will stick with you. The key is to attract them to you initially; the efforts you take to ensure this happens are also the principles you need to consider retaining them. Every element of your practice has a direct effect on the perception of your patient, from your shop front and display, waiting area, receptionist, consultation room, consultation manner, presentation skills, follow-up service, communication style, and so on.

All of these elements combine to support your brand perception; they also encourage a patient to place his or her trust in you. From these beginnings, a great brand will grow, and these strategies will retain patients and drive new patient acquisition. They will ensure the long-term viability of your business; they will build and sustain your brand.

THE PATIENT JOURNEY

Let us look at the patient journey and how within this journey you can best affect your patient's perception of you and your brand. Our patients have become ever more sophisticated, and most businesses should adapt their patient engagement strategy to reflect that. The general model for patient engagement revolves around these five areas:

- Testing
- Fitting
- Rehab visit/fine-tuning visit at 1 month
- Possible further rehab/fine-tuning visit
- Service call at 6 months to continue at 6-month intervals

Having a well-orchestrated plan of patient engagement at each of these critical areas of the patient journey gives you maximum opportunity to shape and enforce a patient's perception of your brand. Mapping out the patient journey in this manner also allows for several communications a year with your patients. These can be either mailings or telephone calls.

Mapping the patient journey in your practice allows you to mail on a regular basis communications that are perceived to have real value for your patients. It also allows you to maintain your patient engagement and keeps you top-of-mind. The structure of the patient journey also allows you to introduce the subject of new technology at the appropriate time.

According to this model, you will mail or call your patients every 6 months to return to your office for service. You can also mail campaign offers on ancillary products perhaps twice a year (e.g., buy two packs of batteries and get one free, or buy refill drying capsules and get cleaning tablets free). It is important that all mailings are structured and well thought out; they must also be pertinent to the patient. Don't forget a Christmas or birthday card; get them printed, take the time to personalize them, have yourself and your staff sign them, and send them out.

If your patient is returning to you every 6 months, you do not need to send them offers on new technology, but you can tell them about it and show it to them in person. If done properly and at the right time, it will not appear to be a sales push; it will merely be more of your famed education and good advice. This is key, but what is the right time to introduce new technology? I think probably from year 4, some patients will ask you about it at year 2. You are best to gauge this individually with each patient.

It is important that you set a structure for each appointment. With a structure, everybody knows what the aim of the appointment is and what needs to happen during the appointment. You should also set a time limit for each appointment.

The Elements of the Patient Journey

As you may be gathering, orchestrating the patient journey is a critical part of your marketing efforts because it builds brand awareness and loyalty. Let's take a closer look at service calls and how they fit into the patient journey. What briefly follows is the structure of the appointments that I adopted in my practice for the first year of service for the typical patient. Note how the time allotments for each appointment vary.

Service Appointment 1: Review patient's experience with amplification; clean aid; clean earmold, wax guard, and/or tubing; fine-tune aid, if necessary; ask about need for ancillary products. Time scheduled 15 to 30 minutes.

Service Appointment 2: Review patient's experience with amplification; complete hearing test; clean aid; clean earmold, wax guard, and/or tubing; fine-tune aid, if necessary; ask about need for ancillary products. Time scheduled 30 to 40 minutes.

Service Appointment 3: Review patient's experience with amplification; clean aid; clean earmold, wax guard, and/or tubing; fine-tune aid, if necessary; ask about need for ancillary products. Time scheduled 15 to 30 minutes.

Service Appointment 4: Review patient's experience with amplification and hearing test; clean aid; clean earmold, wax guard, and/or tubing; fine-tune aid, if necessary; ask about need for ancillary products. Time scheduled 30 to 40 minutes.

This schedule allowed me to be more proactive with my patients, as they were scheduled to see me, rather than seeing me only if they had a problem. It increased my engagement with them and allowed me to build a stronger relationship with them. While orchestrating the patient journey is a major element of a patient retention strategy, it is only as good as your ability to consistently implement it with every patient.

THE COMMUNICATION POLICY

You need to put a clear and stringent communication policy in place in your practice that your staff is aware of and adheres to. The policy should cover everything from how you expect patients to be greeted on the phone and in person to communication messaging and structure. When is mail sent? Two weeks before a service call? Who does a follow-up telephone call to verify the appointment? When a telephone query is made, who actions it, what answers are given, and so on? Exactly how long is too long for the return of a phone call? The key to success with communications strategy and relationship building is a well-designed and well-maintained customer relationship management (CRM) system. A CRM is only as good as the people who enter and read the information on it. I keep a simple word file on every patient with details, name of children, comments made at appointment, membership of groups, interests, and so on. This allowed me to review these notes before every consultation to refresh my memory with these details.

The perception that you and your staff remember the minutia of a patient's life is what builds relationships. Did so and so get that job? Did your grandchild so and so get over the measles? I remember you love the opera; did you hear such and such is coming to town? These comments are the foundations of a relationship; they show that you have a real interest in your patient and their lives. Train everybody in your practice, including receptionists, to prepare their own notes that allow them to maximize their engagements with every patient.

Plenty of commercial CRMs are available that are inexpensive, particularly cloud-hosted ones that allow everybody within your organization to access centralized data. Cloud-based CRM systems allow you to remain current with your patients and their activities. Get a CRM and use it religiously, but put a clear policy in place that every person in your organization follows. That is the only way that it will maintain its usefulness and maximize its full potential for your business.

FRONT-OF-HOUSE OPERATIONS

The patient journey is an all-encompassing concept covering every aspect of a person's interaction with a practice, from the patient's initial contact with your practice to any subsequent phone, Web, or personal face-to-face dealings with your practice. All of these interactions, some that you may not be even aware of, are part of the patient journey and indeed opportunities to begin to build or cement a relationship with a patient.

That is in effect why all practice owners need to plan out a clear, all-encompassing strategy covering patient communications. Within this strategy, they also need to cover all aspects of their marketing and advertising. Marketing and advertising are important facets of the patient journey and extremely important opportunities for a business to shape a patient's perception of your brand.

The front of house (also known as front office) is the real introduction of any business. What does the front of house say about a practice and how they feel about their patients? Particular attention needs to be paid to the answer to this question. I would ask everybody to approach their practice with their eyes wide open. It is easy for us to miss things when we are in the environment day in and day out.

The Shop Window

A shop window is probably the first tangible thing that any prospective patient observes. It needs to be used expertly, signage needs to be fixed, and it must be clean and talk to the image that the practice wishes to portray. A well-designed aluminum shop front with modern recessed lights over the headline signage speaks of modernity and professionalism. No matter which combination or look a business chooses or indeed has, is it clean, in good repair, presentable, and speaking of the brand they wish to portray?

A shop front can be used to effectively communicate the brand of the practice and draw in attention from passers-by; most important, it clearly communicates several things about the practice to their patients. Use a window effectively, plan displays carefully, and change them often; many manufacturers now provide sophisticated point-of-sale (POS) material. The hearing aid manufacturers supply it, and it should be chosen carefully and used for display accordingly. You may also consider creating your own POS materials with a consistent font, logo, and color scheme.

Little touches can make a big impact: The glass in the shop front, with the business logo etched on it prominently in the bottom left corner, particularly as part of a stripe across the bottom of the glass, appears sophisticated and attractive.

For the display behind the glass, use a local shop-fitting business and choose attractive elements that remain constant, such as tables, acrylic cubes, light boxes, and so on. Each business will know what is indeed best for the positioning they are aiming for and indeed their shop front; these items will be the constant base of any display. You should consider having a quasi-living room display, basically a large fixed LCD screen on which can be presented constant-loop videos.

If posters are to be hung, they should be framed, relatively inexpensive aluminum quick-change frames, which can be purchased from a home supply store. Do not hang posters in a display window or indeed the shop with Blu-Tack or sticky tape, as this is likely to portray an image inconsistent with your brand.

The Reception Area

When you walk through the front door, what exactly greets you? The space should be bright, airy, and well decorated. With an eye to the decor inside, are there soothing colors? Think living room or kitchen colors. Think minimalism in this space and contemporary minimalism. If there is a row of those old classroom-type chairs, they should be thrown out. High-seated soft furnishings with perhaps brown or black leather are the way forward. The sofas or chairs need to be relatively high so that older people can sit and raise themselves with ease. They also need to be relatively firm for the same reason, and leather is easy to clean.

If there is a coffee table with magazines, the dog-eared *Vogue* from 1983 needs to be thrown out and also the 20 copies of *National Geographic* from 1968. Honestly, your patients will thank you for it. Speaking of magazine offerings, would it not be better for a business to undertake a quarterly or bimonthly newsletter about its practice and make copies of that available? Instant marketing communications irritate patients by jamming up their mailboxes. News about product lines, information on new treatments for tinnitus, and other similar newsworthy pieces can be communicated with a monthly or quarterly newsletter.

What exactly does the reception desk look like? Is it a typical office desk that the receptionist sits behind, or is it a more substantial purpose-built structure? The purpose-built structure is the way forward; it speaks again to permanence and professionalism. Is it clean and tidy; do the receptionists keep it clean and tidy? The importance of this cannot be overstated. The reception desk and area are the welcome areas to any practice, and they need to be clean, tidy, and, above all, welcoming.

The Receptionist

The receptionist is a pivotal cog in the wheels of every business. I do not think it is too much to say that the business could soar or fail in response to the receptionist that is chosen. A receptionist in most modern practices is, for all intents and purposes, a practice manager who manages the diaries, logistics, mailings, the phones, face-to-face queries, and usually nearly all of the administration. This is a core position within any practice. Finding the right person for the job is often difficult.

Staff need to be encouraged to build a relationship with patients and their families. If need be, instruction should be given about the conversations they should have both in person and on the phone. Make very clear what manner is used to answer the phone and exactly what is said and, most important, what action needs to be taken, when, and by whom in response to most of the usual queries.

In my practice, I have a receptionist who actively forges relationships with our patients to the extent that they would go nowhere else for batteries because they would miss a chat. One of her little tricks is to call patients 2 weeks before Christmas to ask if they need tubing, batteries, drying tablets, or wax caps, because she didn't want them to be without while we were closed over the holiday. She took that upon herself to do; other practices may well have to put that type of practice communication with patients into their communication policy.

All of these elements speak to your brand, by allowing a patient to feel comfortable and nurtured. These elements allow the building of strong relationships with patients, which is the mantra for patient retention. Human contact and the personal touch, particularly with our demographic, delivered in comfortable and welcoming surroundings, are the secret to relationship building, as are open questions from the professional and his or her staff.

YOUR CONSULTATION ROOM

We have now reached the consultation room, the inner sanctum, the place where we have traditionally thought the real action occurs. It is indeed all of those things, but I hope I have showed that it is indeed not the whole story when it comes to the patient journey.

When you enter your consultation room, take a good look around it and ask yourself, what does this room say about me and my day-to-day practice? I undertook this exercise after I had been in practice for a while. Initially when I started my practice, day-to-day thoughts just centered on my audiometry and hearing instrument fitting. My main worry was that I did not make a mess of these elements. After I had settled down, however, I began to concentrate on the commercial elements of my practice, slowly but surely finding my consultation style.

With this done, I began to look at my consultation room, including its appearance and design, and how I could change that to reflect my brand perception. I realized that my consultation room was a mess: hanging cables (the bane of our existence these days), tackle boxes full of tubing, and the usual day-to-day clutter of a practice. It needed to be organized!

I urge you to take a long, careful look at your consultation room. Store your cables and paraphernalia out of site. Whatever you use during one consultation should be put away afterward. The only things that should be visible on your desk are the fixed apparatus that we use every day: an audiometer, a computer monitor and a keypad, your otoscope, and very little else.

If you do not have proper storage, get some built in or indeed buy a nice piece of furniture to store everything in, keep it tidy, and keep everything in its place. There is nothing worse than searching like an idiot for something while your patient looks on. Change the orientation of your desk; place it so that the patient and his or her significant other sit beside you as opposed to across from you. This allows a greater feeling of engagement with your patient. It also closes the physical gap between you and them, allowing the patient to relax somewhat and feel involved.

Position the equipment on your desk, including your computer screen and keyboard, such that it always allows you to be looking toward the patient and the significant other. This allows constant engagement with both of them. If you want real long-term commitment from your patient, you will need to engage with his or her companion or family. This is imperative; engagement with the patient's companion will increase the commitment to you. That engagement needs to start from the initial consultation.

THE CONSULTATION

To have a maximum effect, the actual consultation needs to be well planned and enacted. In the planning stage, you need to think strongly about patient perception of your brand and what indeed you hope to achieve. There are clear stages of a consultation that occur naturally: (1) testing to see if a patient has a hearing loss; (2) overcoming objections to meet any queries, worries, or obstacles that a patient has; and (3) concluding or closing the interaction. The consultation does not necessarily fall in that order. The initial part of the consultation should be a mixture of testing and overcoming objections, which leads to a discussion of options and a conclusion. This is a natural process. Think deeply about this process, come to your own conclusions, and then design a medical record card that follows the flow that you have chosen.

Emotional engagement with our patients is the key to your ongoing success at building your brand. When you make an emotional connection with your patients, it allows them to trust you. It allows them to feel that you not only understand them but also care enough to try your best to fix those problems to the best of your ability. This is the key to patient retention: If a patient feels cared for, you are more likely to have created a "customer for life." This can be a compelling part of your brand story.

Consultation Procedure

Your patient consultation is a core part of your brand, and it should be designed with this in mind. The core principles of the patient consultation are listed in Table 4–3. Each of these stages in the consultation is important to the structure and the goal of building your brand.

The aim of this chapter was to provide the reader with a real-world perspective on marketing. Although audiologists and hearing instrument specialists have been specially trained on auditory physiology and hearing instrumentation, a significant portion of their daily workload must be committed both

Table 4–3. Brand Builders: The Core Components of Your Consultation

Introduction: Who you are
Icebreaking: The weather, holidays, current events
Taking of details: Name, address, date of birth, phone number, etc.
Medical history: The taking of a detailed medical history with questions pertaining specifically to the referable conditions.
COSI: The taking of an individual's needs assessment using a tool like the COSI, gaining clear knowledge of at least three problem areas
Otoscopy: Examine the patient's ears
Audiometry: Testing of the patient's hearing
Explanation: Explanation of the patient's hearing loss and its effect on his or her lifestyle
Live demonstration: Demonstrate the aids to the patient
Options: Always give three hearing system options

directly and indirectly to building their brand within the community. Direct involvement includes creating and implementing an annual marketing plan, complete with a budget and calendar of planned events. Another component to direct marketing includes creating content for direct mail and other forms of advertising.

Indirectly, hearing care professionals are intimately involved in building their brand identity and reputation whenever they are interacting with patients as well as other members of their community. From this perspective, everything an audiologist touches is marketing.

5

DISEASE STATE MARKETING AND INTERVENTIONAL AUDIOLOGY

Brian Taylor and Robert Tysoe

As we grow older, most of us are inclined to ask, what is the secret to a happy life? Fortunately, we live in an era in which the near-infinite processing power of computer algorithms can crunch the data collected by incredibly creative researchers— data that can be used to answer this consequential question. A team of researchers led by George Vaillant at Harvard University has been collecting information for a longitudinal study that is attempting to better understand the secrets of a happy life. Through a painstaking, four-decades-long process conducted by Valliant (2012), 268 men participated in a series of interviews, which researchers used to establish a Decathlon of Flourishing—a set of 10 accomplishments that define success. Two of the 10 items were related to economic success, 4 with mental and physical health, and 4 with social supports and relationships.

Researchers found that a loving childhood, filled with warm relationships through young adulthood, was highly correlated with all items on the Decathlon of Flourishing. On the other hand, there were weak correlations among the other socioeconomic and biologic variables. Their work, *Triumphs of Experience: The Men of the Harvard Grant Study,* demonstrates that an entire lifetime filled with warm and loving relationships (not high IQ, good grades, or wealth) is predictive of a happy life as you grow older. This fascinating longitudinal study serves as a reminder that audiologists and hearing instrument specialists play a crucial role in maintaining the overall health and vitality of all individuals regardless of age. After all, if you have difficulty hearing, those warm and loving relationships that are the secret to a long and happy life are bound to suffer. The primary objective of this chapter is to shed light on the emerging role audiology plays in the long-term delivery of care to patients of all ages, especially those with multiple chronic medical conditions, and how this initiative must be systematically shared with primary care physicians.

It is only through better communication, of which good hearing acuity is imperative, that adults with multiple chronic medical conditions will be better able to more actively participate in their care, including the ability to follow a physician's verbal instructions during a routine appointment. The secret to a healthy practice may be similar to the secrets of a happy life: warm, lasting relationships with patients, colleagues, and other professionals. These interconnected networks may be more critical to your success than effective business management principles or the latest hearing aid technology that you offer in your clinic. After reading this chapter, we hope you take action by fostering deeper relationships with the primary care physicians (PCPs) in your area. (We use the term *PCP* to broadly define physicians, such as family medicine doctors, gerontologists, general practitioners, and others who are often the first to examine individuals who are likely to have hearing loss and other conditions associated with hearing impairment.)

Over the past few decades, interventional medicine has become an important part of health care. As modern science has devised effective treatments for many disease states, health care delivery models have increasingly emphasized the treatment of chronic disease and the promotion of healthy lifestyles. By early detection and noninvasive treatment of various medical conditions, interventional medicine fits squarely within this preventive health care delivery model. It should come as no surprise to most that the fundamental issue driving this change is the growing cost of health care. As costs have increased, so has the urgency to prevent illness whenever possible. The mantra of primary care medicine today is "right care, right time, right provider." This means prevention or the earliest possible intervention with the best possible treatment for chronic illnesses such as diabetes, dementia, cardiovascular disease, and related disorders. In fact, the most common chronic condition experienced by adults is some combination of many of these conditions, which is called multimorbidity. Recent research conducted by Weiss et al. (2007) suggests that almost three in four individuals older than 65 years have multiple chronic conditions. Additionally, one in four adults 65 years of age and younger also have multiple chronic conditions. According to Anderson (2010), patients with multimorbidities are the major users of health care services and account for more than two thirds of the health care spending in this country. To align with the clinical reality of multimorbidity, Tinetti et al. (2012) have called for care to evolve from a disease orientation to a patient goal orientation, focused on optimizing the long-term health of individuals. For numerous reasons, audiologists are well equipped to step into this situation and provide valuable interventional services. This chapter provides a template for raising awareness within the primary care medical community on the importance of interventional services delivered by audiologists and hearing care professionals using the best available evidence from well-designed clinical studies. To fully appreciate this call to action, let's take a look at the American health care system and the possible unintended consequences of an untreated hearing loss in an adult.

We can do this by examining an all too common situation, which until rather recently has been unreported in the literature: An individual, perhaps in his early 70s with type 2 diabetes and mild, sensorineural hearing loss, delays medical care because he hesitates to call for an appointment with his primary care provider due to difficulty understanding the appointment clerk on the phone. Once he finally calls, the patient misunderstands the instructions he is given. Thinking he has been told to alter his medication regimen, his diabetes is soon out of control and he ends up in the emergency room. Such patients are perhaps more common than we realize, and as recent research suggests, mild to moderate age-related hearing loss can contribute to poor health in many ways, including delaying appropriate care as well as being a cause of poor patient compliance due to unintended miscommunication.

There is a constellation of forces at work within the American health care system that may enable hearing care professionals to emerge as integral members of a patient's health and wellness team. The graying of the American population, the notion that baby boomers want to more actively participate in their health care, the emergence of direct to consumer amplification products, the unsustainably rising costs of health care—all of these factors have the potential to profoundly change the way audiology and hearing care are perceived by primary care physicians. Primary care in the United States is changing. Both private and public insurance programs, as well as large employers, are changing the way primary care providers are being reimbursed for their services. The reason for these changes is the rising cost of health care and the realization that primary care is the key to reducing those costs.

The focus of the change is that "value" payments are being added to the traditional "volume"-based fee-for-service reimbursement system in primary care. Reimbursement in traditional primary care is a function of volume: The more patient visits a primary care practice sees in a year, the higher the annual revenue will be. The system is complex in that some patient visits receive higher reimbursement than do others, but historically, the system has nevertheless been purely volume based.

As a result, the efficiency of the primary care office is key. The focus is on seeing the maximum number of patients a day that can reasonably be accommodated with the minimum of overhead expenses. The most successful practices in this traditional volume-based model were usually the busiest. Acutely ill patients were seen promptly, but other patients waited patiently, sometimes for many days and even weeks, for routine appointments.

Over the past decade or two, it has been recognized that this traditional system has a very significant unintended consequence. Primarily because of delays in care, patients became sicker. When they finally had their appointment, they needed more care than would have been the case if they had been seen sooner. As a result, the value of the care was less than what it could have been if the patient had been seen sooner. Volume was consistently trumping value.

There were other problems as well. If patients were not sufficiently motivated to take care of their health, they would often miss recommended screening tests or take medicines irregularly. As a result, they had illnesses that could have been avoided, and caring for those illnesses was a cost to the health care system. That cost is large, and it turns out that paying primary care to focus more attention on prevention and earlier treatment is far less expensive than paying the entire health care system for the cost of caring for patients who had missed opportunities to detect, prevent, or treat illnesses at an earlier stage.

There are many ways being used today to pay primary care practices to improve the value of their services. One common method is to pay the primary care practice a periodic bonus if certain performance standards, usually called "quality metrics," are met. A common quality metric in primary care today focuses on the care of diabetic patients: If laboratory and other tests done to measure the effectiveness of diabetic treatment meet certain standards, the primary care practice receives periodic cash payment from the insurer based on the number of diabetics in their practice and the quality measure performance. This payment is in addition to the usual volume-based reimbursement that the practice receives for each visit.

Numerous quality metrics are being applied to primary care practices today, although the specific value-based payment varies by insurer and location. These payments tend to focus on the quality of care for chronic diseases and also on the percentage of patients who receive preventive treatments (e.g., vaccinations) or screenings (cancer, cholesterol, etc.). The number and sophistication of these quality metrics are rapidly increasing, and as this occurs, the potential dollar value of the payments to the practice is also increasing.

Only a few years ago, most primary care practices had little or no opportunity to receive revenue on the basis of quality metric performance. Today, almost all traditional primary care practices are eligible for such payments. It is not uncommon for practices to receive an additional 10% of their annual revenue from quality metric performance, and 20% or even 30% of traditional volume-based revenue is being seen from high-performing practices. Recent announcements by Medicare suggest that this trend will continue.

The "new money" for primary care actually represents a transfer of money from hospitals and specialists. The key concept is "right care, right provider, right place, right time." If primary care provides patients with "right care/provider/place/time," then the patient will need fewer hospitalizations, fewer emergency room (ER) visits, and fewer specialty referrals. The language being used to capture this idea is that primary care is doing "population health." Hospitals and specialists, naturally, are having trouble accepting the fact that this idea has gained traction with insurers, Medicare, and Medicaid. But it has gained traction, and it does work. The increase in income to primary care is only a small fraction of the decrease in income to hospitals and specialists, and the savings in health care costs for large employers, insurers, and government programs is why this is going to grow.

What does this mean for audiology? Referrals to audiology from primary care in the past were generated for the most part by requests from the patient and their family. Treatment of hearing loss was considered elective, an issue that was almost entirely related to patient preference. Today, if hearing loss is recognized as a factor leading to poor patient compliance with medical care, then the poor compliance will cost the physicians' practice real money. This makes a difference in how hearing loss is viewed by the primary care physician.

In the traditional reimbursement environment, primary care providers are not at financial risk if their patients do not take their medicine, do not have recommended vaccinations or screening tests, or do not follow up after they are seen by another doctor. With value-based reimbursement systems growing rapidly, these same primary care practices are now at a clear financial risk. And that financial risk is large enough that they are paying attention.

The evidence is growing that hearing loss, even mild to moderate hearing loss, interferes with communication and speech understanding at a very basic level. This communication and understanding is critically important for patient compliance with medical care, especially for patients with chronic illnesses and the elderly. And, as any clinician knows, these are the very patients who have the highest incidence of hearing loss. Audiology has a new opportunity to become a partner with primary care providers because the hearing health care specialist can help the primary care provider succeed. Audiologists should understand these new issues in primary care and be clear that the services that audiology offers are not simply services to the patient but represent a service that will help the primary care practice as well. In short, interventional audiology can help primary care practices add value in a way that boosts their bottom line as well as improve the quality of life for many of their baby-boomer patients.

Crash Course: Accountable Care Organizations

An accountable care organization (ACO) is a health care organization characterized by a payment and care delivery model that seeks to tie provider reimbursements to quality metrics and reductions in the total cost of care for an assigned population of patients. According to the Centers for Medicare & Medicaid Services (CMS), an ACO is "an organization of health care providers that agrees to be accountable for the quality, cost, and overall care of Medicare beneficiaries who are enrolled in the traditional fee-for-service program who are assigned to it.

It is imperative for audiology to show ACOs that they can save substantial amounts of money to the system by screening patients at an earlier age and intervening sooner in remediation and management of hearing loss.

INTERVENTIONAL MEDICINE

To gain a deeper appreciation for how the changes in health care may impact the practice of audiology, let's take a look at the concept of interventional medicine and how it may apply to audiology. As previously stated, the rising costs of health care and the growing aging population are on a collision course that requires intervention from audiology. Audiologists have a significant opportunity to become an integral part of a physician's team of trusted advisors and play an essential role in this effort to provide the right care at the right time. With interventional hearing health care strategies that seek to minimize impairment and maximize function, the audiologist will play an increasingly prominent role in the future in controlling health care costs while delivering timely, cost-efficient, and highly effective care.

Before going into the details of the role of audiology in an interventional delivery model, it is helpful to review the history of interventional medicine. Interventional medicine's origins can be traced back to ancient Egypt and the Babylonian period. With long-term accumulation of experiences, interventional medicine evolved as a system with the rise of interventional radiology treatment in the 20th century. New technological advances and innovative procedures have accelerated the improvement of interventional medicine. Interventional medicine techniques and applications have gone beyond its initial use in radiology. Other specialties include interventional oncology, chemotherapeutic drug-eluting systems, and bland beads for the targeted treatment of liver cancer, interventional cardiology, pulmonology, nephrology, pain management, and interventional otology and neuro-otology. The concept of interventional audiology may soon be added to this list, as it offers tremendous promise in helping audiologists as well as hearing instruments specialists expand their reach to greater numbers of patients.

According to MarkeTrak data, the average age of a patient in the United States who is fitted with his or her first pair of hearing aids is approximately 69 years, many of whom are seen for the first time by an audiologist for a hearing test shortly before an initial purchase. This suggests that society categorizes hearing loss as "a disease of the aged." Recent research, however, demonstrates that hearing loss is now "a disease for all ages." For example, research from the federally funded National Institutes of Health (NIH suggests that nearly 80% of men and 70% of women first notice a hearing loss before age 60 years. Evolving to an interventional audiology model means, using one example, that a 21-year-old with a hearing disability caused by the comorbid condition of type 2 diabetes may spend over 60 years of his or her life with communication disorders, an increased risk of depression, enhanced social isolation, and reduced employment opportunities because of a lack of systematic interventional strategies by both primary care specialists and hearing health care professionals. Earlier intervention from an audiologist has the potential to turn a lifelong handicap into a long-term improvement in quality of life that benefits the public good.

Hearing loss is the second leading cause of years living with disability (YLD), second only to depression (Mathers et al., 2003). John Bakke, MD, of Zolo Healthcare Solutions, refers to acquired hearing loss of adult onset as a triple threat to patients. First, clinically significant hearing impairment is itself a disability and is an indication for effective remediation in its own right. Two, hearing loss interferes with a patient's ability to be treated for other medical conditions because it hinders an individual's ability to engage with physicians and understand treatment advice and directives. Finally, emerging research suggests that hearing loss may actually accelerate some disabilities such as cognitive dysfunction and vestibular impairment. The prevalence, comorbidity, and disabling effects of hearing loss underscore the need for aggressive preventive programs that identify conditions such as hearing loss that threaten health outcomes (Weinstein, 2011). Audiology may be an emerging interventional discipline within medicine that has an important role in breaking the cycle of morbidity and mortality associated with a patient's inability to hear. The treatment of hearing loss by audiologists can provide interventional assistance by providing routine hearing evaluations for patients of "patient-centered medical care homes" (PCMHs) that seek to focus on prevention, early detection, and evidence-based treatment. This is likely to result in improved quality of care, patient compliance, improved outcomes, and reduced overall cost of care.

The audiologist is now being increasingly viewed within the wider medical community as an essential component of patient care for a broad range of disease processes, which previously were not considered relevant to hearing impairment. Examples of the value of interventional audiology being included in the comprehensive team of primary caregivers who seek to minimize impairment and maximize function are as follows.

Lin and Ferrucci (2012) recently published research documenting the robust association between high-frequency hearing loss and an increased risk of falls. The researchers found that for every 10-dB increase in hearing loss, there was a 1.4-fold

(95% confidence interval [CI], 1.3–1.5) increased odds of an individual reporting a fall over the preceding 12 months. Early interventional audiologic assessment, as well as balance testing, may allow primary care physicians to prevent unnecessary falls, hospitalizations, and even death associated with complications of hip fracture and other fall-related trauma. Additionally, the diabetic patient is at greater risk due to neuropathies in the feet that may cause ataxic gait and with a twofold increase in the risk of high-frequency hearing loss (Bainbridge et al., 2008). Physicians and hearing health care specialists may jointly counsel this patient type on preventive care strategies that intervene in possible trauma-related health concerns related to falls. Hearing impairment is a hidden disability that is not visible to patients and their support systems, including physicians. Audiologists and other health care professionals would be wise to intervene in the care of individuals with medical conditions and high-risk comorbidities associated with a higher incidence of hearing loss. Although there is a paucity of evidence from randomized controlled trials, early identification, remediation, and treatment of hearing loss are thought to lead to higher overall quality-of-life outcomes. Common sense requires audiologists to educate physicians and other medical practitioners about the linkage between hearing impairment and numerous medical conditions. Let's examine some of these comorbid conditions in greater detail.

Crash Course: What Is a Comorbidity?

In medicine, comorbidity is the presence of one or more additional disorders (or diseases) co-occurring with a primary disease or disorder, or the effect of such additional disorders or diseases. Comorbid conditions shown to be independently associated with hearing loss include dementia, depression, and social isolation. Comorbidity marketing requires that hearing care professionals ethically, accurately, and responsibly communicate these comorbid relationships to all stakeholders in their community, including primary care physicians.

Hearing Loss and Cognitive Decline

By 2050, one in 30 Americans will have dementia. It is thought that delaying the onset of dementia by 1 year could potentially reduce the incidence of dementia by 15%, thus saving billions of dollars in health care costs. Lin et al. (2013) at Johns Hopkins University followed 1,984 individuals between the ages of 36 and 90 years. None of the participants had cognitive impairment as measured on standardized tests at the beginning of the study, while some did have hearing loss. The participants were followed over an 18-year period. The effects of age, medical risk factors, diabetes, and hypertension were controlled in the study design. Results of the study indicated that individuals with hearing loss have a greater risk of subsequently developing dementia than do individuals without hearing loss. Specifically, Lin and colleagues found that study participants with hearing loss at the beginning of this longitudinal study had a 40% chance of a greater rate of cognitive decline compared with those with normal hearing at the beginning of the study. Additionally, the researchers surmise that a mild (25-dB) hearing loss equates to a 7-year cognitive decline. A consequence of the Lin et al. (2013) findings would be to encourage patients to have their hearing screened at an earlier age (before age 55 years) and to actively participate in the appropriate auditory treatment program, if indicated. Although not a cause of dementia, this study suggests a clear link. Thus, earlier intervention of hearing loss may result in a lower incidence of clinically significant dementia.

Hearing Loss and Diabetes

Hearing loss is more than twice as common in adults with diabetes compared with those who do not have the disease, according to a new study funded by the NIH (Bainbridge et al., 2008). Twenty-one percent of the diabetics surveyed had hearing loss, compared with only 9% of nondiabetics in this outcomes-based study, which controlled for other variables. Of the diabetics tested, 68% of them had hearing loss in the higher frequencies. Also, Lin et al. (2011) evaluated NIH data with a higher age cutoff and also showed that diabetics have about twice the prevalence of hearing loss (20%) in the U.S. population compared with those who do not have type 2 diabetes. A certain degree of hearing loss is a normal part of the aging process for all of us, but it is often accelerated in patients with diabetes, especially if blood glucose levels are not being controlled with medication, diet, and exercise. Eighty-five percent of diabetics do not achieve their annual health care goals for hypertension, cholesterol, and blood sugar—poor patient compliance is problematic in this patient population and may be enhanced by diabetics who cannot hear, thus reducing their engagement with their caregivers and increasing the risk of further complications. Henry Ford Hospital in Detroit, Michigan, conducted a study showing that women between the ages of 60 and 75 years with poorly controlled diabetes had significantly worse hearing than those whose diabetes was controlled. Given these findings, diabetic patients and those at risk for developing diabetes should have their hearing screened on an annual basis. Recently, the American Diabetes Association recommended that diabetics who suspect they may have a hearing loss contact their primary care provider, who may refer them to either an audiologist or a licensed hearing aid dispenser for a hearing screening (Taylor et al., 2013).

Hearing Loss and Smoking

Approximately 45 to 48 million Americans currently smoke, with female smokers slightly outnumbering male smokers. Current estimates suggest that approximately 60% of children in the United States are exposed to secondhand smoke each day. Research indicates that smokers are 1.69 to 2.1 times as likely to have a hearing loss as nonsmokers (Cruickshanks et al., 1998). Secondhand smoking also appears to have a deleterious effect on hearing, as individuals exposed to smokers have a 1.83 increased risk of sensorineural hearing loss compared with those not exposed to secondhand smoking (Lalwani et al., 2011).

Research findings show that different mechanisms play a role in hearing loss due to exposure to smoking. The first may be related to tissue hypoxia (lack of oxygen)—nicotine and carbon monoxide may actually deplete oxygen levels to the highly vascularized cochlea, which is bathed in electrolytic fluids. If oxygen is depleted, tissue damage can occur (Katbamna, 2008).

The effect smoking has on hearing also appears to be correlated with the amount of cigarettes smoked. A study conducted on Japanese office workers who smoke (Nakanishi et al., 2000) showed that as the number of cigarettes smoked per day and pack years of smoking increased, the risk of high-frequency hearing loss increased in a dose-dependent manner. In other words, the more people smoked each day and the longer they smoked, the worse the hearing damage—especially in the high-frequency range. Smoking and secondhand smoke are associated with elevated pure-tone thresholds and an increased prevalence of both low- and high-frequency sensorineural hearing loss that is directly related to level of exposure.

Hearing Loss and Depression

Depression is also associated with the elderly patient having acquired hearing loss. Jones and White (1990) conducted a meta-analysis on studies that examined the relationship between hearing loss and mental health. They concluded that individuals with hearing loss were more vulnerable to depression than people from the general population. More recently, Garnefski and Kraaij (2012) examined the relationship between cognitive coping strategies, anxiety, depression, and acquired hearing loss. Their results suggested that maladaptive coping skills and symptoms of anxiety and depression are related issues among individuals with acquired hearing loss. Simply stated, patients with hearing loss tend to have more ill-effects of depression and anxiety compared with individuals with normal hearing. It seems that hearing loss adds to the complexity of the situation for patients with these conditions. Given the paucity of studies in this area, however, further research is necessary to better understand the relationship between hearing loss, anxiety, and depression.

Hearing Loss and Aging-in-Place

The importance of interventional audiology goes beyond its relationship to chronic medical conditions. There are also lifestyle necessities requiring the practice of interventional audiology. The Centers for Disease Control defines "aging-in-place" as the ability to live in one's own home and community safely, independently, and comfortably, regardless of age, income, or ability level. Of course, most adults would prefer to age in place; in fact, 78% of adults between the ages of 50 and 64 years report that they would prefer to stay in their current residence as they age. One third of American households are home to one or more residents 60 years or older. Additionally, those who are not able to age in place, and are therefore institutionalized, become drains on the current health care system and put increasing strain on the currently struggling programs of Medicare and Medicaid. In fact, the CDC estimates that, in the year 2020, Medicare beneficiaries who are admitted to the hospital due to injuries resulting from an accidental fall, will incur hospitalization charges paid by Medicare between $9,113 to $13,507 per incident. As Genther (2013) recently demonstrated, adults with hearing loss have a higher rate of hospitalization and poorer overall health. These data represent an enormous opportunity for audiologists to intervene in the efficient delivery of services that maintain a higher quality of life for a large and growing number of people.

Considering the growing aging-in-place population and the fact that nearly two of every three adults older than 70 years have hearing loss, hearing health care providers certainly have a significant role to play in the aging-in-place movement, and it is reasonable to hypothesize that quicker identification and proper treatment of hearing loss in the elderly population may result in a higher percentage of that population being able to remain in their own homes until a more advanced age than would otherwise be the case.

Hearing Loss and Healthy Aging

Another subcategory of patients that could potentially benefit from interventional audiology services are healthy-agers. Unlike baby boomers, who are defined as those born between 1946 and 1960, healthy-agers are best described as individuals who want to maintain optimal cognitive and physical functioning for as long as possible. In other words, to live to be 100 in the mind and body of a 45-year-old, and they often are willing to spare no expense to accomplish this goal.

Since healthy-agers are defined by lifestyle needs and not year of birth, this segment of the population comprises people of all ages. The role of interventional audiology within the healthy-aging movement is to raise the awareness of the impact that diet and nutrition play on hearing acuity. Additionally, interventional audiologists could demonstrate to healthy-agers the use of downloadable apps, which can be used to improve hearing and overall cognitive function.

Implementation of Interventional Audiology in Your Clinic

Let's examine some specific areas in which audiologists can work in partnership with physicians and other medical professionals to deliver preventive, interventional patient care. Because 80% of older adults make at least one annual physician visit and sections of the Affordable Care Act incentivize younger adults to see their health care provider for routine checkups, it is imperative for audiologists to educate primary care physicians and physician assistants. By adapting a "educate to obligate" communication strategy between audiology and primary care medicine, audiologists can partner with physicians to provide more rapid and effective diagnosis and treatment of hearing loss.

EDUCATION AND AWARENESS

Before examining the three components of an interventional audiology program, let's recognize the challenge and obstacles associated with building referral networks with PCPs. Audiologists must recognize the busy nature of a PCP's practice. Most

PCP practices see patients of all ages with a range of conditions, many of which can be life threatening. For the typical PCP, issues related to hearing loss are a relatively low priority, and therefore audiologists need to be sensitive to the practice's needs. Due to the extremely busy nature of their schedule, audiologists must package educational material so that it is specific and free of jargon. The educational material needs to be in alignment with how PCPs absorb information, and thus materials need to be evidence based and translate research into quality patient care. Finally, the educational material needs to be delivered to the PCP in a familiar format, such as grand rounds or one-page summary sheets.

There are three broad categories of audiologist–PCP engagement. First, physicians must be educated about the impact hearing loss has on their ability to deliver effective care. Systematic, evidence-based targeted education of PCPs is the most fundamentally important component of implementation. Given that most PCPs have had very little formal training on the consequences of untreated hearing loss, the education process must begin by raising awareness with the PCPs in your area. In short, PCPs need to know that untreated hearing loss affects their effectiveness with patients who have hearing impairments. Some of the aspects of patient-physician communication affected by hearing loss include the following:

- Review of medication use, dosage, and so on
- Cognitive assessment when dementia or other cognitive deficits are suspected
- Communicate key components of a treatment plan or follow-up care
- Discussion of palliative care and end-of-life issues
- Cognitive or depression screenings as part of routine practice or in advance of a surgical procedure

A miscommunication because of hearing loss during any of these routine patient-physician interactions may result in the inefficient delivery of care, which undoubtedly increases costs but may result in catastrophic consequences—even death. In regards to education of physicians, audiologists and others within the hearing care industry have a twofold responsibility.

One, the potential catastrophic consequences of untreated hearing loss. Two, the comorbid relationship hearing loss has to the chronic conditions mentioned previously.

Educating the community is another important component to interventional audiology. In addition to the use of traditional newsletters, social media and websites are useful educational tools that raise awareness within the community of the consequences of untreated hearing loss, especially among the chronically ill. An audiology practice's website can be designed to meet the lay public's educational needs, as well as primary care medicine's, with the goal of informing physicians about their interventional capabilities. Audiologists may seek to present the latest preventive and interventional treatment strategies to the medical community through presentations at hospital grand rounds and at primary care physician teaching institutions. Educational opportunities that seek to provide hearing health educational programs in partnership with the American Diabetes Association, the American Cancer Society, and the American Lung Association, as well as attend, display, and educate at cardiology, pulmonology, endocrinology, neurology, trauma, geriatric, and other physician specialty conferences, so that we begin to engage in a more effective partnership with medicine and intervene where it is medically appropriate, are readily available.

Crash Course: The Four Pillars of Interventional Audiology

The goal of interventional audiology is to become directly involved in the care of patients at a younger age when hearing loss is more likely to be prevented. Here is the big picture: It's more than creating and implementing a marketing plan. Practicing interventional audiology requires the full-scale execution of these four "pillar-of-community" tactics:

1. Exerting more positive social pressures on at-risk adults to have their hearing screened through more effective advertising campaigns. See Chapter 2.

2. Engage younger patients, many with milder hearing losses in the process of self-testing and preventive services with audiologists. Use self-testing apps like uHear in this process.
3. Leverage changes in the health care system to partner directly with primary care physicians and other medical gatekeepers, using many of the tactics outlined in this chapter.
4. Modify or update your clinic approach to patient interaction centered on the health behavior change model. Become a student of motivational (also called solution-based) interviewing.

IDENTIFICATION/SCREENING

The second component to implementing an interventional audiology program in your practice is the ability to conduct routine hearing screening. Due to the evolution of digital technology, accurate hearing screenings now can be conducted in an automated fashion using tablet computers or apps on a smartphone. Before using any of these computer-based hearing screening technologies, practitioners are urged to evaluate their reliability and accuracy. When establishing a screening program within a medical practice, there are five Ws that need to be thoughtfully considered.

■ Who does the screening? It is not feasible for the audiologist to conduct the screening in the primary care physician's office, and therefore a nurse or office assistant needs to be trained to conduct the screening or oversee it. Even automated tools (e.g., Ultimate Kiosk system) require the presence of someone to monitor.
■ Who gets screened? It is probably not feasible to conduct the hearing screen on every patient examined by the PCP, even on patients older than 65 years. We recommend the use of a comorbidity risk assessment, like the designed

by Weinstein (2011) and shown in Table 5–1. This assessment can be added to a routine patient intake form, and medical assistants can be instructed to refer anyone with a score of 5 or greater, as this score indicates that hearing loss is more likely to occur.

■ What screen is used? After consideration of who conducts the screening as well as the target population, the next detail is to determine what screening tool you will use. There are many choices from smartphone apps (e.g., uHear, available on i-Tunes) to handheld devices to automated hearing screening programs placed on a

Table 5–1. The Multifactorial Risk Assessment From Weinstein (2013)

Health Condition	Yes 1	No 0
1. Do you smoke cigarettes?	1	0
2. Do you or a family member believe that you have difficulty hearing or understanding?	1	0
3. Have you been told that you now have diabetes?	1	0
4. Have you been told that you have cardiovascular disease at this time?	1	0
5. Have you been told that you now have arthritis?	1	0
6. Are you taking aminoglycoside antibiotics, cisplatin, an anti-inflammatory agent, or a loop diuretic?	1	0
7. Have you had a fall within the past year?	1	0
8. Have you been told that you have low vision or blindness?	1	0
9. Have you been told that you are suffering from depression?	1	0
Total		

Note. Republished with permission of Barbara Weinstein.

tablet computer, such as Ultimate Kiosk. In addition, practitioners may decide to forego a pure-tone screening and use any number of pencil-and-paper questionnaires. The 10-item Screening for Otologic Functional Impairments (SOFI) by Weinstein (2011) can be used to identify patients likely to have hearing loss. The SOFI is high in reliability, valid, and highly correlated with similar hearing handicap self-reports developed by Weinstein (2013). Another pen-and-paper screening tool that has been validated is the Quick Hearing Check by Koike et al. (2010), which can be found at the Better Hearing Institute website (http://www.betterhearing.org/press/pdfs/QuickHearingCheck.pdf).

■ Where does the screening occur? A separate consideration is where the hearing screening will take place. Some of the choices include an examination room, reception area, or even from the comforts of home if an app or questionnaire is used. Locations need to be chosen that have a minimal impact on the normal workflow of a busy practice.

■ When does the screening occur? The final consideration is when the hearing screening should be conducted. Options include before or after the patient's visit with the PCP.

■ What is the referral process? Perhaps the most critical question, you must determine the process by which patients who fail the screening are referred to the audiology practice, establish pass/fail criteria, schedule appointments, and provide follow-up reports.

PROFESSIONAL SERVICES AND AURAL REHABILITATION

Although there is considerable evidence supporting the efficacy of hearing aid outcomes when properly fitted, utilization by those with hearing loss remains relatively low. Thus, audiologists and hearing instrument specialists are encouraged to explore alternatives to them. Clinicians, furthermore, are urged to offer their patients aural rehabilitation, auditory training, and support groups as a means of improving outcomes with traditional hearing aids and as an alternative for those who do not wish to use traditional devices. As Lin et al. (2011) suggest, community-based interventions, such as a hearing loss awareness support group, are needed to ensure that older adults are able to integrate and apply hearing technologies in their daily lives. The role of other alternative models of hearing health care delivery (e.g., through self-fitting of hearing aids), while generally frowned upon by hearing professionals because of concerns about improper programming, also deserves thorough consideration. Primary care physicians need to know that hearing care professionals offer a wide range of services, which have been validated with well-designed clinical research.

Interventional audiology requires hearing health care clinicians to change their orientation toward patient care. Rather than centering on the dispensing of a hearing aid/medical device, interventional audiology revolves around the disease state of hearing loss and its relationship to the chronic medical conditions listed here. In order for the interventional audiologist to become a valuable and respected member of the physician's preventive care team, several items and procedures are needed. These are listed in Table 5–2. Notice there are three distinct phases of interventional audiology: awareness, identification, and treatment/follow-up. Table 5–2 lists the tasks and procedures that many audiologists currently don't possess but are necessary to successfully implement an interventional audiology strategy.

Chronic diseases are the most costly health problem in the United States (Wu & Green, 2000). Some conditions have a higher rate of hearing loss associated with them, and thus audiologists need to be directly involved in all phases of identification and remediation. The process must begin with a dedicated effort on the part of every audiologist and hearing instrument specialist to educate PCPs, as many of them lack the appropriate knowledge base to effectively identify patients with hearing loss and its ramifications to quality of life (Johnson et al., 2008). The broader negative consequences of hearing loss, particularly in older adults, are now beginning to surface. It is the responsibility of audiologists to draw attention to this using the best available evidence.

Table 5–2. Components of an Interventional Audiology Toolkit

Education/ Awareness	Identification/ Screening	Treatment and Follow-up
• Website and social media that provide data on the relationship of hearing loss to various chronic diseases, including links to patient organizations • Informational newsletters with latest evidence on the disease state of hearing loss, delivered to physicians on a monthly basis • Public lectures for the community that discuss disease state of hearing loss and what to do about it • Clinical processes and patient materials that facilitate the practice of healthy hearing behaviors • Evidence-based educational materials on the disease state of hearing loss that can be personally delivered to physicians • Use of a referral form like the one in the addendum	• Multifactorial risk assessment form • SOFI questionnaire • Use of a comprehensive case history form that asks patients about chronic diseases associated with hearing loss • Referral network of physicians who specialize in various chronic diseases • Detailed reports back to referring physicians, outlining auditory assessment outcome and comprehensive treatment options	• Comprehensive habilitation services, aural rehabilitation programs— beyond simply dispensing hearing aids • Active participation in the health and wellness of patients, including providing support on healthy diets and exercise, consistent with regimens recommended by their physician

PILLAR-OF-COMMUNITY STATUS AND PRIMARY CARE PHYSICIANS

This section of the chapter delves into a specific realm of pillar of community—your ability to form meaningful connections with primary care medicine. We examine many of the tactics needed to build an effective network of referring physicians based on mutual respect for the science of age-related hearing loss and its comorbid conditions. There are approximately 260,000 primary care physicians in the United States, who influence 19% of the gross domestic product (Foley et al., 2014). This amounts to $2.7 trillion spent per year on health care in the United States. Each of these primary care physicians has approximately 2,000 patients in his or her practice. On the basis of a review of NIH data, Lin et al. (2011) estimated that 20.1% of Americans (48 million) cannot pass a 25-dB hearing screening in either one or both ears using the World Health Organization's standard hearing screening regimen. Most audiologists would agree that this degree hearing loss is severe enough to interfere with daily communication. Finally, other health care professionals, particularly physicians, are beginning to recognize the growing epidemic of age-related hearing loss and its impact on public health. The pertinent question is, will the relatively small and obscure profession of audiology influence the practice of primary care medicine and nearly a fifth of a nation of more than 200 million people's gross domestic product?

The marvels of modern medicine are so ubiquitous that we often take them for granted. For example, average life expectancy of an American now approaches 79 years, an increase of more than 30 years since 1900! Individuals aged 70 to 75 years, those who are just now beginning to seek the services of audiologists on a massive scale, have scarcely experienced the premature death of siblings, friends, or neighbors, making this group unlike any other generation in history. Thanks to antibiotics, science-based clinical practices, and vaccinations, infectious diseases such as scarlet fever and influenza are no longer a possible death sentence for those afflicted with them. A consequence of this much longer life span is our ability as a society to manage the expenses of a rapidly aging population.

The combination of a rapidly aging population, along with significant increases in the cost of medical care, has necessitated the changes we are beginning to see in how medical care is delivered in the United States. These changes in the U.S. health care system are huge opportunities for audiologists, especially in the context of the increasing awareness of age-related hearing loss as a public health concern.

Crash Course: Hearing Loss and Healthy Living

Science is beginning to catch up with our clinical intuition. A recent keyword search of hearing loss and healthy living revealed more than 100 peer-reviewed studies, many of which have been published in the past 5 years, showing a relationship between hearing loss and several other chronic medical conditions. There is even a study equating erectile dysfunction to hearing loss. For a comprehensive review of current thinking, see the Institute of Medicine's January 2014 two-day symposium on Age-related Hearing Loss and Healthy Aging. The entire 2-day symposium was recorded and archived at http://www.iom.edu/Activities/PublicHealth/HearingLossAging/2014-JAN-13/.

The growing awareness of age-related hearing loss as a public health concern represents a monumental opportunity for audiologists to touch the lives of more patients in need of their services. This can only occur if audiologists are willing to form partnerships with primary care physicians around the triple threat of untreated age-related hearing loss and the comorbid conditions associated with it. From a business perspective, a strategic alliance between audiologists and primary care physicians in communities across the country represents a sustainable revenue stream for clinicians willing to unbundle and charge for professional services. More important, from a patient's perspective, early intervention of age-related hearing loss and its consequences has the potential to allow individuals the ability to maintain an active and participatory life as they age.

Let's deconstruct this incredible opportunity to build bridges with the primary care physician community. Should a hearing health care provider establish a defined market of primary care doctors within a 5- to 10-mile radius from his or her practice, say 50 physicians, with 2,000 patients per practice, the target market is actually 100,000 patients, of whom 20.1% have a potentially treatable loss. That amounts to 20,000 patients. Approximately 25% have already been treated for hearing loss (Pacala & Yueh, 2012), so 15,000 patients remain for audiologists to find mutually beneficial ways to partner with the primary care physician in the comprehensive care of their patients.

MODERN HEALTH CARE: PREVENTIVE, PARTICIPATORY, PREEMPTIVE, AND PERSONALIZED

In Chapter 1, readers were introduced to the four Ps of marketing. In the context of disease state or comorbidity marketing, a different set of Ps can assist in building a formidable referral network with PCPs that uses clinical research in an ethical and responsible manner. *Disease mongering* is a pejorative term for the practice of widening the diagnostic boundaries of illnesses and promoting public awareness of such to expand the markets for those who sell and deliver treatments, which may include pharmaceutical companies, physicians, and other professional or consumer organizations. To avoid being labeled a disease monger, hearing care professionals must take the time to understand the research design, clinical implications, and limitations of every study that examines the relationship between age-related hearing loss and another chronic disease or condition. The Ps of modern health care provide hearing care professionals with an opportunity to educate to obligate. Due to changes in the American health care system, the practice of medicine is expected to see a marked increase in demand for services, especially for primary and preventive care. Because it is not possible to increase the supply of physicians in the short term (and in the long term, increasing the number of physicians is likely to increase the costs of delivering these types of services), the American health care system needs strategies for maintaining access in the face of increasing demand. In view of these proposed changes to the American health care system, Katz (2014) has encouraged physicians to implement the following:

- Create primary care teams in which each member of the team functions at the highest level of his or her license.
- Encourage self-care through better education of patients about their condition.
- Organize seniors who can no longer live independently into patient-centered primary care homes in which the same physician or team of physicians orchestrates delivery of health care, so that the appropriate type of preventive services can be delivered in a consistent manner and duplication of services is minimized.
- Use alternatives to a single patient-physician visit when possible, such as group visits for diabetic patients and the use of telemedicine.
- Eliminate unnecessary testing and overuse of medications.

These recommended changes in medical practice are a golden opportunity to demonstrate how audiology contributes to improving the overall quality of care of patients at risk for hearing loss, while reducing the overall costs to the entire health care system. This process starts with how audiologists fit into the larger picture of health care from the perspective of the gatekeeper, the primary care physician.

The transformation of health care to personalized, preventive, preemptive, and participatory is demanding audiologists to rethink how they create value in the marketplace. In short, the future of audiology may be less dependent on dispensing a device and more dependent on our ability to offer personalized, preventive, preemptive, and participatory services to younger patients with milder hearing losses. At the heart of this transformation from the device being the center of our universe to a myriad of diverse rehabilitative services taking center stage is the audiologist's ability to effectively communicate with the medical community using the three traits shown in Figure 5–1.

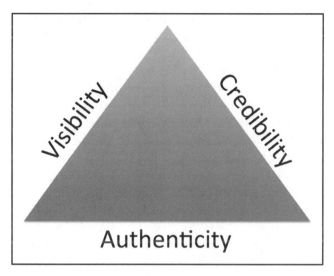

Figure 5–1. The three traits of building an effective relationship with physicians.

BUILDING EFFECTIVE RELATIONSHIPS

In an era of smartphones and Skype, where global communication is instantaneous and almost free, there is something downright old-fashioned and quaint about how to build an effective relationship with the PCP community. After more than a decade of helping audiologists build relationships with physicians, we believe the key drivers of an effective audiologist–PCP relationship in which all parties, including patients, benefit are depicted in Figure 5–1. Let's examine each of the three key drivers more carefully.

Authenticity

Ensuring to the PCP that you have the best interests of the patient as your highest priority begins with the ability to be authentic. Authenticity is best described as the ability to engender trust and respect in another person by putting your true self forward. Due to our increasingly transparent world where information travels at lightning speed to anyone with an Internet connection who happens to be paying attention, the rhetoric of your marketing efforts must be congruent with the reality of how you interact with patients, the community, and other professionals, including PCPs. Other people quickly recognize when a marketing campaign centered on the promise of delivering a transcendent patient experience is overshadowed by the reality of an ordinary, high-pressure sales pitch revolving around hearing aids. In simple terms, authenticity means that you deliver on the promise of your marketing and advertising campaigns. Any disconnect between the two is likely to damage your reputation or brand. Being perceived as authentic—saying what you mean and meaning what you say—can only occur if you are visible within your community and credible in your communication.

Visibility

In a world in which your brand centers on the professional and not the devices you dispense, it is imperative you are visible to the entire community, including PCPs. Despite all the efforts of hearing aid manufacturers, industry consultants, and buying groups to create glossy physician outreach materials, these materials still need to be delivered by the person who is going to be seeing the patient. Taking no more than 2 hours per week to personally visit a PCP practice is a proven approach to becoming more visible and building your brand image.

Credibility

The final section of the PCP relationship triangle is credibility. In short, a credible professional is one who knows the latest science as it relates to hearing loss and amplification and can apply it to clinical practice. From the perspective of building relationships with the PCP community, credibility relates to the fact that you can read, evaluate, apply, and articulate the peer-reviewed research pertaining to age-related hearing loss and its myriad comorbidities.

Physicians are trained in the scientific method and are taught in medical school to evaluate new information with healthy skepticism. Therefore, any communication or attempt to educate medical professions must be grounded in well-reasoned evidence. This will also prevent you from being labeled a disease monger. For example, audiologists would be wise to read the following five studies, which use well-designed methods, have been published in peer-reviewed journals within the past few years, and cite their relevant findings in any professional communication with PCPs.

1. Lin, F., et al (2013). Hearing loss and cognitive decline in older adults. *JAMA Internal Medicine, 173*(4), 293–299.

In total, 1,984 adults between the ages of 70 and 79 years were followed up to 12 years in order evaluate whether hearing loss is independently associated with accelerated cognitive decline. Cognitive testing consisted of the Digit Symbol Substitution (DSS) test and the 3MS, which are two standardized tests of cognitive function in adults.

Results indicated that 1,162 individuals with baseline hearing loss had a 32% poorer score on the DSS and a 41% poorer score on the 3MS compared to those with normal hearing. Compared to those with normal hearing, individuals with hearing loss at baseline had a 24% increased risk for incident cognitive impairment.

The authors concluded that hearing loss is independently associated with accelerated cognitive decline and incident cognitive impairment in older adults. On average, individuals with hearing loss would require 7.7 years to decline by 5 points on the 3MS, while individuals with normal hearing experienced a 5-point decline over a 10.9-year period. Furthermore, the authors indicated that a 25-dB hearing loss equates to 7 years of cognitive decline compared to a similar age group with normal hearing.

2. Fisher, D., et al (2014). Impairments in hearing and vision impact on mortality in older people. *Age and Aging, 43*(1), 69–76.

The main objective of this study was to examine the relationship between hearing and vision impairments and mortality from all causes (all-cause mortality by age group is the annual number of deaths in a given age group per the population in that age group, usually expressed per 100,000) and cardiovascular disease among older people. All 4,926 study participants were from Iceland and 67 years or older.

Participants were placed into one of three categories: vision-only impairment (VI), hearing-only impairment (HI), and dual-sensory impairment (DSI) and followed up to 7 years. After adjusting for age, significantly increased mortality from all-cause and cardiovascular disease was observed for the HI and DSI, especially among men. After further adjustment for mortality risk factors, individuals with HI remained at higher risk for death from cardiovascular disease. Whether hearing loss is an indicator of aging or frailty, physical manifestations resulting in reduced social competence, or a reflection of other adverse health status is unclear; however, results indicated that older men with DSI or HI were at a significantly greater risk for all-cause and cardiovascular death. Regular hearing assessments and rehabilitation services at an earlier age to promote long-term health and longevity are warranted based on these findings.

3. Mick, P., et al (2014). The association between hearing loss and social isolation in older adults. *Otolaryngology-Head & Neck Surgery, 150*, 378–384.

The objective of this study was to determine if age-related hearing loss is associated with social isolation and whether factors such as age, sex, and hearing aid use moderate this association. There were 1,453 male and female participants in this study, all between the ages of 60 and 84 years. Social isolation was defined using the social isolation score (SIS).

Results indicated that greater amounts of hearing loss were associated with increased odds of social isolation in women aged 60 to 69 years. Other groups did not show a significant relationship between hearing loss and social isolation. These results suggest that women within this age range are more likely to alter their lifestyle due to their hearing loss and thus more likely to become socially isolated.

4. Chan-Ming, L. (2014). Hearing impairment with depression in US adults, NHANES 2005–2010. *Otolaryngology-Head & Neck Surgery.* Published online March 6, 2014.

This study estimated the prevalence of depression among adults with hearing loss. Using the nine-item Patient Health Questionnaire (PHQ-9), the prevalence of depression among 18,318 participants of the National Health and Nutrition Examination Survey (NHANES) was examined.

The prevalence of depression increased as hearing loss became worse, except among those self-reported as deaf. Among individuals older than 70 years, no significant association between self-reported hearing loss and depression was found. Adults younger than 70 years, particularly women, had a significant association between moderate hearing loss and depression.

5. Lin, F., et al (2014). Association of hearing impairment with brain volume changes in older adults. *Neuroimage, 90,* 84–92.

Brain volume changes were monitored for a mean span of 6.4 years in 126 adults between the ages of 56 and 86 years. Using sophisticated brain volume measurement techniques, and after adjusting for cardiovascular and demographic factors, the researchers found that individuals with hearing loss had accelerated brain volume declines. These declines in brain volume were primarily confined to the right temporal lobe.

The findings of this study indicate that peripheral hearing loss is independently associated with accelerated brain atrophy in whole-brain and regional volumes concentrated in the right temporal lobe.

Taken as a whole, these five studies suggest that age-related hearing loss has implications well beyond affecting basic communication skills. Although remediating these basic communication skills through early identification using hearing screening has merit in its own right, these five studies provide a high level of evidence demonstrating broader functional implications of age-related hearing impairment on cognitive function, depression, social isolation, cortical changes in the brain, and even early death. Stated differently, there is good evidence to suggest that age-related hearing loss accelerates decline in cognitive, physical, and social function in older adults. Audiologists have a professional obligation, perhaps bordering on a moral imperative, to communicate these findings without hyperbole, inaccuracy, or embellishment. Each study cited here stands on its own as an outstanding contribution to our evolving understanding of the relationship between age-related hearing loss and other common chronic conditions associated with the aging process. By understanding the design of each study, appreciating each study's limitations, and not exaggerating the authors' conclusions, we can begin to develop an evidence-based core message, likely to resonate with the primary care medical community. Audiologists would be wise to develop this core message independent of marketers, who may be tempted to embellish the message, thus jeopardizing the audiologist's credibility.

THE CORE MESSAGE

After reading these five recently published studies and evaluating their findings using your ability to deconstruct each study's design and conclusions, it is likely that you will be able to craft a succinct message similar to the one below. After tailoring it to your liking, the next step is to infuse this message in all your personal communications with the PCP community.

"Age-related hearing loss is a public health concern of very high priority. It's a high priority because several recent studies using randomized controls show age-related hearing loss (AHL) contributes to the acceleration of cognitive and physical decline in adults. Hearing loss imposes a heavy social, economic burden on individuals, families, and communities, as a hearing loss isolates people. Given these findings, all individuals older than 50 years should have a baseline hearing screening, and patients with a history of depression, cardiovascular disease, diabetes, and dementia should have their hearing screened annually."

IMPLEMENTATION: SYSTEMATICALLY COMMUNICATING WITH PCPS

The next questions for audiologists who want to form a strong strategic relationship with primary care medicine are the following: How can I help these patients get the care they so obviously need? Is this an underserved market, and will I be rewarded for investing my time and resources in trying to add new patients to my practice with "physician marketing" strategies? The answer to these questions largely resides in your ability to implement a pillar-of-community communication marketing strategy in place for your practice.

Historically, industry marketing research and testimonials from audiologists who have implemented a physician outreach program support the conclusion that the risk is worth taking and that you will be adequately rewarded.

Pharmaceutical industry marketing research shows it takes five to six calls to a physician to generate a prescription for a new drug. It takes the same number of calls to a primary care physician to generate a new patient referral for an audiologic evaluation. Based on our experience, the number of calls required decreases over time as the relationship between the audiologist and PCP evolves.

Currently, the average audiology clinic in the United States generates $400,000 per year in annual revenue, of which 15% ($60,000) is derived from patients who have been referred by a physician. If one could double the percentage of physician referrals, which is quite attainable based on our experience, then total revenue from physicians is $120,000, of which $60,000 is new income.

To equal this return on investment (ROI), you would need to have $1,000,000 invested in the stock market with an annual return of 12%. For those of you who are not high-risk investors, this may not even be attainable, assuming of course that you have a discretionary $1 million to give to your stockbroker.

Let's revisit the 12,750 patients who will test with hearing loss (TWHL), and assume that all are referred to a hearing health care specialist. We will project that the average number of TWHL referrals to obtain a binaural hearing aid fitting is three, with

4,250 patients who will purchase a pair of instruments. At an average of $5,000.00 per set, the total dollar value of the attainable target market is $21,250,000.

Again, we must ask, "Which patient types in a high-risk patient category older than 12 years should be tested?" The answer lies with those patients with the presence of coexisting conditions or comorbidities that contribute to the cause and increased incidence of hearing loss.

By the numbers, they are as follows:

- 106,000,000 people in the United States who are either diabetic (twice the incidence) or prediabetic (30% increase in the incidence), who have up to two times the incidence of hearing loss versus those who do not have diabetes or prediabetes. Although we did not cite any recent studies showing the relationship between type II diabetes and hearing loss, there are several (Parker, 2009).
- 48,000,000 Americans smoke cigarettes. Smokers have two times the incidence of hearing loss versus nonsmokers, and secondhand smokers have a 1.7 times incidence of hearing loss versus non-secondhand smokers (Katbamna, 2008).
- 30,000,000 of the U.S. working population are exposed to on-the-job toxic noise levels above the Occupational Safety and Health Administration standard of 85 dB every day (May, 2000).
- 140,000,000 Americans are older than 45 years, with 10,000 turning 65 every day. Over 30% of the plus 65 group have a treatable loss, and this number increases with advancing age (2013 United States Census Bureau Data).
- 12,000,000 people in the United States currently have cancer, and over 50% will be treated with chemotherapy, which may include cisplatin-based derivative drugs, and almost 100% will have high-frequency hearing loss after cessation of chemotherapy (Data from American Cancer Society).
- 50,000,000 to 60,000,000 Americans have tinnitus, and approximately 90% have concomitant hearing loss (Data from the American Tinnitus Association).

■ 80,000,000 have cardiovascular disease and its many complications, and patients have three times the incidence of hearing loss versus those who do not have cardiovascular disease. Hypertension (a subcategory of cardiovascular disease), now the most prevalent treatable chronic disease in the United States and the world, is indeed a proven cause of hearing loss (Marchiori et al., 2006).

A pillar-of-community marketing strategy comprising a physician outreach component is a long-term marketing strategy requiring commitment for the entire life of the practice. Given the second author's previous experience working for a leading pharmaceutical company, let's take a look at how those lessons may or may not apply to physician outreach for audiologists.

Marketing research shows that approximately 63% of people with hearing loss ask their primary care medical professional for an assessment, advice, and directions on where to go for treatment. Current market research shows approximately 15% of the revenue associated with all hearing aid fittings are the result of a physician referral. Therefore, it is imperative that the audiology industry develop immediate plans to access the gatekeepers, the physicians/providers of medical care, and inform them about how we can partner with them in providing effective hearing health care to their patients that may result in an improved patient compliance, improved efficacy, improved quality of life, and decreased cost of patient care.

The increase in physician referrals that resulted in hearing aid sales as a result of the physician marketing trial in the Pacific Northwest (Portland and Seattle) grew fourfold in a 5-year period. In Chicago, unit sales dollars from physician referrals doubled within a 1-year period. The Los Angeles area physician marketing program trebled its revenue from physician referrals within a 2-year period. Many testimonials from hearing health care clinics all over the United States report similar results. Why? *Activity* equals *results*. Physician marketing works because the need and the opportunity are there.

An effective physician marketing plan should be specific, measurable, achievable, realistic, and time bound. So let's get started!

Specific: First, define your target market. Make a list of the PCPs, family practice physicians, internal medicine specialists, geriatric specialists, ENT physicians, endocrinologists, diabetes nurse educators, and nurse case managers. Include those who are MDs, GPs, DOs, RNPs, and PAs within a serviceable 5- to 10-mile radius of your audiology clinic—your practice will need a pool consisting of minimum of 40 physicians, if possible. Prioritize the physicians' clinics that you will call upon. That is, the physicians' offices that currently refer to you are the ones with which you need to foster a closer relationship over the course of time. Since you have an established relationship, these physicians are the easiest from which to increase new patient referrals. Also, add the clinics that have multiple physicians. Include those very busy clinics with high potential to refer but do not, and finally be sure to call upon specialists such as endocrinologists, cardiologists, pulmonologists, nephrologists, diabetes educators, and case managers.

Divide the market area into four roughly equal geographic areas, so that there are four weekly call itineraries per month. This allows 12 call cycles per year (i.e., 12 opportunities to establish brand-name recognition and brand-name loyalty with each of our targeted primary care providers). We need an average of five or six calls per provider before they will try our product/ service—which is "you." The number of calls per patient referral decreases over time as you gain likeability, trust, and respect with the physicians and their staff, as well as gain experience with physician marketing. Complement your face-to-face calls with clinically oriented direct mail newsletters or postcards.

When you target clinics with multiple physicians, you get more exposure for the time you commit to being out of the office—block yourself out for 2 to 4 hours per week. Should you decide that as the provider, you cannot get away at all, then delegate the responsibility for making calls to a current member of your staff, or consider hiring a part-time physician liaison. Your return on investment usually justifies the expense.

Assemble 10 or more "patient referral folders" per week that include your referral forms/stationary, business cards, clinic maps, insurance plans/contracts honored, and a list of services provided. Also include evidence-based clinical research about hearing loss, a brochure showing the manufacturer's latest treatment technologies, and examples of patient education material that is available from your clinic. Remember to bring give-aways (e.g., earplugs, pure-tone screeners, earwax removal kits, pocket talkers, amplified telephones, etc.).

Once you have developed brand-name recognition and brand-name loyalty, the following example of results from your activity may be expected within a 12- to 24-month time frame.

- Call goals = 2 clinics per week
- 8 clinics per month = 40 calls/contacts, distributing a referral folder
- 40 calls = 8 to 10 patient referrals
- 10 referrals = 3 opportunities
- 3 opportunities = 1 binaural sales unit
- 1 sales unit = $4,800 to $5,000 per call cycle
- 12 call cycles = $60,000 per year (approximate)

If the current annual revenue for your clinic is $400,000, then $60,000 is approximately 15% of the total target. This is the national average, and it is a realistic goal after spending 12 to 24 months implementing your physician marketing plan. The activity versus results model above closely resembles the pharmaceutical industry models and have been validated based on the physician marketing programs at major audiology companies in the United States, especially when implemented over a period of 2 to 5 years, with demonstrated significant market share and revenue growth.

Crash Course: What Is a Referral Folder?

During any face-to-face communication with a physician or member of their team (e.g., nurse), our experience suggests that educational materials, summarized in bullet point format, should be distributed. The most effective materials condense the published evidence from peer-reviewed journals on the association between hearing loss and other chronic medical conditions. Rather than photocopy peer-reviewed articles, we recommend that you invest in professionally printed materials that summarize key points and a clear call to action that are branded with your practice's name and logo. Any local marketing agency will be able to assist you with this project.

Marketing to physicians is a long-term endeavor. Your success in physician marketing is dependent on building relationships with physicians and nurses, referral coordinators, and receptionists; providing excellent quality service/care; and maintaining communication over an extended period of time, so that you become the "top-of-the-mind" choice for your local hearing health care providers. Once you start, you can't quit or your physician referral pool will decrease and/or dry up.

Conversations with physicians need to include clinical research evidence of the prevalence, the extent of the negative consequences caused by untreated hearing loss to their patients, the benefits of care, and your own strategies to help resolve the problems by focusing on "efficacious" audiology practices. You must coach the whole staff in physicians' offices on how to make a successful patient referral to your hearing health care clinic.

You must provide examples of innovative technology and differentiate your services, as well as explain how your practice can provide the highest quality care to patients without insurance plan benefits, through the use of national contracts, nonprofits, creative financing, and local health plan agreements for discounted private pay audiology services/hearing aids.

Measurable: We need to be accountable by tracking/measuring our activities (i.e., number of "face-to-face" calls, referral folders distributed, introduction letters sent, info mail-outs, lunch and learns conducted, audiogram deliveries with "thank you" cards, etc.). This is how we analyze our "activity versus results," add/delete targeted clinics, and so on. Develop a weekly tracking form for you and your physician liaison to complete on a weekly basis.

Achievable: Your weekly plan must be achievable within the 2- to 4-hour time frame we specified. Allow a half hour per physician clinic call on a Tuesday, Wednesday, or Thursday—this includes travel time. Preassemble the latest information/innovations in your patient referral folders. Stop at your local pastry shop for your relationship-building cream pies. All this can be done with patience and practice.

Realistic: Two physician clinic calls per week is realistic. This typically requires a minimum of 2 hours per week outside the four walls of your practice. If you spend 2 hours per week out of your clinic by going fishing, your opportunity cost is approximately $20,000.00 per year. Replace that fishing/other activity with physician marketing activity, and your return on time invested building relationships with physicians may potentially exceed $60,000.00 per year for the ownership life of your practice.

Time bound: As previously mentioned, it takes time to build relationships with physicians to the point where they will trust you. You must demonstrate ethical behavior, commitment to effective patient care/treatment programs, and excellence in communications.

The first 6 months results will be modest and mostly come from the "innovators and early adopters," and you must invest the time to see a significant return on that investment in the second year, and by the third year, you will have a truly sound physician referral base. Physicians who are the "late adopters" will become evident to you, and you will weed those out of your call cycle. Your time and money need to be spent with that very large group of physician customers in the middle of the bell curve who are "the early majority and the late majority" who need to feel they like, respect, and trust you. While this does take time, it is truly worth the effort in terms of market share and revenue growth results.

It is useful to develop a comprehensive list of clinical research papers on the treatment of hearing loss to discuss with physicians and nurses. This is especially important as more research is published on major populations of patients with comorbid chronic disease states that increase the incidence and severity of hearing loss, such as type 2 diabetes and prediabetes, nicotine addiction, and cardiovascular disease. You will become their valued consultant/health care partner once they feel you have earned their trust. The routine distribution of evidence-based clinical research papers and authoritative journal articles will help grow your credibility and trustworthiness. Local marketing agencies, hearing aid manufacturers, and buying groups often have referral programs that you can use to get your educational materials branded with your practice's name and logo. Also, copy shops, such as Kinko's, can help you develop branded stationery/forms/clinic labels to help promote brand-name awareness on each call. Furthermore, you can use social media tools such as Twitter and Facebook to more consistently communicate with physicians and other medical professionals about the comorbid factors related to hearing loss. We have provided several one-page "Better Hearing Is Better Living" bulletins in Appendix 5–A of this chapter as a guide.

Schedule "lunch and learns" with the physicians' clinics to create face-to-face call opportunities, so that you may enhance the peer-to-peer relationship and discover their patient care needs. There is no need to be lavish. Make it tasty and healthy, with soda/water and a modest dessert. Doctors don't always show up, so be sure that the RNs/MAs/referral coordinators have all the information they need to successfully refer a patient to you. Look and dress professionally, smile like you mean it, always keep your promises, and believe like physicians do, that "the patient always comes first," and you will be well rewarded in this marketplace.

Based on current market trends (one in five Americans have hearing loss), there will be 80 million people in the United States afflicted with hearing loss by the year 2030. This represents a tremendous opportunity for the audiology industry, especially in light of the marketing research that shows that over 60% of patients ask their PCPs first about how to get treatment for their hearing loss. Let us make sure it is you who they call when a patient is diagnosed with impaired hearing and who needs quality care!

In the United States, the pharmaceutical industry's experience, when marketing new medications to physicians, so that they will write prescriptions for the new drugs, closely follows the bell curve in Figure 5–2. Physician outreach programs initiated by the audiology industry in the United States, as well as validated by BHI MarketTrak data and the Hearing Healthcare Marketing Company, verify the identical experience in generating new patient referrals.

Approximately 5% of physicians are "innovators" and "early adopters." They will listen and readily initiate new patient care strategies because of your messaging about which patient types need audiologic care in the first 6 months of your physician marketing program—however, there are not enough of these physician types in your target market to make a return on investment feasible for the long term.

The real rewards are in the "early majority" and "late majority" category of customers. It will take approximately 3 years to

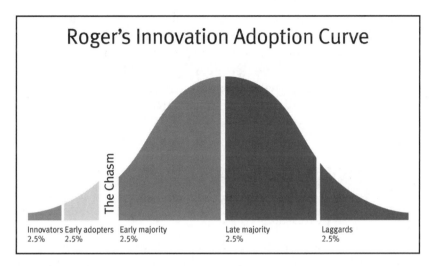

Figure 5–2. Bell-shaped technology adaption curve from Tysoe. Republished with permission of Robert Tysoe.

get to the top of the bell curve with a consistently implemented physician marketing program. You will have another 3 to 5 years of peak sustainable revenue and increasingly profitable returns on your time and resources invested. If there is a single message gleaned from Figure 5–2, it is that you must make a commitment to educate the early and late majority of adaptors. This can take 2 to 3 years based on our experience, but using the findings from well-designed clinical studies showing the comorbid relationship between hearing loss and other common, chronic conditions, you have quality material to sustain those efforts.

New hearing health care technological innovations, enlightened joint clinical research by physicians and audiologists, and expanded services that differentiate you and your practice's patient care capabilities will allow you to maintain a "top-of-the-mind" presence in physicians' clinics, generating another revenue stream and potentially bringing in younger patients for preemptive care.

Now is the time to boldly instill these ideas into your practice by beginning to make calls and develop relationships with the receptionists, referral coordinators, medical assistants and nurses, and the primary care physicians and their office managers. Tailor the core message mentioned above in an authentic manner to build credibility and trust. Ask PCPs to heed our patient care calls to action and accept us as part of the patient care team that seeks to minimize impairment and maximize function in adults with age-related hearing loss. The peer-reviewed articles cited here provide a rational argument. Are you bold enough to bring it to life in your practice by using the tactics shown in Figure 5–3? Only time will tell.

IN-CLINIC SUCCESS AND HELP-SEEKING BEHAVIOR

Interventional audiology strategies certainly are not confined to our marketing efforts, as recent reports have indicated that a recommendation for a hearing screening often does not prompt individuals to take action to resolve a suspected hearing problem. This inability to take swift action can be explained through the lens of help-seeking behavior. Over the past few years, several studies have enriched our knowledge of how adults with

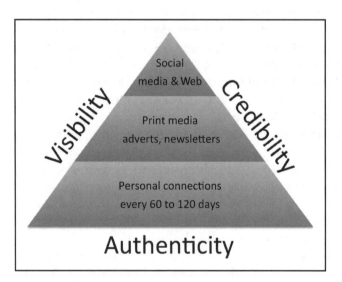

Figure 5–3. The marketing tactics needed to create a sustainable physician outreach program are listed inside the pyramid.

chronic medical conditions, such as age-related hearing loss, manage their condition and what cues to action may influence their behavior change. Various models have been proposed to explain the process of coping with chronic conditions, some of which have been applied to age-related hearing loss.

The "transtheoretical stages of change" model has been used to describe how adults with hearing loss cope with their condition (Proschaska & Velicer, 1997). The "stages of change" model suggests that an individual's ability to change passes through four distinct levels, which are summarized in Figure 5–4. These levels are best summarized as follows:

1. *Precontemplation,* at which time individuals cannot even consider acknowledging a problem exists and that behavior change is needed

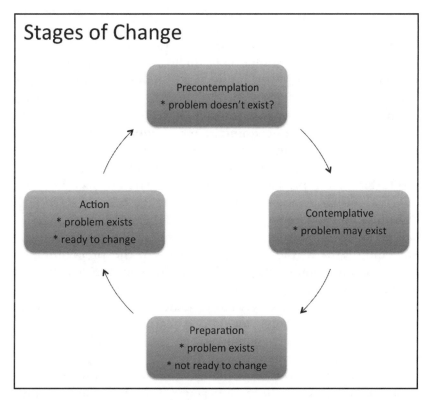

Figure 5–4. The transtheoretical model of behavior change.

2. *Contemplation,* at which time individuals are ambivalent about the existence of a problem and the need to change behaviors
3. *Preparation,* at which time individuals are preparing to make changes by seeking information and talking about this possible change with others
4. *Action,* during which time individuals make actual changes to their behaviors

The literature also mentions a fifth stage, called *maintenance,* at which time individuals make a deliberate attempt to maintain their changed behaviors.

Two self-report questionnaires have been used in "stages of change" research to ascertain the underlying decision-making process of individuals with hearing loss. The Health Belief Questionnaire (HBQ), created by Saunders et al. (2013), is a 33-item assessment that measures five constructs: severity, benefits, barriers, self-efficacy, and cues to action on a 10-point scale. A summary of the five constructs comprising the health belief model is shown in Figure 5–5. Additionally, the University of Rhode Island Change Assessment (URICA) by McConnaughy et al. (1983) is a 24-item self-report assessing the four stages of change, using a 5-point scale. Although both tools have been validated, given their length, neither questionnaire is considered a viable clinical tool in their current form.

Research using the health belief model and stages of change model have attempted to better understand behaviors of individuals with hearing impairment who have failed hearing screening. Milstein and Weinstein (2002) evaluated the "stage of change" in 147 older adults participating in hearing screening. Before the screening, 76% of the participants were in the precontemplative or contemplative stages. Stages-of-change scores did not significantly change as a result of the screening. More recently, Laplante-Levesque et al. (2012) evaluated the stage of change of 224 adults who failed an online hearing screening. In this study, 50% of the participants were in the preparation stage of change, while 38% were represented by the contemplation stage and another 9% by the precontemplation stage. Only 3% of the participants were in the action stage. Together, these studies suggest that hearing screening alone is not enough to improve

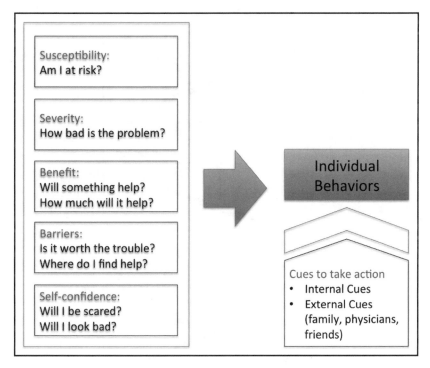

Figure 5–5. The health belief model for age-related hearing loss.

help-seeking rates. Clearly, there are opportunities beyond the offering of an easy-to-use automated or online hearing screening tool that must be considered if our profession is to improve hearing aid usage rates.

Another line of research attempting to explain the underlying decision-making process of hearing-impaired individuals was proposed by Carson (2005). The spiral of decision-making model explains the "push-pull" between seeking and not seeking help that many patients with hearing loss of gradual onset experience. Carson based her spiral of decision-making model on the longitudinal study of a group of women between the ages of 72 and 82 years. Her model, which is summarized in Figure 5–6, suggests that individuals with gradual hearing loss evaluate, analyze, and make decisions around three themes that define self-assessment: comparing/contrasting, cost versus benefit, and control. Carson's model proposes that this spiral of

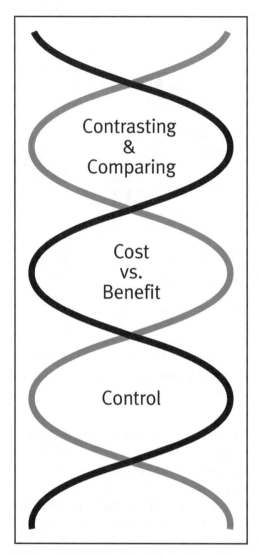

Figure 5–6. The spiral of decision-making model proposed by Carson (2005).

decision making is ongoing, even after remediation for hearing loss has begun.

Changes in the primary care delivery model and implementation of knowledge-based marketing tactics intended to foster a deeper relationship between audiologists and physicians do not change the fact that hearing loss of adult onset is a stigmatizing condition. To embrace the health belief models shown in Figures 5–3 through 5–5, hearing care professionals are encouraged to view the condition of age-related hearing loss through the lens of the social model of disability. Given the ambivalence of all stakeholders—patients, families, professionals, and so on—toward hearing loss of adult onset, the social model of disability, shown in Figure 5–7, is the common thread tying together the concepts discussed in this section.

The social model of disability identifies systemic barriers, negative attitudes, and exclusion by society for individuals with a

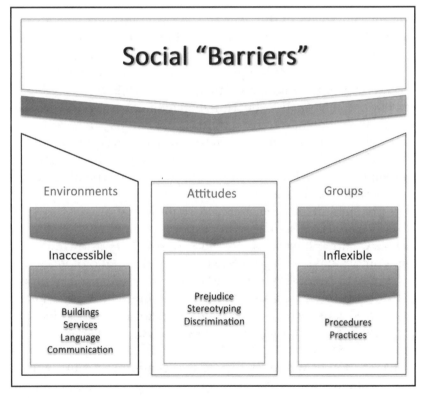

Figure 5–7. The social model of hearing loss based on the work of Goodley (2001).

chronic condition, such as age-related hearing loss. While physical, sensory, intellectual, or psychological variations may cause individual functional limitation or impairments, these do not have to lead to disability unless society fails to take account of and include people regardless of their individual differences. In an evolving health care system, the role of physicians, audiologists, hearing instrument specialists, and others is to ease, reduce, or eliminate environmental, attitudinal, and societal barriers of patients.

Given the unprecedented advances in diagnosis, treatment, and long-term management, the challenge for all health care professionals is to identify and deliver the most appropriate care for the needs of each individual patient. Audiologists are advised to engage in the process of implementing the shared decision-making model of patient care delivery. Under this model, every patient, regardless of the degree of hearing loss, is given a summary of all possible remediation options appropriate for his or her condition. For example, the typical adult presenting to the audiology practice with age-related sensorineural hearing loss would be given a summary of the pros and cons associated with traditional hearing aids, hearing management (support) groups, cochlear implants, auditory training programs such as LACE, and doing nothing. Under a shared decision-making paradigm, each of these five options would be mutually exclusive, and the patient makes the final decision concerning the type of remediation best suited for his or her needs.

Changes in health care also require audiologists to take a more proactive stance with respect to their relationship to primary care physicians. By leveraging their knowledge of the comorbidities of age-related hearing loss, audiologists are equipped to become part of the "pit crew" of the primary physician's team of trusted advisors. Considering that most primary care physicians know very little about hearing loss and its consequences, it is imperative that audiologists do all they can to educate them. With this in mind, we have provided an educational toolkit in Appendix 5–B of this chapter that can be used to educate medical professionals in all health care arenas on the importance of early hearing screening and appropriate remediation and management. The guiding principles of this toolkit can be summarized by these three essential points:

1. The way primary care medicine is practiced is changing, and this change affords audiologists and hearing care professionals an opportunity to get more directly involved in the care of patients, many at younger ages with milder hearing loss.

2. If hearing care professionals are to leverage these opportunities, they must use evidence from peer-reviewed studies, which shows a relationship between various medical conditions and age-related hearing loss as a key part of their marketing message. This change requires a significant shift away from price-driven, product-centric advertising to knowledge-based marketing strategies, which places the skills of the practitioner at the center. For this reason, clinicians are strongly encouraged to learn how to use motivational interviewing techniques when working directly with adults suspected of having hearing deficits.

3. Given the psychologic nature of age-related hearing loss, long-term professional success is largely predicated on what happens once a patient decides to seek the services of a practitioner. The essence of the practitioner's skills rests with his or her ability to unravel the so-called spiral of decision making. Ultimately, it is the personal relationship between the hearing care professional and primary care physician, as well as hearing care professional and patient, that drives the sustainability of our profession. Viewing our value proposition through the lens of the social model of disability, rather than through the lens of the medical model of disability in which the dispensing of hearing aids is at the center, has the potential to transcend the marketplace.

REFERENCES

Anderson, G. (2010). *Chronic care: Making the case for ongoing care.* Princeton, NJ: Robert Press.

Bainbridge, K. (2008). Diabetes and hearing impairment in the United States (NHANES). *Annals of Internal Medicine, 149*(1), 1–10.

Carson, A. (2005). "What brings you here today?" The role of self-assessment in help-seeking for age-related hearing loss. *Journal of Aging Studies, 19*, 185–200.

Cruickshanks, K., Klein, R., Klein, B., Wiley, T. Nondahl, D., & Tweed, T. (1998). Cigarette smoking and hearing loss: The epidemiology of hearing loss study. *JAMA, 279*(21), 1715–1719.

Foley, D., Frick, R., & Lin, F. (2014). Association between hearing loss and healthcare expenditures in older adults. *Journal of the American Geriatric Society, 62*(6), 1188–1189.

Garnefski, N., & Kraaij, V. (2012). Cognitive coping and goal adjustment are associated with symptoms of depression and anxiety in people with acquired hearing loss. *International Journal of Audiology, 51*, 545–550.

Genther, D. (2013). Association of hearing loss with hospitalization and burden of disease in older adults. *JAMA, 309*(22), 2322–2324.

Goodley, D. (2001). "Learning difficulties," the social model of disability and impairment: Challenging epistemologies. *Disability & Society, 16*(2), 207–231.

Johnson, C., Danhauer, J., Koch, L., Celani, K., Lopez, I., & Williams, V. (2008). Hearing and balance screening and referrals for Medicare patients: A national survey of primary care physicians. *JAAA, 19*, 171–190.

Jones, E., & White, A. (1990). Mental health and acquired hearing impairment: A review. *British Journal of Audiology, 24*, 3–9.

Katbamna, B. (2008, October 28). Effects of smoking on the auditory system. *Audiology Online.* Retrieved May 13, 2014, from http://www .audiologyonline.com

Katz, M. (2014). Health insurance is not health care. *JAMA Internal Medicine, 174*(6), 859–860.

Koike, J., Hurst, M., & Wetmore, S. (2010). Correlation between the American Academy of Otolaryngology-Head and Neck Surgery five minute hearing test and standard audiological data. *Otolaryngology-Head and Neck Surgery, 111*(5), 625–632.

Lalwani, A., Liu, Y. H., & Weitzman, M. (2011). Exposure to second-hand smoke associated with hearing loss in adolescents. *Archives of Otolaryngology-Head and Neck Surgery, 7*, 655–662.

Laplante-Levesque, A., Knudsen, L. V., Preminger, J. E., Jones, L., Nielsen, C., Öberg, M., . . . Kramer, S. E. (2012). Hearing help-seeking behavior and rehabilitation: Perspectives of adults with hearing impairment. *International Journal of Audiology, 51*(2), 93–102.

Lin, F., & Ferrucci, L. (2012). Hearing loss and falls among older adults in the United States. *Archives of Internal Medicine, 172*(4), 369–371.

Lin, F., Niparko, J., & Ferrucci, L. (2011). Hearing loss prevalence in the United States. *Archives of Internal Medicine, 171*(20), 1851–1853.

Lin, F. R., Yaffe, K., Xia, J., Xue, Q-L., Harris, T. B., Purchase-Helzner, E., . . . Simonsick, E. M. (2013). Hearing loss and cognitive decline in older adults. *JAMA Internal Medicine, 173*(4), 293–299.

May, J. (2000). The New York Center for Agricultural Medicine: Occupational hearing loss. *American Journal of Industrial Medicine, 37*, 112–120.

Marchiori, L., Ferreira dos Anjos, M., Takata, T., Chaim, R., & Barros, F. (2006). Hypertension as a factor associated with hearing loss. *Brazilian Journal of Otolaryngology, 72*, 4.

Mathers, C., Smith, A., & Concha, M. (2003). *Global burden of hearing loss in the year 2000*. Geneva, Switzerland: World Health Organization. Retrieved September 3, 2013, from http://www.who.int/heath careinfo/statsitics/bod_hearingloss.pdf

McConnaughy, J., Prochaska, J., & Velicer, W. (1983). Stages of change in psychotherapy: Measurement and sample profiles. *Psychotherapy: Theory, Research and Practice, 20*, 268–376.

Milstein, L., & Weinstein, B. (2002). Effects of information sharing on follow-up after screening for older adults. *Journal of the Academy of Rehabilitative Audiology, 35*, 43–58.

Nakanishi, N., Okamoto, M., Nakamura, K., Suzuki, K., & Tatara, K. (2000). Cigarette smoking and risk for hearing impairment: A longitudinal study in Japanese male office workers. *Journal of Occupational and Environmental Medicine, 42*(11), 1045–1149.

Pacala, J. T., & Yueh, B. (2012). Hearing deficits in the older patient: I didn't notice anything. *JAMA, 307*(11), 1185–1194.

Parker, P. (2009). Diabetes and hearing loss. *Audiology Practices, 2*, 22–23.

Proschaska, J., & Velicer, W. (1997). The transtheoretical model of health behavior change. *American Journal of Health Promotion, 12*, 38–48.

Saunders, G., Frederick, M., Silverman, S., & Papesh, M. (2013). Application of the health belief model: Development of the Health Belief Questionnaire (HBQ) and its association with hearing health behaviors. *International Journal of Audiology, 52*, 558–567.

Taylor, B., (2013). Diabetes: A roundtable discussion. *Audiology Practices, 5*(3), 18–22.

Tinetti, M., Fried, T., & Boyd, C. (2012). Designing health care for the most common chronic condition—multimorbidity. *JAMA, 307*(23), 2493–2494.

Vaillant, G. (2012). *Triumphs of experience: The men of the Harvard Grant Study*. Cambridge, MA: Harvard University Press.

Weinstein, B. (2011). Screening for otological functional impairments in the elderly: Whose job is it anyway? *Audiology Research, 1*, e12, 42–48.

Weinstein, B. (2013). Tool kit for screening otologic function of older adults. *American Journal of Audiology, 22*, 179–182.

Weiss, C., Boyd, C., Yu, Q., Wolff, J., & Leff, B. (2007). Patterns of prevalent major chronic disease among older adults in the United States. *JAMA, 298*(10), 1160–1162.

Wu, S., & Green, A. (2000). *Projection of chronic illness prevalence and cost inflation.* Santa Monica, CA: RAND Health.

APPENDIX 5-A

BETTER HEARING IS BETTER LIVING

Better **Hearing**
is Better **Living**
No. 1

Evidence of a Dementia – Hearing Loss Link

By 2050 one in 30 Americans will suffer from dementia. It is thought that delaying the onset of dementia by one year could reduce the prevalence of dementia by 15%, thus saving billions of dollars in health care costs.

Frank Lin MD and colleagues at John Hopkins University followed 1984 individuals between the ages of 36 and 90 years of age. None of the participants had cognitive impairment as measured on standardized tests at the beginning of the study, while some of them did have hearing loss. The participants were followed over an 18 year period. The effects of age, medical risk factors, diabetes and hypertension were controlled in the study design.

Results of the study indicated that individuals with hearing loss have a greater incident of dementia. Specifically, Lin et al found that study participants with hearing loss at the beginning of this longitudinal study have a 40% chance of a greater rate of cognitive decline compared to those with normal hearing at the beginning of the study. Additionally, the researchers surmise that a mild (25 dB) hearing loss equates to a seven year cognitive decline.

Conclusions: The results of this prospective study indicate that hearing loss increases the risk of cognitive decline in older adults, with the rate of cognitive decline associated with the degree of the hearing loss. Encourage your patients to have their hearing screened and to actively participate in the appropriate auditory treatment program, if necessary.

Reference

Lin et al. *JAMA Intern Med.* 2013;173(4):293-299.

Lowery Mayo, Au.D.
Advanced Hearing & Balance
636 Church St. #307
Evanston, IL 60201

Better **Hearing**
is Better **Living**

No. 2

The Triple Threat of Hearing Loss

Hearing loss is the second leading cause of years living with disability (YLD), second only to depression. John Bakke, MD of Zolo Healthcare Solutions, refers to acquired hearing loss of adult onset as a triple threat to patients. Here is why:

1. Clinically significant hearing impairment is itself a disability and is an indication for effective remediation in its own right.

2. Hearing loss interferes with a patient's ability to be treated for other medical conditions because it hinders an individual's ability to engage with physicians and understand treatment advice and directives.

3. Emerging research suggests that hearing loss may actually accelerate some disabilities such as cognitive dysfunction and vestibular impairment. The prevalence, co-morbidity and disabling effects of hearing loss underscore the need for aggressive preventive programs that identify conditions such as hearing loss which threaten health outcomes.

Conclusion: Encourage your patients to have their hearing screened and to actively participate in the appropriate auditory treatment program, if necessary.

References

Mathers, C. et al (2003). Global burden of hearing loss in the year 2000. Geneva: World Health Organization. www.who.int/heathcareinfo/statsitics/bod_hearingloss.pdf. [Accessed September 3, 2013.

Weinstein, B. (2011) Screening for otological functional impairments in the elderly: whose job is it anyway? Audiology Research. 1:e12,42-48.

Lowery Mayo, Au.D.
Advanced Hearing & Balance
636 Church St. #307
Evanston, IL 60201

Better **Hearing**
is Better **Living**

When you make a referral to an independent hearing care professional you can expect your patients to be treated with care and respect. You can also expect to receive a detailed and timely report of assessment results. Independent practitioners stake their reputation on word-of-mouth referrals from individuals in your community. By developing a personalized and comprehensive "communication plan," independent practitioners are better-equipped to deliver thorough care to patients of a variety of ages and backgrounds. In addition to high quality, personalized care, you can expect:

• A comfortable, professional and no-pressure environment

• Timely service without long waits

• Direct access to experienced clinicians

• Use of latest diagnostic equipment and assessment techniques

• Wide range of hearing devices and therapeutic approaches

• Private pay and many insurances accepted

The Co-Morbid Condition of Hearing Loss

Your local independent hearing care professional is now being increasingly viewed within the wider medical community as an essential component of patient care for a broad range of disease processes which, previously, were not considered relevant to hearing impairment. Examples of the value of interventional audiology being included in the comprehensive team of primary care-givers who seek to minimize impairment and maximize function are as follows:

1. Recently published research documenting the robust association between high frequency hearing loss and an increased risk of falls. The researchers found for every 10-dB increase in hearing loss, there was a 1.4-fold (95% CI, 1.3-1.5) increased odds of an individual reporting a fall over the preceding 12 months.

2. Researchers at John Hopkins University followed 1984 individuals between the ages of 36 and 90 years of age. None of the participants had cognitive impairment as measured on standardized tests at the beginning of the study, while some of them did have hearing loss. The participants were followed over an 18 year period. The effects of age, medical risk factors, diabetes and hypertension were controlled in the study design. Results of the study indicated that individuals with hearing loss have a greater risk of subsequently developing dementia than do individuals without hearing loss. Specifically, Lin et al found that study participants with hearing loss at the beginning of this longitudinal study have a 40% chance of a greater rate of cognitive decline compared to those with normal hearing at the beginning of the study. Additionally, the researchers surmise that a mild (25 dB) hearing loss equates to a seven year cognitive decline.

3. Hearing loss is more than twice as common in adults with Type II diabetes compared to those who do not have the disease, according to a 2008 study funded by the National Institutes of Health.

Conclusions: Hearing impairment is a hidden disability that is not visible to patients and their support systems, including physicians. Hearing loss is often linked to other chronic medical conditions. Encourage your patients to have their hearing screened, especially if they have one of these common, chronic conditions.

References: Lin, F. & Ferrucci, L. (2012). Hearing loss and falls among older adults in the United States. *Arch Intern Med*. 172,4,369-371; Bainbridge et al. (2008) Diabetes and Hearing Impairment in the United States (NHANES) Annals Intern Med. 149,1,1-10; Lin, F. et al (2013) Hearing loss and cognitive decline in older adults. *JAMA Intern Med* 173,4, 293-299.

Better Hearing is Better Living

No. 4

What Happens When Your Patient Doesn't Hear You

Recently published data from NIH suggests that one-third of individuals between the ages of 65 and 74 and one-half of individuals over 75 have hearing loss. Hearing loss is known to be the third most common chronic medical condition, yet many people fail to take the time to have their hearing checked. In brief, more patients than you think have trouble following the conversation during a consult in your office.

Some of the aspects of patient-physician communication affected by hearing loss include:

• Review of medication use, dosage, etc.

• Cognitive assessment when dementia or other cognitive deficits are suspected

• Communication of key components of a treatment plan or follow-up care

• Discussion of palliative care and end of life issues

• Cognitive or depression screenings as part of routine practice or in advance of a surgical procedure

Conclusions: Hearing impairment is a hidden disability that is not visible to patients and their support systems, including physicians. Hearing loss is often linked to other chronic medical conditions. Encourage your patients to have their hearing screened, especially if they are over the age of 60.

References: Lin, F. & Ferrucci, L. (2012). Hearing loss and falls among older adults in the United States. *Arch Intern Med.* 172,4,369-371; Bainbridge et al. (2008) Diabetes and Hearing Impairment in the United States (NHANES) Annals Intern Med. 149,1,1-10; Lin, F. et al (2013) Hearing loss and cognitive decline in older adults. *JAMA Intern Med* 173,4, 293-299.

Lowery Mayo, Au.D.
Advanced Hearing & Balance
636 Church St. #307
Evanston, IL 60201

Better **Hearing**
is Better **Living**

No. 5

Hearing Loss and Depression

Recent research suggests that individuals suffering from hearing loss are more likely to also suffer from the ill-effects of depression. Jones & White conducted a meta-analysis on studies that examined the relationship between hearing loss and mental health. They concluded that individuals with hearing loss were more vulnerable to depression than people from the general population. More recently, Garnefski & Kraaij examined the relationship between cognitive coping strategies, anxiety, depression and acquired hearing loss. Their results suggested that maladaptive coping skills and symptoms of anxiety and depression are related issues among individuals with acquired hearing loss. Simply stated, patients with hearing loss tend to suffer more from the ill-effects of depression and anxiety when compared to individuals with normal hearing. It seems that hearing loss adds to the complexity of the situation for patients suffering from these conditions. Given the paucity of studies in this area, however, further research is necessary to better understand the relationship between hearing loss, anxiety and depression.

Conclusion: An untreated hearing loss may be a contributing factor associated with depression. In addition to standard treatment options, patients over the age of 65 who are at-risk for suffering from depression would benefit from a hearing screening to rule out hearing loss.

References: Jones, E. & White, A. (1990). Mental health and acquired hearing impairment: a review. *Brit Jour Aud.* 24, 3-9; Garnefski, N. & Kraaij, V. (2012). Cognitive coping and goal adjustment are associated with symptoms of depression and anxiety in people with acquired hearing loss. *Inter Jour Aud.* 51, 545-550.

Lowery Mayo, Au.D.
Advanced Hearing & Balance
636 Church St. #307
Evanston, IL 60201

Better **Hearing** is Better **Living**

No. 6

The Manifestations of Age-Related Hearing Loss

The manifestations of age-related hearing loss in many older adults are subtle—having to increase the volume of the television, missing words of a conversation—and hence, hearing loss is often perceived as an unfortunate but inconsequential part of aging. An estimated one in three adults between the ages of 65 and 74 have some degree of hearing loss, while one in two individuals over the age of 74 have hearing loss.

Although hearing loss is the third most common chronic medical condition, a relative few have their hearing screened. According to one study, just under one-third of all adults suspecting a hearing loss had their hearing screened. The consequences of untreated hearing loss are well-known and debilitating.

Conclusion: If you encounter patients who you suspect have a hearing loss, encourage them to have their hearing screened or evaluated by a local hearing care professional.

References: Lin, F. et al. (2011) Hearing Loss Prevalence in the United States. Archives Intern Med. 171, 20, 1851-1853; Genther, D. (2013) Association of hearing loss with hospitalization and burden of disease in older adults. *JAMA.* 12,309, 22.

Lowery Mayo, Au.D.
Advanced Hearing & Balance
636 Church St. #307
Evanston, IL 60201

Better **Hearing**
is Better **Living**

No. 7

Cognition and Hearing Aid Usage

Northwestern University researchers report that the cognitive skills of the patient affects hearing aid benefit. They report that older adults with hearing loss and poor working memory are "more susceptible to hearing aid distortions from signal-processing algorithms." Cognitive function also appears to impact speech-in-noise perception of older adults. Imaging studies reveal when older adults listen to speech in difficult listening situations with challenging signal-to-noise ratios, the older adults activate more of their memory and attention centers (than do younger adults), indicating that older adults are using more of their cognitive resources (than younger adults) to understand the same speech task.

The researchers report 120 adults (aged 55 to 79) with normal to moderate sensorineural hearing loss were evaluated with regard to cognitive, hearing and neural processing ability. The tests administered included tests of memory and attention as well as standard audiometric tests using speech in noise.

The authors report, "We found that cognitive function and neural processing were the biggest contributors to variance in speech-in-noise perception. Interestingly, the contribution of hearing thresholds was not significant...." They suggest that "the recent focus on the importance of cognitive function perhaps argues for the incorporation of a quick cognitive screening into the audiology battery in the near future."

Conclusion: Patients suspected of hearing loss can be referred to a local hearing care professional who is well-versed in speech in noise and auditory working memory testing.

Reference
Kraus N, Anderson S. (2013) The Auditory-Cognitive System: To Screen or Not to Screen. *Hearing Journal.* 66(7):36.

Lowery Mayo, Au.D.
Advanced Hearing & Balance
636 Church St. #307
Evanston, IL 60201

Better **Hearing** is Better **Living**

No. 8

Hearing Aids and Comprehensive Care

Several peer review studies indicate that hearing loss is associated with poor quality of life among older people and may lead to increased health and mood disorders (i.e., depression and anxiety); hearing loss may also increase the risk of mortality. McCormack and Fortnum (2013) report that in the United Kingdom, the average age of the first-time user (FTU) of hearing aids is 74 years of age, while in the US it is under the age of 70.

These authors performed a "scoping study" based on extensive quantitative and qualitative findings from PubMed, which revealed the most common reasons people did not wear their prescribed hearing aids were (lack of) "value" followed by "fit and comfort" issues. (Scoping studies are used to indicate where knowledge has been established and where findings are suggestive, yet not definitive. Scoping studies summarize and disseminate findings.) Specifically, McCormack and Fortnum report their scoping study indicated for non-users hearing aids were not effective in noise, provided poor benefit or sound quality and were not suitable for the hearing loss. Further, they report the patient's manual dexterity and their ability to insert/remove the hearing aid was an issue for some patients.

In another study, using survey data collected from American hearing aid users, patients that received a comprehensive battery of tests and personalized follow-up attention, reported better outcomes from their hearing aids. Specifically, patients that reported that they received more than nine important tests and procedures were more likely to achieve improved satisfaction from their hearing aids when listening in noise.

Conclusion: Refer patients that you suspect have hearing loss to a local hearing care provider that delivers comprehensive testing and follow-up services.

References: Kochkin S, Beck DL, Christensen LA, Compton-Conley C, Fligor BJ, Kricos P et al. (2010) MarkeTrak VIII The Impact of the Hearing Healthcare Professional On Hearing Aid User Success. *Hearing Review* 17(4):12-34; McCormack A, Fortnum H. (2013) Why Do People Fitted With Hearing Aids Not Wear Them? *International Journal of Audiology.* 52:360-368.

Lowery Mayo, Au.D.
Advanced Hearing & Balance
636 Church St. #307
Evanston, IL 60201

Better **Hearing**
is Better **Living**

No. 9

Impact of Self-assessed Hearing Loss on a Spouse: a Longitudinal Analysis of Couples

Hearing loss is increasingly common among older persons and is negatively associated with health and well-being. Its impact on spouses, however, is poorly researched. This study analyzed the relationship between a spouse's self-assessed hearing loss and his or her partner's physical, psychological and social well-being five years later.

Subjects were 418 older married couples from the Alameda County Study. Hearing loss and adjustment variables were assessed in 1994 and outcomes in 1999. Longitudinal analyses included multivariate statistical models using generalized estimating equations to adjust for paired data and partners' hearing loss, age, gender, chronic conditions and financial problems.

Results indicated that spouse hearing loss increased the likelihood of subsequent poorer physical, psychological and social well-being in partners. The negative impact of husbands' hearing loss on wives' well-being appeared stronger than the reverse.

Findings suggest that early diagnosis and treatment of hearing loss constitute important clinical strategies to enhance the well-being of both hearing-impaired individuals and their spouses and support policy change to cover hearing devices by insurance.

Conclusion: Hearing loss negatively effects spousal relationships. Encourage your older married patients to have their hearing screened – it just might lead to a longer, healthier relationship!

References: Wallhagen MI, Strawbridge WJ, Shema SJ, Kaplan GA. *J Gerontol B Psychol Sci Soc Sci* 2004;59:S190-S6.

Lowery Mayo, Au.D.
Advanced Hearing & Balance
636 Church St. #307
Evanston, IL 60201

Better **Hearing**
is Better **Living**

Experience the Independent Difference

When you make a referral to an independent hearing care professional you can expect your patients to be treated with care and respect. You can also expect to receive a detailed and timely report of assessment results. Independent practitioners stake their reputation on word-of-mouth referrals from individuals in your community. By developing a personalized and comprehensive "communication plan," independent practitioners are better-equipped to deliver thorough care to patients of a variety of ages and backgrounds. In addition to high quality, personalized care, you can expect:

- A comfortable, professional and no-pressure environment
- Timely service without long waits
- Direct access to experienced clinicians
- Use of latest diagnostic equipment and assessment techniques
- Wide range of hearing devices and therapeutic approaches
- Private pay and many insurances accepted

Don't Let Unaddressed Hearing Loss Spiral into Depression

If your quality of life, relationships and emotional and mental wellbeing are important to you, then get your hearing checked, the Better Hearing Institute (BHI) is advising in recognition of World Mental Health Day and National Depression Screening Day on October 10th. Research shows that unaddressed hearing loss is associated with depression; but studies also show that people with hearing loss who use hearing aids often have fewer depressive symptoms, greater social engagement and improved quality of life.

Happiness and hearing aids: Is there a connection?
Perhaps.

In fact, a recent Italian study published in Geriatrics & Gerontology International concluded that the benefits of digital hearing aids in relation to depressive symptoms, general health and social interactivity, but also in the caregiver-patient relationship, were clearly shown. In fact, reduction in depressive symptoms and improved quality of life at statistically significant levels were observed early on with the use of hearing aids.

This Italian study, in fact, echoed the general findings of research conducted more than two decades ago. A 1990 study—published by Cynthia D. Mulrow, MD, MSc and co-investigators in the Annals of Internal Medicine—concluded that hearing loss is associated with important adverse effects on the quality of life of elderly persons—effects which are reversible with hearing aids.

Research shows that hearing loss is frequently associated with other physical, mental and emotional health conditions and that people who address their hearing loss often experience better quality of life. Eight out of ten hearing aid users, in fact, say they're satisfied with the changes that have occurred in their lives specifically due to their hearing aids—from how they feel about themselves to the positive changes they see in their relationships, social interactions and work lives.

When people with even mild hearing loss use hearing aids, they often improve their job performance, enhance their communication skills, increase their earnings potential, improve their professional and interpersonal relationships, stave off depression, gain an enhanced sense of control over their lives and better their quality of life.

Lowery Mayo, Au.D.
Advanced Hearing & Balance
636 Church St. #307
Evanston, IL 60201

Better **Hearing**
is Better **Living**

No. 11

Experience the Independent Difference

When you make a referral to an independent hearing care professional you can expect your patients to be treated with care and respect. You can also expect to receive a detailed and timely report of assessment results. Independent practitioners stake their reputation on word-of-mouth referrals from individuals in your community. By developing a personalized and comprehensive "communication plan," independent practitioners are better-equipped to deliver thorough care to patients of a variety of ages and backgrounds. In addition to high quality, personalized care, you can expect:

- A comfortable, professional and no-pressure environment
- Timely service without long waits
- Direct access to experienced clinicians
- Use of latest diagnostic equipment and assessment techniques
- Wide range of hearing devices and therapeutic approaches
- Private pay and many insurances accepted

Here Are Five Little-Known Facts about Today's Hearing Aids...

1. They're virtually invisible. Many of today's hearing aids sit discreetly and comfortably inside the ear canal, providing both natural sound quality and discreet and easy use.

2. They automatically adjust to all kinds of soundscapes. Recent technological advances with directional microphones have made hearing aids far more versatile than ever before—and in a broad range of sound environments. Recent research suggests that advanced noise reduction technology reduces auditory fatigue.

3. You can enjoy water sports and sweat while wearing them. Waterproof digital hearing aids have arrived. This feature is built into some newly designed hearing aids for those concerned about water, humidity and dust. This feature suits the active lifestyles of swimmers, skiers, snowboarders, intensive sports enthusiasts and anyone working in dusty, demanding environments.

4. They work with smartphones, home entertainment systems and other electronics. Wireless, digital hearing aids are now the norm. That means seamless connectivity—directly into your hearing aid(s) at volumes that are just right for you—from your smartphone, MP3 player, television and other high-tech gadgets. In addition, a growing number of hearing aids are equipped with a telecoil, which allows the device to seamlessly connect to telephones and loop systems.

5. They're always at the ready. A new rechargeable feature on some newly designed hearing aids allows you to recharge your hearing aids every night, so they're ready in the morning. It's super convenient—and there's no more fumbling with small batteries.

Lowery Mayo, Au.D.
Advanced Hearing & Balance
636 Church St. #307
Evanston, IL 60201

Better **Hearing**
is Better **Living**

Experience the Independent Difference

When you make a referral to an independent hearing care professional you can expect your patients to be treated with care and respect. You can also expect to receive a detailed and timely report of assessment results. Independent practitioners stake their reputation on word-of-mouth referrals from individuals in your community. By developing a personalized and comprehensive "communication plan," independent practitioners are better-equipped to deliver thorough care to patients of a variety of ages and backgrounds. In addition to high quality, personalized care, you can expect:

- A comfortable, professional and no-pressure environment

- Timely service without long waits

- Direct access to experienced clinicians

- Use of latest diagnostic equipment and assessment techniques

- Wide range of hearing devices and therapeutic approaches

- Private pay and many insurances accepted

Hearing Loss and Social Isolation

Hearing loss is the most common sensory deficit in the elderly, and it is becoming a severe social and health problem. Especially in the elderly, hearing loss can impair the exchange of information, thus significantly impacting everyday life, causing loneliness, isolation, dependence and frustration.

Due to the aging of the population, presbycusis is a growing problem that has been reported to reduce quality of life (QoL). Progression of presbycusis cannot be remediated; therefore, optimal management of this condition not only requires early recognition and rehabilitation, but it also should include an evaluation of QoL status and its assessment.

In brief, hearing loss is also a social loss. Reported effects of presbycusis on Quality of Life are:

- emotional reactions, such as loneliness, isolation, dependence, frustration, depression, anxiety, anger, embarrassment and guilt
- behavioral reactions, such as bluffing, withdrawing, blaming and demanding
- cognitive reactions, such as confusion, difficulty focusing, distracting thoughts, decreased self-esteem and communication disorders

Identifying individuals with hearing loss, supplying appropriate hearing aids or other listening devices and teaching coping strategies may have a positive impact on the quality of life of older people. A recent episode of Charlie Rose (October 11, 2013) was devoted to scientific breakthroughs associated with the sense of hearing. Among the many illuminating points made by the panel of experts was that individuals over the age of 55 should have their hearing screened due to the many negative consequences outlined here.

Reference

Ciorba A, Benatti A, Bianchini C, et al. High frequency hearing loss in the elderly: effect of age and noise exposure in an Italian group. *J Laryngol Otol*. 2011;125(8):776–780.

Lowery Mayo, Au.D.
Advanced Hearing & Balance
636 Church St. #307
Evanston, IL 60201

APPENDIX 5–B

HEARING HEALTH CARE TOOLKIT FOR USE IN PRIMARY AND GERIATRIC CARE

Hearing healthcare toolkit for use in primary and geriatric care

Barbara E. Weinstein, Ph.D., The Graduate Center, City University of New York

Brian Taylor Au.D., Director of Practice Development & Clinical Affairs, Unitron, Plymouth, MN

THE GRADUATE CENTER
CITY UNIVERSITY OF NEW YORK

unitron

3605 MANL 06-14

Hearing healthcare toolkit for use in primary and geriatric care

According to the World Health Organization estimates, 299 million men and 239 woman have hearing loss (Pacala & Yueh, 2012). Globally, adult onset hearing loss is the second leading cause of years living with disability (YLD) behind depression and is a larger non-fatal burden than alcohol use, osteoarthritis and schizophrenia (Mathers, Smith & Concha, 2003). Approximately 34 to 36 million Americans report suffering from some degree of hearing impairment and this number is projected to rise to 52.9 million by the year 2050. Extrapolating from a number of population based studies, hearing loss prevalence ranges from 30 to 47 percent among persons 65+ years.

Age-related hearing loss is considered a "triple threat" to patients for the following three reasons:

1. Clinically significant hearing impairment is itself a disability and is an indication for effective remediation in its own right.

2. Hearing loss interferes with a patient's ability to be treated for other medical conditions because it hinders an individual's ability to engage with physicians as well as other caretakers and understand treatment advice and directives.

3. Research suggests that hearing loss may actually accelerate some disabilities such as cognitive dysfunction and vestibular impairment. The prevalence, co-morbidity and disabling effects of hearing loss underscore the need for aggressive preventive programs that identify conditions such as hearing loss which threaten health outcomes.

Demographics

What follows is a more detailed explanation of the relationship between age-related hearing loss, other chronic medical conditions and their impact on the overall health and wellness of individuals. Hearing loss shares many unique characteristics with **dementia**. Hearing loss is a highly prevalent condition, increasing in prevalence with increased longevity. While high in prevalence, it typically goes unrecognized. Invisible at first, the person with the condition often does not know they are missing important aspects of communication with others. Hearing loss is often invisible to healthcare practitioners, as well. It is insidious, taking about seven to ten years before people realize that the condition is problematic and is interfering with aspects of their lives. The inability to communicate effectively which is a hallmark as the condition progresses, robs the individual from being a productive member of society. Hearing loss has various consequences in the physical, behavioral and social domains. It is indirectly associated with **mortality** and directly associated with **functional disability, social isolation** and **poor self-reported health and depression**. Hearing impairment is a risk factor for cognitive decline, falls and mobility decline. Older adults with hearing loss have the increased burden of medical co-morbidities relating to aging such that more than 50% of older adults have three or more chronic diseases (i.e., multimorbidities) (American Geriatrics Society, 2012). Individuals with hearing loss, vision loss and dual sensory loss have an increased likelihood of presenting with co-morbid conditions ranging from falls and walking difficulty to hypertension to cardiovascular disease. There is a higher prevalence of diabetes in those with hearing impairment, as well.

Present in nearly two-thirds of persons 70 years of age and older, hearing loss remains untreated in the majority of persons in this age group (Chien and Lin, 2012). While the prevalence of hearing loss is nearly 80% among persons 80-plus years of age and older, only 14% reported owning hearing aids; among persons 70–79 years of age, with a prevalence of hearing impairment of nearly 50%, approximately 8% reportedly used hearing aids (Chien & Lin, 2012). Older adults are prone to impacted cerumen which can lead to temporary or exaggerated hearing loss and can also obstruct hearing aids interfering with their function. Overall, the majority of persons with hearing loss do not use hearing aids or other sensory aids despite their proven effectiveness in reducing some of its negative consequences. Hearing aids may not be an option for some and the advent of hearing assistive technologies and personal amplifiers as inexpensive alternatives opens the door to numerous options from which to choose. Of course older adults with severe to profound hearing loss who are no longer candidates for hearing aids are increasingly being referred for cochlear implants with excellent outcomes emerging.

> Nearly 50% of inviduals between the ages of 70 to 79 have hearing loss, yet only 8% use hearing aids.

Hearing loss is independently associated with increased burden of disease, poorer self-reported health, increased odds of hospitalization and healthcare use. Specifically, as compared with normal hearing adults 70 years of age and older, individuals with hearing loss had more hospitalizations and had a positive history of cardiovascular disease. Hearing loss was associated with any hospitalizations and number of hospitalizations (Genther, Frick, Chen, Betz, & Lin, 2013). After hospital discharge, nearly half of hospitalized patients experience at least one adverse event. It has recently been acknowledged that most errors result from a breakdown in communication between parties (e.g., the hospital team and the patient or primary care physician) Specifically, upon discharge, physicians tend to rely on verbal instructions and the entire interaction is typically rushed (Kripalani, Jackson, Schnipper

& Coleman, 2007). People with age-related hearing loss by virtue of the cognitive and central changes which compromise auditory processing will by definition be at a considerable disadvantage.

Case Presentation

Background Information: The oldest old (85 years and older) represent the fastest growing segment of the United States population. Mr. X an 86-year-old man is typical of individuals in this age cohort. He suffers from multiple chronic conditions including cerebrovascular disease and has experienced multiple falls over a period of one year. He lives with his wife and is committed to aging in place. He is socially engaged in that he visits with his children and does have dinner with friends approximately once a week. Having first noted difficulty hearing when he was 80 years of age, he chose to ignore it as it was his understanding that hearing loss was to be expected with advancing age. While performing otoscopy, Dr. Jones asked Mr. X about his hearing. Mr. X, did not understand the question so he asked his doctor to repeat the question. Mr. X then proceeded to describe the many situations which were problematic for him. Dr. Jones suggested that he schedule an appointment for a hearing test with a local audiologist. Mr. X asked for a recommendation, but Dr. Jones was unable to provide any names. After about six months, Mr. X was finally able to find a local audiologist with whom he scheduled an appointment.

The Assessment: Pure tone tests revealed a mild sloping to profound sensorineural hearing loss in each ear. Word recognition ability in quiet was poor in both ears and speech understanding in noise testing confirmed considerable difficulty in suboptimal (noisy) listening environments. The Hearing Health Care Intervention Readiness (HHCIR) scale which assesses perceived social and emotional effects of hearing loss, self-efficacy, social isolation and readiness to proceed with a hearing health care intervention was administered. Responses to the HHCIR suggested that Mr. X experiences difficulty understanding in most social situations and is very frustrated with the difficulty communicating. He also feels that his hearing loss is interfering with the ability to hear environmental sounds, compromising a sense of security.

Similarly, the hearing loss makes him feel isolated and lonely even though objectively his social network is relatively large in terms of number of social contacts. The HHCIR score of 26 suggested that he is handicapped by his hearing loss, is a good candidate for a hearing aid and feels somewhat confident that he would be able to learn how to use hearing aids. We administered the De Jong Gierveld Loneliness Scale. The baseline score suggested that he is feeling isolated and lonely. Hearing health care intervention options ranging from situation specific hearing assistive technologies (e.g., for the phone and the television) to hearing aids were presented using a Decision Aid listing options and evidence of outcomes. Mr. X decided to purchase hearing aids for each ear. As part of the hearing aid fitting he and his wife were instructed on use, care and operation of the hearing aids. Communication strategies to promote more effective communication were outlined.

The follow up: Mr. X returned three weeks after the hearing aid fitting. When tested with the hearing aids, speech understanding ability improved dramatically in noise, the score on the De Jong Gierveld Loneliness Scale revealed that he was no longer feeling isolated, this was also confirmed by a score of 4 on the HHCIR suggesting that he was no longer feeling lonely or having difficulty in the majority of listening situations. The self-reported improvement also coincided with a report that he no longer feels as depressed.

Implications: This case highlights a number of important features of hearing loss and hearing health care interventions. We spoke to Dr. Jones following the hearing aid fitting to communicate our findings and he volunteered that it requires less effort to communicate with Mr. X and that his mood seems to have improved according to the impressions relayed by his wife. His wife also reported that the volume of the television no longer has to be turned up and conversations with family members reveal that Mr. X is more engaged.

Hearing healthcare toolkit for use in primary and geriatric care

The need to strengthen the primary care system and improve chronic care management has become a focus of the U.S. healthcare system.

It is well accepted that errors and adverse events in discharge planning are attributed to breakdowns in communication between the hospital team and the patient or primary care physician (Kripalani, Jackson, Schnipper, & Coleman, 2007). Further, more effective transitions of care, notably, greater clarity in physician–patient communication and adoption of strategies to promote communication might potentially contribute to reductions in medical errors in discharge planning. It is our conviction that identifying persons with hearing loss and utilizing technologies and communication strategies to overcome or compensate for hearing loss and facilitate improved communication in primary care can improve provision of high quality care and promote more effective care transitions be it at hospital discharge, during home visits or during routine office visits.

In sum, as is shown in Figure 1, the unique features of age-related hearing loss can be summarized using 4-Is.

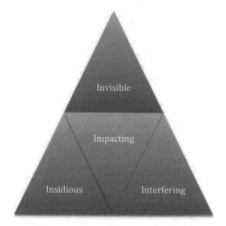

Figure 1. The 4-Is of Age-Related Hearing Loss

Insidious: Age-related hearing loss usually develops so gradually that the individual and those around him don't notice it for a few years. As the hearing loss progressively worsens, the individual's personality, behaviors and outlook toward life may change.

Interfering: Age-related hearing loss interferes with communication in many daily listening situations

Hearing healthcare toolkit for use in primary and geriatric care

Impacting: The consequences of age-related hearing loss impact self-esteem, sociability and overall quality of life, if left untreated

Invisible: Similar to other chronic medical conditions, individuals suffering from age-related hearing loss often adapt or use avoidance behaviors that enable them to "get by" in many social situations. Additionally, society tends to ignore the long-term implications of hearing loss of adult onset. For these reasons, age-related hearing loss is often referred to as an invisible handicap.

Why untreated hearing loss matters

Given the insidious and invisible nature of untreated age-related hearing loss, it is not surprising that its consequences interfere with many facets of daily life for individuals and their families. At the very heart of the issue is the ability of individuals suffering from the consequences of age-related hearing loss to maintain an independent lifestyle as they age. Figure 2 summarizes some of the potential impacts of untreated age-related hearing loss on well being and health care transitions of these individuals.

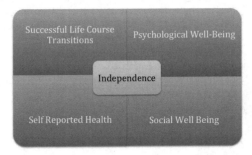

Figure 2. Domains of Quality of Life and Quality of Care Affected by Untreated Hearing Loss

It is imperative that primary care physicians ask about their patient's hearing status and encourage those over the age of 55 and/or suffering from one of the many chronic medical conditions associated with hearing loss (e.g., diabetes, cognitive decline) to undergo a hearing screening. Figure 3 summarizes the primary advantages to be gained in primary care by identifying and screening at risk older adults for hearing impairment.

Hearing healthcare toolkit for use in primary and geriatric care

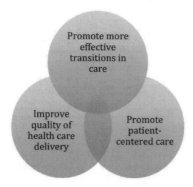

Figure 3. Why Identify and Refer At-Risk Older Adults

Toolkit for hearing loss

This virtual toolkit is meant as a resource for health professionals who care for older persons at risk for burdensome, age-related hearing loss. It includes an assessment algorithm, in- office assessment tools, as well as strategies for communicating with persons with hearing loss.

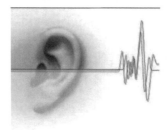

The Affordable Care Act and Hearing Care

Hearing loss is not a normal part of the aging process, as not every older person has impaired hearing. Among persons with impaired hearing, most do not even realize or admit to have hearing difficulties until its social and emotional impacts begin to be felt. The typical older adults tends to think that since hearing loss is a normal part of aging there is little to be done and it is not a major concern. When asked, your older patient may state the following: "they can hear people speaking, but they cannot make out the words." This statement is synonymous with the presence of age-related hearing loss (ARHL).

The higher the number of co-morbidities and communication breakdowns that your patient exhibits, the higher the risk that he/she may have a hearing impairment which may interfere with quality of care and life.

In an effort to remove barriers to preventive services under the Affordable Care Act and acknowledging the importance of hearing status, Medicare covers an Annual Wellness Visit (AWV) which provides Personalized Prevention Plan Services (PPPS) at no cost to the beneficiary (not subject to a co-payment and the physician can bill Medicare for the visit). This benefit enables you to work closely with your patient to develop a personalized prevention plan as shown in Table 1 (Medicare, 2012).

Key elements of the first AWV providing PPPS include, among other things, detection of any cognitive impairment, review of potential risk factors for depression, review of functional ability based on direct observation or appropriate screening questions, or a screening questionnaire including a minimum assessment of:

(1) hearing impairment
(2) ability to successfully perform ADLs
(3) fall risk
(4) home safety

Following the assessment the provider must furnish personalized health advice and a referral, as appropriate, which should be aimed at community-based lifestyle intervention to reduce health risks. The personalized health advice given to the beneficiary must include a referral, as appropriate aimed at community-based lifestyle interventions to reduce health risks and promote among other things self-management, wellness, fall prevention, etc.

Table 1. Sample Action and Planning Form

[Modified from Medicare(2012)]

Patient Name: _____

Date: _____ Age: _____ Gender: F or M

PATIENT ASSETS

FUNCTION	HABITS	REFER
☐ Difficulty hearing and understanding family members ☐ Difficulty communicating with healthcare professionals	☐ Difficulty understanding over telephone ☐ Difficulty understanding physician recommendations (e.g., prescriptions, discharge, return visits) ☐ Home safety concerns	Yes No

Recommendations

Please schedule the following appointment(s):

Audiologists

☐ Please contact one of the following audiologists

1._____

2._____

3._____

Otolaryngologists

☐ Please contact one of the following Otolaryngologists

1. _____

2. _____

3. _____

Hearing risk assessment

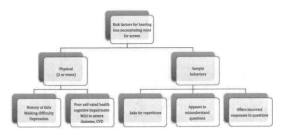

Figure 4. Sample Risk Factors for Hearing Loss and Need for Hearing Screen

Before proceeding with the screening protocol, if upon otoscopic examination there is visible evidence of significant cerumen accumulation referral, cerumen removal is an important first step. The screening protocol is a risk-based approach(Table 2) with the goal being to identify older adults with multiple chronic conditions with an untreated hearing loss which may interfere with care, independence and well being.

Figures 4 and 5 show the risk factors suggesting need for a hearing self-test(Table 3). A sample referral form which grows out of the risk assessment is shown in Table 4.

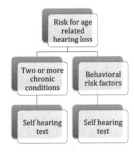

Figure 5. Screening Protocol

Hearing healthcare toolkit for use in primary and geriatric care

Step 1: Assess Co-Morbidities

Does the patient have two or more of the following conditions?

☐ History of falls within past year

☐ Complaint of acute or chronic dizziness

☐ Diabetes

☐ Poor self-rated health

☐ Inability to perform routine activities of daily living

☐ Cerebrovascular disease

☐ Mild cognitive impairment

☐ Depression

☐ Sudden or rapidly progressive hearing loss within the previous 90 days

☐ Significant visual loss

☐ At Risk – 2 or more conditions, proceed with hearing self-test

Step 2: Assess Behavioral Risk Factors

There are a number of behaviors typically exhibited by patients who have difficulty understanding. Hence, if the patient has one or more of the following behavioral signs of hearing loss, this is indicative of possible risk for hearing loss and need for referral to a hearing healthcare professional:

☐ Does the patient consistently ask "what" when you are asking questions?

☐ Does the patient offer incorrect responses to simple questions?

☐ Does the patient appear confused at times because of misunderstanding?

☐ Does the patient spouse or caregiver answer questions for patient?

☐ Does the patient turn his/her head toward you to better understand what is being said?

☐ At Risk – Yes to two or more behaviors, proceed with hearing self-test

Hearing healthcare toolkit for use in primary and geriatric care

Table 2. Risk Assessment

Note that when a patient exhibits behaviors consistent with hearing loss, it is important to use communication strategies(Table 5) and possible communication aids (e.g., Pocket Talker or smartphone Apps–Table 5) to facilitate patient-centered care, transitions in care and adherence.

The questions below include items highly associated with the need for a follow-up hearing test. Built into the questionnaire are indicators of patient acceptance of hearing difficulties, readiness to speak to someone regarding concerns about hearing and questions about social isolation which is highly correlated with mortality and is a condition physicians are likely to address and rarely associate with hearing loss (although it is associated with moderate to severe hearing loss).

Table 3. Self Hearing Test – Hearing Health Care Intervention Readiness (HHCIR) Questionnaire (Weinstein, 2013 .)

	Item	4	2	0	NA
H-1	Does a hearing problem cause you difficulty when listening to the television or to the radio?	Yes	Sometimes	No	
R-1	How important is it for you to have less difficulty when listening to the television or radio?	Very	Somewhat	Not Very	
H-2	Does a hearing problem cause you difficulty when visiting with friends, relatives or neighbors?	Yes	Sometimes	No	
R-2	How important is it for you to experience less difficulty when visiting with friends, relatives, or neighbors?	Very	Somewhat	Not Very	
H-3	Does a hearing problem interfere with your ability to hear environmental sounds such as the telephone ringing or car horns honking?	Yes	Sometimes	No	
H-4	Does a hearing problem cause you to feel frustrated when communicating with friends, co-workers or members of your family?	Yes	Sometimes	No	
R-3	How important is it for you to feel less frustrated when communicating with friends, co-workers or members of your family?	Very	Somewhat	Not Very	
SI-1	Do you experience feelings of loneliness or not belonging due to your hearing loss?	Yes	Sometimes	No	
SI-2	Do you perceive yourself to be isolated from friends and/or family members due to your hearing loss?	Yes	Sometimes	No	
SE-1	How confident are you that you would follow the recommendations of a hearing healthcare professional (e.g. undergo a hearing evaluation, use hearing aids, use a hearing assistance technology, participate in a communication program)?	Very	Somewhat	Not Very	

AT RISK = Y/S to SI – 1 or SI-2 or H or R TOTAL score > 4

Hearing healthcare toolkit for use in primary and geriatric care

Table 4. Sample Risk Assessment Referral Form

Risk Level	Co-Morbidities	Behaviors	Self-Test SI (>2)	Self-Test H or R > 4	Targeted Recommendations
High Risk	+	+	+	+	1. Referral to audiologist for diagnostic test to determine if hearing loss exists 2.Communication strategies–setting specific
Moderate Risk	+	-	-	+	1.Referral to Audiologist for diagnostic test to determine if hearing loss exists 2.Communication strategies
Mild Risk	-	+	-		Counseling and communication strategies
No Risk	-	-	-		Ask at subsequent visits if patient feels they have a hearing loss

Communicating with your hearing impaired patient

There are several easy ways to make communicating with hearing impaired individuals easier. Six of the most straightforward ways for improving face-to-face conversations with patients with hearing loss are listed in Table 5.

Table 5. General communication strategies and assistive technology for individuals at risk for hearing loss

1. Make sure face and mouth are visible when speaking to the patient

2. Make sure to keep distractions(auditory and visual)to a minimum when speaking to the patient

3. Make sure to sit within three to six feet of the patient

4. If the patient is a hearing aid user, make sure hearing aids are turned on, in the ear and working

5. If the patient is not a hearing aid user, but exhibiting difficulty understanding (e.g., asks you to repeat what you have said), then use a commercially available personal sound amplifier, such as the Pocket Talker shown, available from https://www.oaktreeproducts.com. You may also consider smartphone Apps listed in Table 6 to make communication easier during examination and discharge planning (Appendix A includes tips for use of the Pocket Talker).

6. Ask your patient to explain in their own words what they need to know based on their encounter with you. This teach-back method offers a way to check for understanding and, if needed, to restate or clarify any information you wanted to convey. This promotes health literacy, as well.

Alternative communication aids: Smartphone apps

A number of companies have successfully turned IOS or Android devices into an amplifier. Since smartphones have built in microphones, they can play audio through a personal headset. Thus, ear buds or headphones are needed when using an amplifier app. The app is programmed to pick up the signal from the microphone, amplify it and relay it to the listener through the headphone. Apps differ in terms of the algorithms used to filter out or amplify certain frequencies or sounds(e.g., background noise), and this is controlled by the user. The noise cancelling capabilities and frequency sound analyzers differ across apps. Some apps are free and some carry a small fee. Table 6 includes a listing of a smartphone apps you may wish to recommend or utilize with your patients. As you may know, new smartphone apps are being developed all the time. Since this is an under-regulated area of healthcare, readers are advised to be cautious about the recommendations of specific amplifier apps.

> Smartphone apps may be a reasonable alternative to the Pocket Talker

Table 6. Smartphone apps that turn device into an amplifier

uHear	SoundAMP-R from Ginger Labs
BioAid	FiRE
EarMachine	Hearing Aid from TIAuEngineering UG
EQ HearAid	

Hearing healthcare toolkit for use in primary and geriatric care

As previously stated, there are many relatively easy ways to enhance communication between the patient and the medical provider that do not rely on the use of a customized hearing aid. This is especially true for patients who have milder degrees of hearing loss. In order to optimize communication so that medical directives are clearly understood, medical professionals are advised to utilize the following communication strategies. Table 7 indicates the most useful communication strategies for the various environments in which care is delivered.

Table 7. Setting Specific Communication Strategies

	Office Visit	Hospital	Home Visit	Palliative Care	LTC
Make sure to look at patient when speaking	+	+	+	+	+
Turn television off if it is playing in the background	-	+	+	NA	+
Use Pocket Talker or smartphone app if patient exhibits difficulty communicating	+	+	+	+	+
Position self at same height as patient*	+	+	+	+	+
Stand or sit within three to six feet of patient	+	+	+	+	+
Confirm patient's level of understanding or make sure they are able to perform the self care activities and medication management required following discharge	+	+	+	-	
Use audiovisual modalities and provide written instructions to reinforce what is communicated	+	+	+	-	-
Use "teach-back" method by asking patient to repeat back what they understand from discharge instructions	-	+	+	-	-
Rather than asking yes/no questions, ask open-ended questions such as "What questions do you have?"	+	+	+	+	+

*If patient is in a wheelchair, be sure to sit down; if patient is standing, remain standing

+ denotes a viable communication strategy

Referral to medical professional, audiologist or hearing instrument specialist

Hearing healthcare professionals, by virtue of their training are uniquely qualified to care for persons at risk for hearing loss. Physicians are encouraged to refer their patients to either:

A. An otolaryngologist or otoneurologist should an acute (e.g., sudden hearing loss) or chronic ear related medical condition present or when symptoms (e.g., dizziness, tinnitus) suggest a possible medical etiology. The medical professional to whom you are referring should practice patient-centered care following an approach which is best illustrated in Figure 6.

B. A local audiologist or hearing instrument specialist for treatment of a patient at risk for hearing related concerns based on the risk assessment described above. Be sure to refer to a hearing specialist who delivers patient centric and individualized care based on an understanding of the patient's listening needs and goals. The hearing healthcare professional should send you a summary of the effectiveness of the hearing intervention for the patient you referred. A sampling of interventions offered by audiologists or selected hearing instrument specialists is listed in Table 8.

Table 8. Possible Hearing Health Care Intervention Options

Hearing Aids
Cochlear Implants, BAHA, other implantable devices
Hearing & Communication Exercises /Aural Rehabilitation Group
Hearing Loss Support Group (HLAA)
Hearing Assistive Technology
Personal Sound Amplifier (PSAP)
Web-based or DVD-based training focusing on promoting Auditory Cognitive Skills (LACE, GROUP)

Audiologists and hearing instrument specialists are two specific groups of professionals who work with hearing impaired individuals. Audiologists have a broad scope of practice, specializing in the long-term management of hearing loss, balance disorders and tinnitus. Although an essential component of their work revolves around the selection and fitting of hearing aids, Table 8 lists many of the other services – beyond hearing aids – offered by audiologists. Figure 6 outlines three essential drivers of an effective therapeutic relationship between patient and hearing healthcare professional (audiologist or hearing instrument specialist).

> Audiologists provide serveral options to patients for improving communication beyond hearing aids

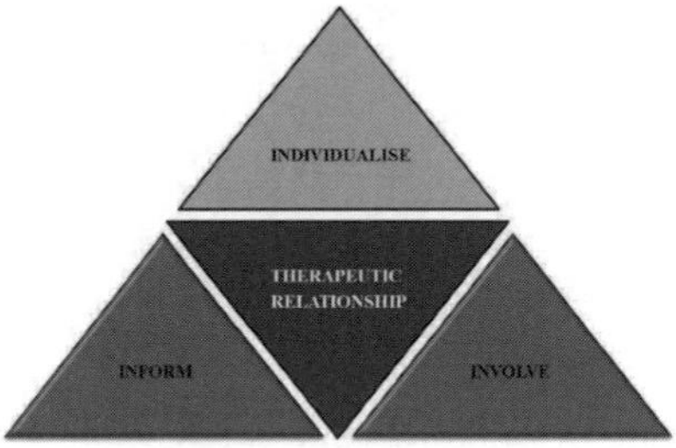

Figure 6. The standard for hearing care provided otolaryngologists, audiologists and hearing instrument specialists are summarized by the 3-Is of the therapeutic relationship. Source: Grenness, et al. (2014) with permission.

The latest evidence linking age-relating various medical conditions to the acceleration of age-related hearing loss

Recent research in peer reviewed medical journals suggests that age-related hearing loss is a growing public health concern requiring pre-emptive attention from physicians. Here are seven recent studies supporting this claim.

1. Lin, F. et al. (2013) Hearing Loss and Cognitive Decline in Older Adults. JAMA Internal Medicine 173, 4, 293-299.

One thousand nine hundred eighty-four (1984) adults between the ages of 70 and 79 were followed up to 12 years in order evaluate whether hearing loss is independently associated with accelerated cognitive decline. Cognitive testing consisted of the Digit Symbol Substitution (DSS) test and the 3MS, which are two standardized tests of cognitive function in adults.

Results indicated that 1162 individuals with baseline hearing loss had a 32% poorer score on the DSS and a 41% poorer score on the 3MS compared to those with normal hearing. Compared to those with normal hearing, normal hearing individuals with hearing loss at baseline had a 24% increased risk for incident cognitive impairment.

The authors concluded that hearing loss is independently associated with accelerated cognitive decline and incident cognitive impairment in older adults. On average, individuals with hearing loss would require 7.7 years to decline by five points of the 3MS, while individuals with normal hearing experienced a five point decline over a 10.9 year period. Furthermore, the authors indicated that a 25 dB hearing loss equates to 7 years of cognitive decline when compared to a similar age group with normal hearing.

2. Fisher, D. et al. (2014). Impairments in Hearing and Vision Impact on Mortality in Older People. Age and Aging. 43, 1, 69-76.

The main objective of this study was to examine the relationship between hearing and vision impairments and mortality from all-cause (all-cause mortality by age group is the annual number of deaths in a given age group per the population in that age group, usually expressed per 100,000) and cardiovascular disease among older people. All 4,926 study participants were from Iceland and 67 years of age or older.

Participants were placed into one of three categories: vision-only impairment (VI), hearing-only impairment (HI) and dual sensory impaired (DSI) and followed up to seven years. After adjusting for age, significantly increased mortality from all-cause and cardiovascular disease was observed for the HI and DSI, especially among men. After further adjustment for mortality risk factors, individuals with HI remained at higher risk for death from cardiovascular disease. Whether hearing loss is an indicator of aging or frailty, physical manifestations resulting in reduced social competence or a reflection of other adverse health status is unclear; however, results indicated that older men with DSI or HI were at a significantly greater risk for all-cause and cardiovascular death. Regular hearing assessments and rehabilitation services at an earlier age in order to promote long-term health and longevity are warranted based on these findings.

3. Mick, P. et al. (2014). The Association between Hearing Loss and Social Isolation in Older Adults. Otolaryngology-Head & Neck Surgery. 150, 378-384.

The objective of this study was to determine if age-related hearing loss is associated with social isolation and whether factors such as age, gender and hearing aid use moderate this association. There were 1453 male and female participants in this study, all between the ages of 60 and 84 years. Social isolation was defined using the social isolation score (SIS).

Results indicated that greater amounts of hearing loss were associated with increased odds of social isolation in women aged 60 to 69. Other groups did not show a significant relationship between hearing loss and social isolation. These results suggest that women within this age range are more likely to alter their lifestyle due to their hearing loss; thus more likely to become socially isolated.

4. Chan-Ming, L (2014) Hearing Impairment with Depression in US Adult, NHANES 2005-2010. Otolaryngology-Head & Neck Surgery. Published on-line March 6, 2014.

This study estimated the prevalence of depression among adults with hearing loss. Using the 9-item Patient Health Questionnaire (PHQ-9), the prevalence of depression among 18,318 participants of the National Health and Nutrition Examination Survey (NHANS) was examined.

The prevalence of depression increased as hearing loss became worse, except among those self-reported as deaf. Among individuals over the age of 70, no significant association between self-reported hearing loss and depression was found. Adults under the age of 70, particularly women, had a significant association between moderate hearing loss and depression.

5. Lin, F. et al. (2014). Association of hearing impairment with brain volume changes in older adults. Neuroimage. 90, 84-92.

Brain volume changes were monitored for a mean span of 6.4 years in 126 adults between the ages of 56 and 86. Using sophisticated brain volume measurement techniques, and after adjusting for cardiovascular and demographic factors, the researchers found that individuals with hearing loss had accelerated brain volume declines. These declines in brain volume were primarily confined to the right temporal lobe.

The findings of this study indicate that peripheral hearing loss is independently associated with accelerated brain atrophy in whole brain and regional volumes concentrated in the right temporal lobe.

6. Kamel, et al. (2014). Association between hearing impairment and frailty in older adults. Journal of the American Geriatric Society. 62, 6, 1186-1188.

Data from 2,109 individuals aged 70 and over from the NHANES served as the study population. The association between hearing loss and frailty was examined using logistic regression models adjusted for demographic factors, cardiovascular risk factors, health status and hearing aid use. The result of this analysis showed that self-reported hearing loss is independently associated with frailty in women aged 70 and above. Potential explanations for this association between frailty and hearing loss in older women include a shared microvascular disease etiology, effects of frailty on self-perceptions of hearing, social isolation, stress or lack of awareness of the auditory environment affecting mobility.

7. Foley, et al. (2014). Association between hearing loss and healthcare expenditures in older adults. Journal of the American Geriatric Society. 62, 6, 1188-1189.

Using data collected from 34,981 individuals aged 65 and over, 23.7% had self-reported hearing loss. Individuals with hearing loss were more likely to be older, male, of lower socioeconomic status, have cardiovascular conditions and be diabetic. The authors concluded that individuals with hearing loss had higher levels of medical expenditures compared to those with normal hearing of similar age. These greater amounts of medical expenditures were for office-based, outpatient and emergency room visits.

Taken as a whole, these studies suggest that age-related hearing loss has implications well beyond affecting basic communication skills. Although remediating these basic communication skills through early identification using hearing screening has merit in its own right, these five studies provide a high level of evidence demonstrating broader functional implications of age-related hearing impairment on cognitive function, depression, social isolation, cortical changes in the brain and even early death. Audiologists have a professional obligation, perhaps bordering on a moral imperative to communicate these findings without hyperbole, inaccuracy or embellishment. Each study cited here stands on its own as an outstanding contribution to our evolving understanding of the relationship between age-related hearing loss and other common chronic conditions associated with the aging process.

Age-related hearing loss is a public health concern of very high priority. It's a high priority because several recent studies using randomized-controls show AHL contributes to the acceleration of cognitive and physical decline in adults. Hearing loss imposes a heavy social, economic burden on individuals, families, and communities, as a hearing loss isolates people. Given these findings, all individuals over the age of 55 should have a baseline hearing screening, and patients with a history of depression, cardiovascular disease, diabetes and dementia should have their hearing screened annually.

Medical Referral Criteria

The FDA requires hearing healthcare professionals to refer a patient to a physician, preferably an otolaryngologist when one or more of the following conditions exist. Otherwise, a medical waiver can be signed by the patient prior to be fitted with hearing aids.

1. Visible deformity to the outer ear
2. Visible evidence of significant cerumen accumulation or a foreign body in the ear canal
3. Any history of active drainage from the ear within the previous 90 days.
4. Any history of sudden hearing loss within the previous 90 days
5. Any acute or chronic dizziness
6. A hearing loss in one ear of sudden or rapid onset within the previous 90 days
7. Ear pain or discomfort
8. An air bone gap on the audiogram of more than 15 dB at 500, 1000 and 2000Hz

Hearing healthcare toolkit for use in primary and geriatric care

Hearing health care resources:

Appendices A – C includes a list of helpful resources including instructions in use of a Pocket Talker, links to articles linking hearing loss to negative health outcomes including falls, and a list of frequently asked questions along with answers.

Appendix A

How to use a pocket talker

1. Ask patient if they would like to try the new "hearing helper" you have been experimenting with
2. Explain that you are merely going to place the headphones over their ears so they will hear your voice more easily
3. Before you put the headphones on, turn the volume of the pocket talker to 2 so that you can talk to the patient as you are placing the headphones
4. Talk to the patient through the microphone, while placing the headphones, so they can immediately experience hearing your voice more easily

Appendix B

Important Resources on Hearing Health Care

Hearing Loss and Falls
http://archinte.jamanetwork.com/article.aspx?articleid=1108740

Falls, injuries from falls, health related quality of life and mortality in older adults with vision and hearing impairment—is there a gender difference?
http://ac.els-cdn.com/S0378512211001733/1-s2.0-S0378512211001733-main.pdf?_tid=b5419c10-9d8e-11e3-9f6d-00000aacb35f&acdnat=1393272380_75aed48b3e7d2aa7e55e3f76e9adaa69

Hearing handicap, rather than measured hearing impairment, predicts poorer quality of life over 10 years in older adults
http://www.sciencedirect.com/science/article/pii/S0378512212001144

Associations Between Hearing Impairment and Mortality Risk in Older Persons: The Blue Mountains Hearing Study
http://ac.els-cdn.com/S1047279710000578/1-s2.0-S1047279710000578-main.pdf?_tid=71276a78-9d8e-11e3-a115-00000aacb361&acdnat=1393272266_e1277aa9ad31b36df48daeeb76954f14

Incidence and Predictors of Hearing Aid Use and Ownership Among Older Adults With Hearing Loss
http://ac.els-cdn.com/S1047279711000858/1-s2.0-S1047279711000858-main.pdf?_tid=026dabfa-9d8f-11e3-8e38-00000aabof27&acdnat=1393272509_62a26268e8230cab203994888778db0a

Appendix C

Frequently Asked Questions

1. Can I bill Medicare for hearing screening?
   Yes.

2. Why do hearing aids cost so much?
   There is a wide range of prices and insurance does not always cover even a portion of the expense. In general, hearing aids are customized devices that require time and expertise to optimize. Beyond the fitting of hearing aids, the personal adjustment counseling provided to the patient by the clinician is spread over several months and necessitates 3 to 5 appointments. The time and expertise provided to the patient that helps overcome years of maladjusted coping behaviors is typically bundled into the price of the hearing aids and represents a significant part of the overall expense.

3. Do all patients with hearing loss need hearing aids?
   No, there are many other options, some of them not requiring the use of hearing devices. Clinicians typically share several options with patients, depending on individual needs, test results and lifestyle requirements.

4. Why do some patients do better than others with hearing aids?
   Individuals outcomes are dependent on several factors, such as motivation, expectations, cognitive ability, physical ability (finger dexterity), type of hearing loss, family support, even personality can have an effect.

5. Is there direct evidence of a link between hearing loss and falls?
   Yes.

6. Is there direct evidence of a link between hearing loss and incident dementia?
   Yes.

7. Is there direct evidence of a link between handicapping hearing loss and poor self- rated health?
   Yes.

8. How can I tell if my patient is: (1) hearing impaired, (2) depressed or (3) has mild cognitive impairment or dementia?
   Behavioral symptoms are often difficult to distinguish, so a hearing loss must be ruled out.

9. What can I tell my patients they should be asking or looking for when purchasing hearing health care interventions?
   Individualized and personalized care informed by an assessment of hearing, speech understanding in noise, sound annoyance considerations, listening needs and hearing related goals. They should be given choices and input into the decision making process.

Hearing healthcare toolkit for use in primary and geriatric care

10. Why should I recommend that my patient consider trying hearing aids?
    a. Hearing aids are less noticeable than hearing loss
    b. Hearing aids are discreet and virtually invisible
    c. Performance of hearing aids has improved significantly with high-fidelity sound processing and background noise suppression
    d. Hearing aids can enable your patient to remain socially engaged and often make listening and communicating easier and less stressful

11. What is a cochlear implant?
    A cochlear implant is a surgically implanted device to be considered by persons with severe to profound hearing loss who do not benefit from hearing aids. Older adults increasingly should consider this option as the evidence points to improvements in function and quality of life among older adults who have undergone cochlear implant surgery.

12. Is my patient a candidate for cochlear implants?
    Their health status, hearing loss severity, aided speech understanding and functional ability are all factors to be considered.

13. Is there objective evidence that hearing health care interventions such as hearing aids or cochlear implants improve hearing quality of life?
    Yes.

References

American Geriatrics Society (AGS) (2012). Expert Panel on the Care of Older Adults with Multimorbidity. Guiding principles for the care of older adults with multimorbidity: An approach for Clinicians. (2012) Available from http://www.americangeriatrics.org/files/documents/MCC.principles. Retrieved April 7, 2014.

Chien W. & Lin, F. (2012) Prevalence of hearing aid use among older adults in the United States. Archives of Internal Medicine. 172: 292-293.

Genther, D., Frick, K., Chen, D., Betz, J. & Lin, F. (2013). Association of Hearing Loss With Hospitalization and Burden of Disease in Older Adults. JAMA. 309: 2322-2324

Grenness, C. et al. (2014) Patient-centered audiological rehabilitation: perspectives of older adults who own hearing aids. International Journal of Audiology. 53, S68-S75.

Kripalani, S., Jackson, A., Schnipper, J. & Coleman, E. (2007). Promoting effective transitions of care at hospital discharge: A review of key issues for hospitalists. Journal of Hospital Medicine. 2: 314-323.

Mathers, C., Smith, A., & Concha, M. (2003) Global burden of hearing loss in the year 2000. [Internet] Geneva: World Health Organization. Available at http://www.who.int/healthinfo/statistics/bod_hearingloss.pdf [Accessed April 3, 2014].

6

SOCIAL MEDIA AND DIGITAL MARKETING

Brian Taylor

The purpose of this chapter is to provide you with a working knowledge of digital marketing strategy and how that strategy fits into a more comprehensive, pillar-of-community marketing plan. Although it may be tempting to hand your digital marketing strategy off to your 19-year-old nephew, this chapter intends to deliver the reader with some cutting-edge digital tactics, mainly revolving around website development and social media. Search engine optimization (SEO), hyperlinks, and Google analytics are among the terms that confuse and confound the most seasoned tech-savvy professionals; therefore, this chapter doesn't intend to make you into a digital marketing or social media expert. The intent, rather, is to guide your thinking on how digital marketing and social media can be a powerful and trusted part of your overall marketing plan. As you may have guessed, a single tactic using social media is not a magic bullet that suddenly transforms your practice. But when employed as part of a more comprehensive marketing plan, social media can amplify your message to a larger number of people, particularly those that influence our core demographic.

To truly appreciate the potential of social media and digital marketing, it helps to get in a time machine and go back about 25 years. Let's disembark from our time machine in the year 1990. A quarter of a century ago, we did not use the Internet or smartphones, and Facebook was but a gleam in Mark Zuckerberg's eye. Although the traditional marketing tactics used in 1990 appear stark and antiquated by today's standards, they did many of the things—albeit much slower—that we take for granted with social media and websites today, namely, create demand for your services. Lead generation, for example, has been a staple of marketing plans for generations. Using postcards and, and in later decades, television, lead generation advertising was effective but cumbersome by today's standards. Digital social media are tools that allow businesses a more diverse array of customer touch points, often at a faster speed than traditional forms of advertising.

The ability to communicate, interact, and even gawk at the near speed of light didn't exist in 1990, but that didn't stop people from trying to connect. Back in 1990, we relied heavily on direct mail, newspaper advertising, and the Yellow Pages to make these connections. The hugely important difference with digital media with respect to older, analog technology is that it allows for direct, seamless back-and-forth communication between the sender (your business) and the receiver (your customers). Perhaps another way to think about the power of social media and digital marketing (and something that sounds like it might be spouted by your 19-year-old nephew) is that traditional media distribute propaganda, while social media encourage participation. No matter how you view social media (if you have teenagers in your household, you probably think of it more as a curse than a blessing), exactly how these digital media are used by your business will be the focus of this chapter.

Probably the most critical initial question is, what exactly is digital marketing? Simply defined, digital marketing is the ability to communicate your brand message and everything else important about your practice using all forms of high-speed, low-cost computer-based connectivity. Connectivity refers to everything from websites to social media, from television to signage—yes, even a billboard that allows the message to be changed instantaneously via computer would be considered a form of digital marketing. Granted, it's a broad definition that encompasses media that have been around for generations, but in its most practical sense, digital marketing tools allow you to interact with your customers in the virtual world.

Another pertinent question surrounding the development and implementation of your digital marketing strategy is, what should you expect from it? After all, there is no shortage of creative and energetic young professionals willing to create a cutting-edge website complete with blogs, video, and other flashy accessories. And, in case you haven't figured in out by now, the author is not an expert on the constantly changing social media and digital marketing landscape. Keeping this in mind, we will take a practical, big picture view of how digital media can complement, enhance, and otherwise make your current marketing plan more effective.

It takes a long time to gain the trust of a customer. According to data compiled by the Pew Research Center, individuals typically look at six pieces of research before they buy. A big reason consumers are likely to look at so many pieces of research before they make a purchasing decision is quite simply because they have the ability to instantaneously use their computer or smartphone to access the Internet. Virtually every American household has access to the Internet, which enables them to use Google, Facebook, and myriad other sites to do their homework, prior to making a purchasing decision. If it really is true that the majority of customers are doing that much homework on a product or service before they buy, it stands to reason that we have to have a presence on as many of the places that they do this homework and comparison shopping. It is imperative for your practice to be part of the conversation by using social media and various other digital marketing media.

Optical, Inc, a leading customer experience vendor in the elective medical care sector, reported in 2014 that patient appointments from "Internet sources" are now equal to "word-of-mouth" as a primary source for patient referrals and leads in an elective medical practice. This is a noteworthy statistic because it indicates that Web-based and social media are an integral part of the patient journey. Considering that most people now go to the Internet to learn about possible medical conditions, it is not too surprising that the social and other digital media have such an influential reach.

Most marketing experts agree that word-of-mouth referrals are still highly prized. Nothing beats the power of a personal testimonial. However, social media have the ability to amplify the traditional person-to-person referral process: A positive referral from a friend, colleague, or neighbor is likely to prompt an Internet search and social media qualification. People in the market for hearing care are likely to visit your website, like your Facebook page, follow you on Twitter, or peruse your blog after they have learned from a trusted friend that you offer a particularly high level of professionalism and service. If these important website and digital media sources are woefully outdated (i.e., looks like they were designed in 1998) or uninteresting, the prospect is likely to continue shopping around—even though you may have received a glowing person-to-person referral.

People will visit your website to learn more about your professional experience, product line, and prices, but more often than not, they are also interested in online reviews and testimonials. These testimonials can be written, videotaped, and even podcasted. So-called online reputation management sites like Review Buzz help develop trust between patient and provider by readily sharing these reviews and testimonials around cyberspace. Much like Amazon, Review Buzz and similar services allow patients to rate practices on a one- to five-star scale. When prospects are online conducting an educational search, they are more likely to schedule an appointment with the practice that has several five-star reviews compared to the practice with mainly three-star reviews. Review Buzz and other online reputation managers allow providers to send an email directly to patients who opt into the system. (Patients can opt into the system in a Health Insurance Portability and Accountability Act [HIPAA]–compliant way by completing a simple form in your office.) This email encourages the patient to write a review and provide a one- to five-star ranking. Poor ratings are an opportunity for the practice to improve, while high ratings can be linked to the practice's website and used as testimonials to attract more patients.

One example of an online review site in the audiology industry is Hearing Tracker, created by Dr. Abram Bailey. Hearing Tracker.com is a HIPAA-compliant system that allows audiologists to privately track the results of hearing aid outcome measurements and customer feedback surveys. Audiologists are given the option to publish customer feedback to their profile page, providing the opportunity to benefit from high levels of customer satisfaction. HearingTracker.com has often been described as a Yelp for hearing aids and for hearing providers, but there are a few notable differences:

- On HearingTracker.com, the provider has full control of its customer reviews. Customer feedback surveys are published individually by the provider, and only authenticated patients may leave reviews.
- Hearing aid outcomes may be kept private or shared publicly. This is an all-or-none decision; cherry-picking is not allowed.
- HearingTracker.com administrators respond immediately to audiologist service requests, adding a level of security that larger online review sites cannot offer.

HearingTracker.com helps make collecting and aggregating customer surveys simple and provides a number of tools to help audiologists identify strengths and weaknesses in their services.

Crash Course: The Power of Online Reviews

Social media experts tell us that people are more likely to visit websites listing positive reviews from other customers. Companies like Review Buzz and Call Course make it easy for you to encourage satisfied customers to write and post testimonials about the quality of services provided by your practice. When others are conducting an online search, a snippet of a four- or five-star review appears next to your listing on page 1 of Google. People searching for hearing care services are inclined to click on websites that have glowing testimonials next to the listing on Google. Since we are not allowed to post a page from Google for you, try this: Type hearing aid + your local community into your favorite search engine. Notice that one or two of the listings you receive for hearing aids have a four- or five-star review listed next to it on page 1. If you are like the average person, you are more likely to click on the listing with the testimonial listed next to it.

The website also provides tools to help audiologists learn more from their outcome measurements (i.e., which hearing aid models are producing the greatest success among patients with mild hearing loss). By amassing a large set of outcome measurements, providers will be able to make evidence-based hearing aid recommendations, based on their own clinical history. A testimonial for an audiologists is shown in Figure 6–1.

CONTENT IS KING

Now that you've been given a brief introduction to social and digital marketing, let's delve into the two most critical aspects

Figure 6–1. An example of a testimonial page for an online reputation management system. Republished with permission of Hearing Tracker.

of it: content creation and electronic distribution of this content. Building true social media engagement means creating a content strategy to hook the audience. It is not just being on social media. Content is king! The following analogy might be helpful: Those who love to drink coffee often have a favorite place to indulge. They frequent a chosen venue because it's a great place to hang out. Perhaps they know the owners or the other customers who, like them, regularly drop in to socialize. But without the rich aromas and great-tasting coffee that they serve, would they still go there if there was nothing to drink? Your practice is the coffee shop, and your social media content is the coffee. If you have fresh content, you are more likely to engage the crowd. More often than not, practices tend to focus on how their message gets distributed. This is perhaps due to the strong media presence of players such as Facebook, Google+, or LinkedIn or to the dizzying numbers they are typically associated with; Facebook alone has now 1.11 billion people using the site each month. The reality for the hearing care practice is that any competent social media marketer can get your website hooked up to these engines, but only you and your staff can provide the unique and engaging content.

In practical terms, social media enable consumers to interact with your practice. Unlike traditional advertising media, such as direct mail, social media allow for more direct, almost immediate interaction with consumers. In short, consumers can now push information in the form of opinions, links to articles, Tweets, and so forth back to you.

Crash Course: Useful Digital Marketing Terms

By no means an exhaustive list. Here are some important terms your favorite 14-year-old may know but you may never have heard of and find useful:

Webmaster: The person responsible for maintaining your website and many of the other social media platforms that are linked to it. The duties of the webmaster may include ensuring that the Web servers, hardware, and software are operating correctly; designing the website; generating and revising Web pages; providing you with marketing analytics; replying to user comments; and examining traffic through the site. Most practices hire a webmaster to oversee their digital marketing portfolio.

Web 2.0: A newer generation of website that become common around 2006–2007. Web 2.0 uses technology that allows for more interaction with the viewer. Major features of Web 2.0 include social networking sites, user-created websites, self-publishing platforms, tagging, and social bookmarking. Users can provide the data that are on a Web 2.0 site and exercise some control over that data. Blogs, wikis, and RSS are essential parts of Web 2.0.

RSS: Rich Site Summary uses a family of standard Web feed formats to publish frequently updated information: blog entries, news headlines, audio, and video. An RSS document (called "feed," "Web feed," or "channel") includes full or summarized text and metadata, like publishing date and author's name. Subscribing to a website RSS removes the need for the user to manually check the website for new content. Instead, their browser constantly monitors the site and informs the user of any updates. The browser can also be commanded to automatically download the new data for the user.

Memes: An idea, behavior, or style that spreads from person to person. Nothing accelerates a meme faster than social media.

Social media: Like many things, social media are easy to identify and rather difficult to define. Social media might be defined as a group of Internet-based applications that build on the technological foundations of Web 2.0 and that allow the creation and exchange of user-generated content. Social media depend on mobile and Web-based technologies to create highly interactive platforms through which individuals and communities share, co-create, discuss, and modify user-generated content. They introduce substantial and pervasive changes to communication among organizations, communities, and individuals.

Search engine optimization (SEO): The process of getting your practice listed at (or near) the top of page 1 of a Google search. Since most people don't go beyond the first page of an online search, webmasters use all types of tips and tricks, many of which are secret to have a better chance of being listed near the very top of page 1. The primary objective of search engine optimization is to obtain free nonpaid/unsponsored Web traffic by influencing search engines to display your Web content (Web pages, videos, local listings, etc.) high in search engine listings for keywords that target your particular market.

HTML: HyperText Markup Language is the standard markup language used to create Web pages.

Cookie: A small piece of data sent from a website and stored in a user's Web browser while the user is browsing that website. Every time the user loads the website, the browser sends the cookie back to the server to notify the website of the user's previous activity.

Web browser: Software applications used for searching the Web. The major Web browsers are Firefox, Internet Explorer, Google Chrome, and Safari.

Pay per click (PPC): This is an Internet advertising model used to direct traffic to websites, in which advertisers pay the publisher (typically a website owner) when the ad is clicked. It is defined simply as "the amount spent to get an advertisement clicked." Anecdotally, experts in the audiology industry belief that PPC is not very effective, especially for independent businesses.

MailChimp: The most popular email marketing service provider. It has 7 million users that collectively send over 10 billion emails through the service each month. It is a tool that helps manage and track your digital media effectiveness.

The best content is authentic. This means that it is created by you and your staff. Of course, you could find someone to professionally craft content for your digital media messaging. Companies such as Content Marketing World (http://www.contentmarketingworld.com) provide a steady stream of good content, but it is unlikely to sound like it is coming from your practice. This means you probably need to spend at least an hour or so each month doing some writing.

The most useful content inspires and evokes passion. Telling stories about patient success in your practice is a good way to inspire and inform. For every patient success in your practice, take a few moments (with their permission, of course) to write about how you changed his or her life for the better through your recommendation and treatment. When you can communicate through patient success stories, you are more likely to evoke an emotional response from your readers. Not a good writer? Instead of writing the story, take out your smartphone and record a testimonial that you can post on your website or Facebook page.

Your content should position you as a local thought leader. Once you decide on a few specific topics within the field of audiology in which you want to be recognized as an expert, start writing about them. For example, you could position yourself as a thought leader around amplification devices for adults. Any time a new product or gadget is introduced to the market, you could post a brief commentary on your blog with a link for the reader to find more information about a new product. You could position your thought leadership around a service (aural rehabilitation) a certain demographic (healthy-agers or baby boomers) or communication disorder (tinnitus). The main point is to align your thought leadership position around a specific topic and consistently generate thoughtful musings.

Your content must be written with the layperson in mind. The challenge for academically trained professionals is to distill highly technical content into easy-to-read snippets of information. When you come across technical content, say from an academic journal, think about how you would discuss the article with a precocious 12-year-old. This will help you craft a message that is clear and to the point. And, don't be afraid to be entertaining, whimsical, and slightly irreverent. If these traits are authentic to your personality, it is okay to weave a little entertainment into your message when posting on a blog or on social media.

Here are a couple of questions that will help you fine-tune your content. Who is your target audience? What group of patients are you trying to attract to your office? Most independent audiology practices are likely to say adults older than 60 years. Therefore, make sure all of your content is interesting to people older than 60 years. Seek out content from others that cater to this market. Sites such as http://www.aarp.com can provide you with fodder to blog about or re-tweet that will be relevant to your target audience. What is your content strategy? This question gets at what you are likely to be writing about. Since you probably have a limited amount of time to create content and search the Web for links, you'll need to spend some time developing content around your business strategy. For example, if you want your office to be perceived as a leader in delivering a personalized service experience, much of your content needs to revolve around the benefits of high-quality service.

Dozens, if not hundreds, of digital media platforms and services can help you aggregate content and disseminate it to your audience. Two tools that are easy to use and allow you to tailor the message with a level of authenticity are blogging and a personalized content aggregator called Zite.

Zite evaluates millions of new stories every day, looking at the type of article, its key attributes, and how it is shared across the Web. Zite uses this information to match stories to your personal interests and then delivers them automatically to your iPad or iPhone. Once you have developed a quick list of topics, such as hearing aids, aging, healthy living, and geriatrics, you can personalize a message around a link to an important article or video that appears on your Zite quick list. In addition to Zite, Feedly is another content aggregator that makes seeding your social media sites quick and easy. After downloading either the Feedly or Zite app to your smartphone or tablet PC, you can set up quick lists that enable you to personalize messages for each bit of content you post on your social media sites. This task can be completed in 1 to 2 minutes per day.

Another way to deliver content that is personalized and authentic is through blogging. A blog is nothing more than a series of short articles or posts that are archived on a website. Blogging is a great way to establish a following or fan base for your practice. In addition to the written word, a blog can consist of audio or video content. An audio blog is commonly called a podcast and has the advantage of being listened to while performing another task, such as driving a car. Since there are so many platforms (WordPress is a popular one) that allow you to blog, it is best to talk to your local webmaster to find the one that will provide you with the most bang for your buck.

TRENDS IN SOCIAL MEDIA

The thing about social media and the Web is that they are always changing. What was cutting edge last year may quickly become obsolete. There is no need to sweat the details or spend hours outside your clinic trying to use new social media tools in your marketing plan. Networking with a few social media experts will help you stay ahead of the curve. Below are hot trends, according to the experts, that are likely to become part of an effective social media marketing strategy. Readers are advised to find a local marketing firm or a nationally known company that knows the hearing care industry and hire them to implement the following trends into your broader marketing plan:

Visual Content Will Be a Focus

From memes to infographics to in-the-moment Instagram images, brands big and small are already getting huge engagement from visual content; over the next few years, that visual content will be extremely popular in social media.

A common misconception is that visual content requires significant resources to create, which is simply not true. In fact, simple content that is easy to navigate often receives the highest volume of engagement. According to research from Social Media Examiner, 70% of marketers plan to increase their use of visual assets over the next 2 years. Audiologists are encouraged to work with their marketing professionals to find visual content that is representative of their brand and resonates with consumers in their local market.

The Growth of Adaptive and Responsive Websites

As you might expect, website design and function continue to evolve. Audiologists are urged to keep a steady eye on how they can readily adapt new technology into their websites. For example, responsive websites are designed to display well on any screen size. They are optimized for viewing on any smartphone. Responsive websites are not just a resize of the entire website to the screen size. The website displays differently for desktop and mobile, even differently for mobile on landscape and portrait. In this way, the different elements of the site are always displayed in the best manner possible.

On the other hand, adaptive sites display differing elements depending on the viewing device. In this way, you can ensure that only the elements that are suitable for differing smartphones are displayed. For instance, a slider that works well on a full screen or landscape view of a tablet may well not look so good on a phone.

It is now imperative for your website to be smartphone optimized. Today, customers now use smartphone and tablet apps more than PCs to access the Internet. Pew Research says that 91% of American adults now own a cell phone, and 61% of those are smartphones. This means that a large swath of the population is using smartphones to access the Internet, and you want to make it easy for them to do so. If you don't have a responsive website, there is an increasing chance that people will land on it and leave immediately. When working with a webmaster (someone who creates and manages your website), be sure to ask about adaptive and responsive website technology.

Blogging Will Continue to Rule

Business blogging has seen a meteoric rise in the past few years, and all signs point to the trend continuing in force over the next 3 to 5 years. A successful business blog is a platform you own and thus should serve as the hub of your social presence. While curated content is a key piece of a successful content strategy,

58% of marketers, according to the Pew Research Center, say that original content is still the most important content asset for their business. Blogging is a great way to speak your brand's unique voice. Audiologists are encouraged to spend 1 or 2 hours per week writing short articles for their blog. (Don't worry, your website creator can help you create and disseminate the content.)

Podcasting Will Dramatically Increase in Popularity and Reach

One of the biggest advantages of podcasts is that the format lends itself to reaching your audience at a time when few other digital channels can, in the car. Given the average podcast is around 30 minutes, what other channel can you routinely expect to engage with your audience in an intimate environment for such an extended period of time? With social media evolving at an incredible speed, it's vital for businesses to stay on top of these trends to get the most value from their social marketing investment.

BROADCASTING YOUR CONTENT

Once you have created a coherent content strategy, it is imperative to get your message out to the world. There is no shortage of social media platforms to broadcast your content. Prior to about 2005, you could broadcast your message using television and radio. Before the advent of Internet cable TV, your message was likely to be passively broadcast to a large segment of the population. Today, given the abundance of media, your message can be tailored to match the interests of your target population, and that target population can be part of the conversation when social media are employed to disseminate the message.

Let's confine our discussion to using social media, and not television and radio, which are more traditional forms of broadcasting. Given the sheer number of social media platforms, it is critical to know which social media platforms are the most popular for your target audience. Experts suggest that Facebook is extremely popular among those individuals older than 60 years. Thus, it is imperative that our message has a presence there. Additionally, the choice of social media in which your message is delivered is determined by search engine optimization factors. In other words, your presence on certain popular platforms will help drive your standing on Google, which is still by far the most widely used search engine. The total number of Twitter and YouTube users also makes them reasonably good choices for broadcasting your message. Since millions of people older than 65 years use Twitter and YouTube each day, it will help raise your search engine optimization standing on a Google search of keywords, such as *hearing aids* and *hearing care services.*

Rather than provide you with mundane technical details of search engine optimization, find a webmaster that will seamlessly deliver your content across the most popular platforms. Although it is subjective to change, Twitter, YouTube, and Facebook would be excellent content delivery mechanisms. The key is to get people talking with you and about you on social media. The key to broadcasting your content starts with the selection of the social media platform that your target audience is likely to use. In an era in which content is king, strive to inspire people to post questions to your practice using the most popular social media platforms for your target audience. At the end of the day, it's the virtual conversation that matters!

Do the above and people will share links to your interesting, relevant, and sometimes provocative content on Facebook, Google+, Twitter, and Pinterest, and you'll get even more likes and followers. Ultimately, this is what Google and other search engines, like Bing, are designed to do—boost your search engine rankings.

THE IMPORTANCE OF A GOOD WEBSITE

You don't have to look too far back in time to conjure memories of life without the Internet. For those of you younger than 35, yes, we did manage to run successful practices without a wireless Internet connection, laptop computers, and smartphone apps. Today, not having those things is likely to get you labeled a Luddite or, worst-case scenario, a Neanderthal by a rancorous, impatient teenager. Even though websites have been around for about 20 years, they continue to be the lynchpin of a sustainable digital marketing strategy. Gone are the days when you could rely on a splashy ad in the Yellow Pages or the newspaper to grow your business. Today, more and more customers want to hear from a far more powerful resource: each other. Thus, social media, as we have already mentioned, along with websites are a critical component to any marketing strategy.

Unlike most investments we make to the infrastructure of our practice, which have a shelf life of several years, a good website needs to be refreshed fairly often. Experts say a refresh is required about every 2 to 3 years. Consumers today are using the Web in a number of ways. Specific to our industry, consumers are using search engines (Google, YouTube, Bing, and Yahoo) to find information on hearing aids, hearing loss, hearing tests, tinnitus, and so on. Consumers have always consulted others before making purchases of "big ticket" items; what's changed over the past decade is that consumers can consult many additional opinions using online resources, like websites.

When a consumer searches "hearing aids, Golden Valley, MN," for example, this is considered a local search. Searching locally often indicates that a consumer is ready to take action. He or she is looking for a provider nearby. There are three areas within search results for a practice to rank: paid ads and local and organic listings. Each requires different action by the office or their Web provider(s) to ensure visibility.

As consumers land on a practice's website from search results, this is often their "first impression." Relevant content to the search terms, quality Web design, and site usability will determine whether the visitor will remain on the site or return to the search results. Print and other media outlets often lead back to a practice's website. If a practice runs a direct mail campaign, it is advantageous to include the website domain name near the phone number. Consumers are more likely to visit the website before making a phone call to schedule an appointment.

The goal of the visitor to a practice website is to contact the office or schedule an appointment. Upon first visit to the practice, it is important to ask specific questions regarding their experience with your website: Have you visited our website? Did you find the information you were searching? Was there further information you were looking to obtain that you could not find?

CONTENT IS STILL KING

Once a consumer has visited a hearing practice and a communication deficit is identified, he or she has a lot of choices on next steps. No matter how the patients initially found the practice, it is critical for the website to have all of the information they may be seeking in follow-up. A cutting-edge website has content that keeps patients tied to your office. For example, a new patient recently fitted with hearing aids can go to your website to download written documents on hearing aid use and care. Patients should be able to find links on your website that allow them to learn more about advocacy groups, such as the Hearing Loss Association of America or the Better Hearing Institute. Additionally, hearing aid orientation videos that reiterate your face-to-face counseling process with patients are extremely beneficial and help foster loyalty, which results in repeat business and more word-of-mouth referrals.

Here are a few other aspects of an effective website that cannot be overlooked: The use of an introductory video prominently placed on the center of your landing page is a great way to capture attention. This introductory video, which should be about 60 to 90 minutes in duration and narrated by the audiologists in the practice, should talk about the benefits of better hearing and communication. Short, emotionally compelling videos introducing prospects to your practice are a proven way to draw attention because they tap into the brain's emotional center, the limbic system. Blogging, which has already been mentioned, is another way to capture the attention of patients and prospects. Providing emotionally captivating commentary on issues relevant to healthy aging, hearing, and communication is sure to keep your target audience engaged. Furthermore, practices are urged to get listed on the "Find a Provider" on their preferred manufacturer websites. This will help drive additional traffic to your website.

Crash Course: Website and Social Media Marketing With Kelly O'Keefe of Audiology Design

To learn more about the importance of a fresh website and how it can be used by consumers in their decision-making process, you can turn to Kelly O'Keefe, director at Audiology Design, for some answers. Find out what he had to say about the latest in consumer-oriented websites and social media and their role in an audiology practice.

Kelly: A website is often a prospective patient's first impression of a practice. Make sure the website is professionally designed and provides the proper representation of the practice. If the site does not engage the visitor, they become a "bounce rate" statistic. This indicates that they quickly left the site without clicking through additional pages. The most critical component of an effective website is the content, which includes written copy, images, and videos. The general consumer should easily understand the language. For example, use the term *hearing aid* versus *hearing instrument*. Not only is it easily understood by the consumer, but it is the way in which they are searching the information. A large part of a website's performance is its ability to appear in search engine results. Search engines will index a site based on the content and the way in which it is optimized. Ensure usability on all devices. Websites today should be built using "Responsive Design." This is a development technique that enables your site to automatically adjust to any size screen. In 2010, the average number of unique screen resolutions was 97. In 2013, that number rose to 232. Mobile browsing continues to rise along with the number of screen resolutions. Test the website for optimal usability on desktop, laptop, tablet, and mobile devices. If the site requires pinching and zooming on a mobile phone, it may be time for an update to Responsive Design. Another critical component of an effective website is call-to-action (CTA) buttons. CTAs are often used to highlight the most visited pages or encourage the visitor to take the next steps. Some examples include

- Schedule an Appointment
- Take a Survey
- Learn More
- Meet Our Staff
- Watch Our Video

Use a variety of techniques to engage visitors and retain them on the site. In addition to written content, incorporate photos or videos that assist in telling the story of your unique value proposition in your local marketplace. If personal videos are not an option, manufacturers typically have YouTube channels that allow video to be embedded on the site.

Republished with permission of Kelly O'Keefe.

There are many ways to use a hearing practice website. The main purpose is to introduce prospective patients to the practice, including your staff, services, and products. Think of your website as a resource for those looking for information on all matters related to hearing, hearing preservation, healthy aging, and communication. Using personalized photography of the staff and office allows the visitor to virtually "meet" the team and see the practice prior to walking in the front door. It creates a warm and welcoming website for the visitor. Clinic and testimonial videos also help to engage visitors and keep them on the site. Consumers, in general, are lazy, so they would rather watch a video versus reading a page of text.

NUTS AND BOLTS OF AN EFFECTIVE WEBSITE

Yes, content is still king, but it is helpful to know a little about the inner workings of a good website. It is recommended that all offline activity is consistent online. For example, when running promotions and special events, many practices update their information on the website and social media properties. Consider every touch point with the prospective patient and be consistent across all mediums. Patient forms on the website allow the patient to complete these documents prior to their initial appointment. It may assist in expediting the process for the practice, while providing the patients the ability to complete the forms on their own time. A website and social media can engage new and existing patients. Connect the practice website to all social properties and engage the visitors with regularly updated content. A big part of an effective website is getting people to view it. That is why search engine optimization tactics are so important.

Various factors play a role in how a practice can improve its chances of being ranked higher in search engine listings. However, they can be divided into two categories:

1. On-page optimization, which covers what can be done on the pages of a website itself. This pertains to all elements of the practice website.
2. Off-page optimization, which covers activity that takes place elsewhere or "off site." This includes social profiles, local listings, and sites that link back to the practice website. Off-page is primarily the process of building a profile of links that point back to your website through various means.

The following is a list of essential elements that affect on-page optimization and recommendations for each:

■ Keyword research and searcher intent: Target keywords and search phrases that you know your patients will be searching for.
■ Title tags: One of the most important parts of on-page optimization. They should be between 65 and 75 characters long. They should be unique per Web page and use the targeted keyword at the beginning of it.
■ Meta description tag: These are on each individual Web page. They should be no more than 165 characters long

and provide a description of what the Web page is about, while using a target keyword in the description.

■ Heading tags: These tags essentially are the "layout" of the Web page. They allow users to skim through content and find the information they are looking for. Best practice is to use a primary keyword in your headings and do not duplicate them throughout the page.

■ Image optimization: Name image files properly. Example: if you have an image of a staff member, you should use his or her name, "johnsmith.jpg," rather than "DCM38745. jpg"; also use an ALT tag to provide additional information. Search engines cannot "read" images, but they will read this information if you provide it.

■ Body content: The most important aspect of on-page optimization is to write compelling content that engages your users by either capturing their interest and/or answering their questions. Focus on the services your practice provides and educate them on ailments, products, and your practice. This is where most practices fail.

■ Internal link anchor text: Link from within your content to other relevant pages. For example, if your home page has "hearing aids" mentioned on it, you should link that text to your hearing aids page.

The following is an essential element that affects off-page optimization and recommendations:

■ Create social media profiles: Social media are fundamentally the way to own all the "shelf space" for your brand on the Internet and expand your reach from outside of your website(s). They allow for great link building and circulation of your Web content that increases not only the visibility of your pages but also the rate at which your pages are indexed. Sites with more pages indexed lead to more traffic, and more traffic leads to more prospective patients for practices.

The following is for obtaining more exposure through local listings. These appear within organic search results but are separate from website listings. This is also considered off-page implementation as these are other properties that link back to your website.

- Register Google Plus Local Business page
- Sign up for Yahoo Local
- Create an account at Bing Local
- Reserve your Yelp! Page
- Make a listing on Yellow Pages
- Register with City Search
- Comment on local blogs
- Guest blog on local blogs
- Provide testimonials for local businesses

Finally, mobile-friendly pages rank higher in mobile searches and desktop organic searches, so it is wise to ensure that practice websites opt for a "responsive" site that will conform to whatever device is being used to view their Web page.

WEBSITE ANALYTICS

A credible webmaster will insist that your website have the ability to track the number of unique visitors, how they got to your site, what they did on the site, and how long they were there. For example, Google Analytics provides a huge amount of customized data and can be tied with other digital media platforms you may be using. Although no performance benchmark exists, webmasters agree that your website should have dozens of visitors per day with approximately 20% of the traffic spending more than 5 minutes on your website. Given the nature of social media and website activity, and unlike traditional forms of media, it is virtually impossible to reliably track the return on investment of a website. This is because the current generation of customers participates in the buying process in a much more circular fashion than previous generations. This is the so-called loyalty loop, depicted in Figure 6–2. Notice there are six distinct stages of the buying experience. Customers may interact with your practice at each of the stages using your website. From an analytic view-

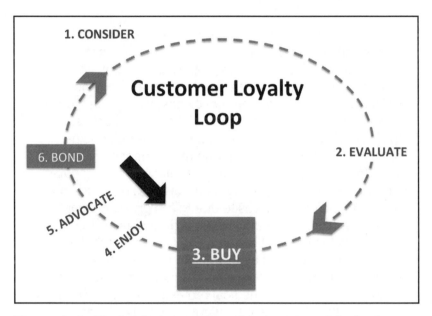

Figure 6–2. The loyalty loop outlines the six stages of the buying process. Your website plays an important role in each stage.

point, the more times, and the longer, an individual spends on your website, the more effective the website is thought to be. Furthermore, the loyalty loop also explains why you must have educational content in which products and services can be compared, patient testimonials, links to support groups, and even a mechanism for purchasing items like hearing aid batteries.

Crash Course: Updating Your Website With Kelly O'Keefe

A practice should make updates to its website on a fairly regular basis. Keep up to date with current events, promotions, staff, and hearing aid product information. A complete website overhaul/redesign should occur every 2 to 4 years to remain at the forefront of website design and development techniques. Many practices could improve their website by making it more personable and professional. As previously mentioned, this is a practice's opportunity to make a first impression for the visitor. Build a site that has character and properly represents the practice. Do-it-yourself websites can be an inexpensive solution; however, there are costly mistakes. It may require a Web expert's assistance for the site to be effective. Website content, design, development, search engine optimization (SEO), hosting, and maintenance are a lot of work for hearing professionals in addition to their regular work. We recommend hiring a professional organization to build and maintain a website due to the growing complexity of the Web today. The other main area that websites could improve is their overall content. Quality content that is properly optimized will allow the site to be found in search engines. It is important to remember that you are attracting consumers, not fellow medical professionals. Use common language that the consumer would understand. For example, use the term *hearing aid* versus *hearing instrument*. Practices sometimes want to move away from a negative connotation associated with some of the standard industry terms; however, you also have to consider the terms that consumers are using to search for the practices' products and services.

Republished with permission of Kelly O'Keefe.

FACEBOOK

A critical part of any marketing strategy employing social media is the use of Facebook. Facebook has over 750 million users worldwide and has become a ubiquitous part of our lives. As a practice owner or manager, it presents a tremendous opportunity to spread the word about your business in an instant. Social networks work differently than traditional advertising. For most small business owners, one glowing recommendation from a patient can loom larger than an entire billboard. Therefore, the power of social media marketing is that it taps into these organic communities to sell and recommend your business. Offers and endorsements spread instantly through groups of friends. News stories and opinions rocket through communities in a flash. These "friend of friend" networks are deep, fast, and free. To harness the power of social media, you need to get in on the conversation, share your news, and broadcast special offers to the people best equipped to spread the word: your patients.

The most common question posed by audiologists is, "Most of my patients are 60 and over. Are those folks really on Facebook?" The answer, which is surprising to some, is a resounding yes. According to a recent Pew report, social networking use among Internet users age 60 years and older nearly doubled from 22% in 2009 to 64% in 2014. More than half (57%) of Internet users ages 50 to 64 years and one in three (36%) users age 65 years and older now use social networking sites. In the United States alone, more than 22 million people older than 55 years use Facebook. The "stickiness" of the sites is also notable. Among the pool of adults age 50 years and older who use social networking sites, 54% used them on the day prior to their being contacted for the Pew report survey.

The primary reasons cited by older generations for using Facebook seem to be fairly consistent across those surveyed. Some users sign up for Facebook to see pictures of their grandchildren, while others are interested in reconnecting with people from their past to build a support network as they enter retirement. Others reach out for support online to help them deal with a chronic illness such as hearing loss.

There is no question that Facebook is a popular site for our target market. The good news is that setting up a Facebook page for your practice couldn't be any easier. But before we dive into the details, let's first distinguish between a "profile" and a "page." Profiles represent individuals and must be held under an individual name. In contrast, pages allow a business to maintain a professional presence on Facebook. You may only create a page to represent a real organization of which you are an authorized representative.

To create a page, you first login to your personal Facebook profile and click the "profile" button in the upper left corner. Once you are on your main profile page, scroll to the bottom of the page and select the link labeled "create a page." This will open up a separate page with six choices. You will select the first option, "local business or place." From here, you will be asked to "choose a category." The most likely choices are either "health/medical/pharmacy" or "hospital/clinic." The additional information required is self-explanatory: business name, address, and phone. The last step is to agree to the Facebook pages terms and click "get started."

Once you have created a page, you will be listed as an "admin." It is important to understand that pages are managed by admins who have personal profiles. Pages are not separate Facebook accounts and therefore do not have separate login information. You access your business page by logging into your personal profile.

You might be wondering how to build your initial fan base. As part of the initial setup process, Facebook now allows "admins" to "invite friends." For example, if John Smith is one of my friends, I can highlight his name and the tool will send a notification to John suggesting that he like my business page. This type of outreach can jumpstart growth for new pages or help facilitate further viral growth for established pages. The other resource for generating awareness about your Facebook page is called "Tell Your Fans." Using this tool, "admins" can upload their current patient email list and create a customized email that will be sent through Facebook to all patients with a personal Facebook profile. Like the "Invite Friends" tool, the "Tell Your Fans" tool is a great way to recruit fans and spread the word about your new Facebook page.

The final option for building a broad base of fans is to create incentives to encourage current or potential patients to "like" your Facebook page. The choice of incentives depends entirely on your preferences. Some might prefer to choose a more altruistic incentive such as offering to donate $1 to a specified charity on behalf of each person who "likes" the page. Others might have more success with low-cost product giveaways such as, "Like our page and receive a month's worth of replacement batteries for free." Whatever type of incentive you choose, the idea remains the same—there is value in having a broad base of followers, and successful practices should be willing to offer nominal compensation to build their fan base.

Search engine optimization (SEO), which we have mentioned more than once in this chapter, confounds and confuses even the most savvy Web marketers. However, it is critically important to the success of your business because it increases the visibility of your practice and drives engagement on your Facebook page. There are three ways to help ensure that your Facebook page will appear on page 1 of the search engine results for major search engines like Google and Bing.

The first strategy is to add links from your website to your Facebook page. Ideally, those links will appear not only on your home page but also on your subpages. The easiest way to ensure that the links appear on multiple pages is to include the link as part of your standard website design template. Typically, this means placing the link in either the header or footer. You also want to make sure that your link includes your practice name (e.g., "Happy Hearing Solutions on Facebook"). Finally, you must link directly to your "Vanity URL," which is simply the short version of your Facebook Web address. To register your "Vanity URL," you first need to have 25 "likes." Once you meet that threshold, you can replace your original Facebook Web address, which includes a random string of alphanumeric characters, with a more succinct Web address like http://www.facebook.com/ProfessionalHearingSolutions. As with domain names, being able to secure your preferred "Vanity URL" depends entirely on availability, so the sooner you get 25 "likes," the better.

The second way to help ensure that search engines pick up your Facebook page is to include your practice name in your wall posts. This is critical because search engine algorithms analyze the content of Facebook pages to determine whether a particular Facebook page is a relevant match for the requested search. Therefore, the more times your practice name appears on your "wall," the higher likelihood that the search engine algorithm will consider the page relevant and post the link.

The final way to improve search engine performance for your Facebook page is to increase the number of "likes" and the number of posts. Calculating the number of people who "like" your Facebook page helps search engines evaluate the level of social engagement with your practice. For example, all of the people who "like" your Facebook page also have a Facebook profile. The links to these user profiles are picked up by "spiders" (i.e., Web-crawlers used by search engines). Therefore, to increase the probability that these "spiders" find your page, you want to have as many links to people who "like" your page as possible. Similarly, you also want to post regularly to your wall to ensure that these posts routinely appear in the "news-feed" for the people who like your page. This strategy is analogous to buying lottery tickets—would you rather have 1 lottery ticket or 1,000 lottery tickets?

Crash Course: How to Advertise on Facebook With Doug Richey of Demand Street

Doug Richey, CEO of Demand Street, is a leading Facebook expert in the health care arena. Here is his crash course on using Facebook to advertise.

Doug: Creating an advertisement on Facebook might sound like a daunting task, but in fact, the process is both simple and intuitive. To get started, you simply login to Facebook and type http://www.facebook.com/ads in your browser.

Once you are on the "Advertise on Facebook" page, the first step is to choose a "destination" for your ad. There is a dropdown menu next to "destination" that allows you to select any of the "pages" for which you are an "admin." After you've selected your "destination," your next step is to design your "Facebook ad." You write your ad copy in the section labeled "Body," and you are limited to 135 characters. Next you will upload an image that appears alongside the ad copy. The "Preview" space highlights how the ad will appear on the profile pages for your target audience.

Selecting a target audience is the next step, and Facebook allows you to be as general or as specific as you prefer. Under "Location," the options include "Country," "State/Province," or "City," with the most likely choice being city, which also allows you to specify a proximity range of 10, 25, or 50 miles. With "Demographics," you select an age range and gender. For "Interests," you are able to target specific interests based on user profiles. For example, if you type "Hearing" as an interest, you will notice that there are 2,880 people in the United States older than 18 years who like "Hearing." This information can be found on the right-hand side of the page listed under "Estimated Reach." You will notice that as you modify your target selections, the "Estimated Reach" will fluctuate dynamically. Finally, with "Connections," you can choose whether to target people who already "like" your page or people who do not yet "like" your page. You can also decide to only show your ad to friends of people who "like" your page.

The final step is to set a budget, outline a schedule, and choose your pricing model. When establishing your budget, you can choose between a daily budget and a lifetime budget that will span the duration of the campaign. The schedule options are to either "Run my campaign continuously starting today" or specify a date range. In both cases, the schedule will be limited by your budget constraints. The final step is to choose your pricing model. Facebook offers two options: "Pay for Impressions (CPM)" and "Pay for Clicks (CPC)." Most advertisers prefer the CPC model because they only pay when a user actually clicks on their ad and visits their page. Yet, the ad still generates impressions even when users are not clicking. The bid price for either CPC or CPM is simply the maximum price you are willing to pay per click or per impression.

Republished with permission of Doug Richey.

Database Marketing

The real value of Facebook might be that it is arguably the easiest way to leverage the referral potential of your existing patient base. Existing patients that "like" your page are going to receive your "wall posts" as part of their "newsfeed." If anything catches their eye (e.g., an interesting story of a success patient or a 50%

discount on a 6-month supply of batteries), they can easily share the post with their friends by clicking the "Share" button in the bottom right corner directly beneath the post.

When users click the share button, a separate window opens up inviting them to write a message to accompany the post. Additionally, users are given the option to share the post on their own wall, on a friend's wall, in a group, or in a private message. In most cases, your existing patients will probably choose to send a private message directly and discreetly to a friend or group of friends.

The great news is that the demographic profile of the people who are friends with your existing patients probably closely resembles the demographic profile of your existing patients. Age, income, and lifestyle all tend to be highly correlated within social networks. So in all likelihood, your ideal patient is probably going to have a lot of friends who are also ideal patients. And, who could be better to help validate your professionalism and quality of care than your most loyal advocates. These days, anything that can be posted on your website can be posted on a Facebook page. The advantage of using Facebook is that news about your practices travels like a virus.

Facebook recently announced it had reached the threshold of 1 billion users, now constituting almost 75% of all activity on the Internet. Half of those users report using Facebook on a daily basis. To give you a sense of how quickly this has become the primary site for not only personal use but for business use as well, in August 2008, Google overtook Yellow Pages as the number one source for information on products and services.

With this explosion in activity has come a new terminology in marketing—inbound versus outbound. Outbound is the new way of referral to traditional marketing forms: putting mail inside people's mailboxes, showing images on TV screens, sending patients in your database a monthly newsletter. Today, the emphasis is on putting content (giving birth to another new phrase: content marketing) into cyberspace and allowing people to find you as a result. Some media experts predict that by 2016, more business will be done via inbound marketing than outbound marketing. Facebook should be thought of as one of several pillars of an overall foundation of inbound marketing. Others should include blogs and other platforms like Twitter.

Given its popularity, ease of use, low opportunity costs, and the viral nature of social media, Facebook needs to be a cornerstone of your digital marketing campaign.

DIGITAL SIGNAGE

Digital out-of-home (DOOH) marketing is a term used to describe advertising you are likely to encounter in a medical office's waiting room television. It is important to understand how it compares to traditional out-of-home (TOOH) marketing. Highway billboards, banners on the sides of buses, and signs posted on the outfield walls of your favorite ballparks are some of the more common types of TOOH you are likely to encounter every day. Because TOOH relies almost exclusively on visual appeal, it is easy for consumers to ignore. Just think how many times you have driven by the same static billboard on your way to work. After seeing the unchanging image a few times, most people completely tune it out.

On the other hand, DOOH combines audio and video to generate a dynamic and, ultimately, more emotionally appealing message. It's this emotional appeal that attracts attention and enables customers to take action. As the price of digital advertising becomes less expensive, DOOH becomes more widely used by businesses trying to attract more customers. DOOH is quickly supplanting TOOH as a more popular choice relative to TOOH.

The core to DOOH marketing is the use of digital signage, which is displayed in the reception area on a flat-screen television. The content of the digital signage displayed on the flat-screen television is usually controlled using basic personal computers, by way of proprietary software programs. This keeps the costs of DOOH manageable by avoiding any large capital outlays for the controller equipment. Most systems automatically update themselves using a high-speed Internet connection, which reduces clinic staff involvement and keeps fresh content in front of your patients. The audiologist or clinic manager simply has to inform the service (HNN) of changes and updates in content displayed on the flat-screen TV.

Crash Course: DOOH Marketing With Brad Dodson of Clear Digital Media, Inc.

Brad: Here are four things to do when getting started with DOOH:

1. Obtain a large flat-screen television and wall mount for your reception area.
2. Connect the television to a high-speed Internet connection. Although a wireless connection is sufficient, a high-speed wired Internet connection works best.
3. Subscribe to a DOOH service (e.g., HNN).
4. Identify and/or create the content you want to run on your 10- to 20-minute loop. This should include a video introducing you and your staff as well as services you offer. Public service videos can also be included. The video content is broadcast in the theater portion of the screen, which comprises about 85% of the area of the flat screen. Local weather is broadcast on the right margin of the TV screen and national news on the bottom.

Republished with permission of Brad Dodson.

CLOUD-BASED MARKETING TOOLS

Historically, audiologists have done a reasonably good job of fostering an emotional connection with their patients. This connection is largely predicated on the personal, face-to-face interaction between the professional and patient during a routine appointment. Monthly patient newsletters, birthday cards, and reminder phone calls are outbound marketing strategies that have been used traditionally to grow these relationships. Recently, cloud-based marketing tools from companies such as Solution Reach and Call Source allow practices to engage with patients in novel ways using social media. By interfacing with your existing office management software, cloud-based marketing tools allow practices to send appointment reminder texts to patients, personalized happy birthday videos, and instantaneous patient surveys via text or email directly to patients. In addition to cloud-based tools that allow practices to engage, retain, and educate patients, these tools have robust analytics that help practices gauge the return on investment from their marketing efforts.

Crash Course: Using Social Media With the Mature Marketplace With Don Marsh

Don Marsh is recognized within the profession as a real expert on marketing to individuals older than 65 years. Let's find out some of the latest marketing trends with respect to this all-important age group.

Don: No matter how you read the statistics, the bottom line remains the same: These are challenging times for those in the audiology profession. Even if the daily economic news wasn't so up-and-down, there's ample evidence to suggest it's time to look outside the usual comfort zones when it comes to marketing hearing health care services.

Newspaper ads have long been a staple for hearing health care marketers. Now newspapers themselves are fast becoming a dying breed, as evidenced by a Pew Report that showed readership down more than 26% in the last 3 years. During that same time frame, more than 200 newspapers throughout America have ceased publication. Many have attempted to recapture the same readership— and ad revenues—by going online, but for most that effort has yet to become fully productive. In addition, Yellow Page ads are costly, with the results often difficult to track. And raise your hand if the response rate from your last direct mail campaign even came close to the former gold standard of a 2% return. In an era when decreasing resources are more often than not matched up against increasing competition, nowhere is that challenge more complex than when your target audience is the mature marketplace.

These five key concepts are considered universal truths in defining what motivates the 50+ mature marketplace. The more these concepts can be incorporated into not only your marketing materials but also conversations with patients and family members, the more success will come by way of enhancing the patient experience and ensuring business growth.

The five key concepts are the following:

1. Autonomy or self-sufficiency: Regaining the ability to pursue the interests and activities that age or illness may have taken away is a recurring theme in the mature marketplace. From a marketing perspective, offering choices as opposed to only one solution, whether in the way of medical treatment or even financing options, is a way to help older patients use their need for autonomy and self-sufficiency as part of the decision-making process.

2. Connectedness: This is an audience that have reached a station in life when "trigger events" begin to affect their everyday lives—children growing up, selling the family home, retiring from a long-enjoyed career, perhaps even losing a spouse. Because contact with patients is typically infrequent, handwritten notes, phone calls, newsletters, and other means of communication answer their need to stay connected to your staff, services, and place of business.

3. Altruism: Fund-raising experts will tell you that people 50 and older traditionally make up the largest segment of any donor population. Engaging your health system, clinic, or practice in community-based charitable activities, while at the same time encouraging patients to participate, will allow them to engage in this concept, defined as a concern for others.

4. Personal growth: The growth of organizations like Elder Hostel is a prime example of how important this concept

is to the mature marketplace. It may also be the most easily understood, simply by drawing the connection between better health and the ability to enjoy new, enriching experiences. The moral here is that no matter how old we become, we never, ever, leave behind the need for personal growth.

5. Revitalization: One of the recommendations I offer clients when reviewing their marketing materials is to use models who appear to be 10 to 12 years younger than the target audience. This is a practical application of the fact that the older we are, the younger we still like to think of ourselves as being. Use this concept to reinforce the notion that better health leads to feeling younger and more alive again.

Republished with permission of Don Marsh at marketservices@ sbcglobal.net.

Social media represent a significant opportunity for audiologists to build awareness of their brand within the community. Rather than rely on the pull of traditional marketing campaigns to attract clients, digital media, such as Facebook and the deployment an interactive website, allow audiologists to interact with a virtual community of their target audience. Social media experts suggest that the key to successful use of digital marketing is having content that is easy to digest and willingly shared by followers of your practice. Old-fashioned values, like empathy and warmth, still have tremendous value in the digital era. The traits that help patients emotionally connect with professionals can generate activity of platforms such a Facebook and Twitter when audiologists take the time to write stories about their favorite patients and share ideas they are passionate about. When audiologists commit 1 to 2 hours per month writing content that reflects the mission and purpose of their practice, they are more likely to gain a following and become a pillar within their community, regardless of the social media platforms they use.

SUMMARY

An audiology practice would be wise to do the following three things when creating a digital marketing strategy:

1. Maintain a captivating website with personalized video content, educational materials for patients with links to other relevant websites, and your social media platforms. Additionally, the use of online reputation management systems that allow patients to record, share, and view testimonials is an excellent way to generate word-of-mouth advertising.

2. Create interesting content that resonates with your target audience. This content can be posted on a blog, broadcast through Facebook or Twitter, or placed in a newsletter. Rely on social media platforms that are most popular with your target audience. Content does not have to be confined to the written word; video and audio can also be used. Finally, you can complement your own content by finding links to other bloggers and Web pages that are of interest to your target audience.

3. Hire a professional webmaster, preferably one that understands both the hearing care industry and your local market. The webmaster can be contracted to work a few hours per month overseeing and orchestrating all aspects of your digital marketing strategy. Be sure that your webmaster shares the analytics of how many people have visited your website and how much time the average person spends on it.

7

MARKETING UNIVERSITY AND OTHER NONPROFIT AUDIOLOGY CLINICS

Donald W. Nielsen

"Do today what others will not do, so tomorrow
you will have what others do not have."
—Anonymous

Too many university audiology clinics complain they are the best-kept secret in town. The reason for this is simple; they have not planned to make their clinic known, valued, and trusted in the community. Until recently, marketing has been nonexistent and even frowned upon in university audiology clinics. But competition now threatens most university and other nonprofit audiology clinics. An extensive survey by *Strategy & Consumer Survey* (Estupianan, Fengler, & Kaura, 2014), of 2,339 U.S. residents that mimicked the total U.S. population demographics paints a clear picture of a population displeased with its overall health care experience—and with rising expectations for transparency, value, and customer service, as well as a willingness to seek health care from less traditional sources such as big-box stores, the Internet, and manufacturers. Forty percent of respondents said they would trust a large retailer for health services. Transparent markets and an ever-increasing range of choices mean that maintaining "no marketing" status quo is no longer an option for audiologists. To survive, university and other non-profit audiology clinics must become market driven and develop marketing skills. Competition is most obvious in hearing health services and providing hearing aids, so we focus on those services and products in this chapter, but the strategies presented here can be generalized to other services and products in your clinic.

This chapter helps university and nonprofit clinics struggling to succeed in this increasingly competitive environment. Marketing nonprofit clinics uses many of the same techniques and procedures as for-profit clinic marketing, but there are some important differences and clear strategic advantages for nonprofit clinics; those differences and advantages are the subject of this chapter and at the core of the recommended marketing strategies below. To many university and nonprofit audiology clinics, marketing is new and much needed. Marketing planning will help you define your unique niche and reach the patients you want with a message that motivates them to action.

To understand why marketing nonprofit clinics differs from marketing for-profit clinics, we must understand how the two types of clinics differ and how to turn those differences into advantages in the marketplace.

NONPROFIT/FOR-PROFIT DIFFERENCES

Nonprofit status is based on federal tax law. According to Salamon (1999), "U.S. tax law contains no fewer than 27 separate sections under which organizations can claim exemption from federal income taxes as nonprofit organizations." Exemption from federal income tax assumes that a nonprofit will produce profit; otherwise, there would be no need for the exemption. The label *nonprofit* is widely misunderstood to assume that no profit will be made. That is incorrect. In nonprofit organizations, profit can be made, but it must be reinvested in the organization's mission. The tax exemption, as well as nonprofit status, is granted because the clinic serves the public good. Nonprofit clinics are human change agents. Their products or outputs are changed human beings: a patient who hears better or young women who become competent professional audiologists.

For this chapter, we consider a nonprofit audiology clinic as a clinic with nonprofit tax status and whose mission serves public purpose, such as the advancement of health, education, scientific progress, or social welfare. This definition includes freestanding nonprofit clinics and clinics in private nonprofit universities. In addition, we include audiology clinics at city- or state-funded universities because the marketing techniques and advantages described here also can apply to those clinics. University clinics that reside within medical schools and want to increase patient flow to audiology will find this chapter useful, but these audiology clinics usually have a sufficient patient base created by a constant stream of referrals from their own physicians, so additional marketing may not interest them. This chapter is focused primarily on AuD teaching clinics not in medical environments and other nonprofit clinics to whom marketing is now important. If you are in a university setting or other nonprofit audiology clinic and want to increase the flow of patients to your clinic, this chapter is written for you.

In a for-profit business model, the input to the business is money, and the output of the business is also money (Collins, 2005). Ideally, the for-profit clinic adds value and grows the input so the output is greater than the input creating profit, which is its sole measure of its success. For-profit clinics serve patients and change those patients, but patient changing is the process that enables them to create a profit; the changed patient is not the output—it is the means by which the output, profit, is created. Our colleagues in for-profit clinics will argue that they are patient focused, and many are, but the degree to which they put patient interests above making profit varies widely. The real test of how patient focused a clinic is comes when making difficult decisions about the patient's interests versus making a profit. If making a profit ever exceeds operating in the patients' best interests, the clinic should be a for-profit clinic. If patients' interests always trump making a profit, the clinic should be a nonprofit clinic and benefit from some of the advantages explained in this chapter.

Nonprofit clinics differ from the for-profit model because money is an input and not a measure of success. To be clear, money, even profit, may be part of the nonprofit clinic's output, but never the sole output, and not the measure of success. In nonprofit clinics, profit must be reinvested in the clinic to advance the mission. The output measure that indicates nonprofit success is the output that shows how well the clinic's mission is being accomplished: Did you change a human being such as a patient or a student?

When made clear, the difference in commitment between for-profit and nonprofit clinics is important to patients. For-profit clinics are in business to make money by helping patients. Nonprofit clinics are committed to helping patients, and they make money to pay their bills and serve more patients. To potential patients, this difference results in an immediate increased level of trust for nonprofits. This trust advantage is the most significant differentiator between nonprofit clinics and their competition and is central to university and nonprofit marketing strategies suggested here.

Many marketing plans are available for university and nonprofit clinics to modify for their use, such as Business Plan Pro and Marketing Pro by Palo Alto Software, and planning advice on the U.S. Small Business Administration's website (http://www.sba.gov). This chapter will help you with that process by discussing some of the marketing problems exclusive to university clinics and by focusing on unusual and sometimes unique marketing strategies that lend themselves best to successful marketing of university and other nonprofit audiology clinics.

MISSION

Many university audiology clinics have not clarified their mission with a mission statement. The clinic's mission is at the heart of its business plan, crucial to measuring success, and central to marketing. It is critical to create a mission if you do not have one or to reexamine your mission if you have one.

Because mission statements should answer the following: *What is your clinic's reason for being? Who do you serve? Why do you do what you do? For what do you want to be remembered?* University clinics are often confused about their mission and may feel they have four missions:

1. Providing hearing health care services for the community or some segment of the community
2. Training future doctors of audiology
3. Participating in translational research: partnering with department researchers to move research from the lab to the clinic and providing researchers with subjects with hearing losses
4. Creating operating revenue for the clinic

Mission confusion can be caused because the clinicians, teaching faculty, research faculty, department management, and the university may all have differing ideas about the clinic's purpose. Strategic planning and business planning at the department level should clarify the purpose of the clinic, and once this is clear and agreed upon, everyone can focus on that common mission. To arrive at a mission to which all parties can agree requires that everyone be represented in the decision process.

Some university clinics create mission statements with two, three, or four purposes to satisfy several viewpoints. That practice dilutes the mission. As you will see in the example mission below, that dilution is unnecessary. From the discussion of nonprofit clinics above, it should be clear that the university clinic's purpose should not be to make money. Money may be necessary to operate the clinic but it is not the raison d'être for a nonprofit clinic. The university clinic would not exist if there were not a need to train students, so university clinicians often feel their primary purpose is to train students. But because university clinics train students to identify and serve patients' needs, the training clinic must be focused on what they are teaching: serving patients. The clinic cannot train students without patients, translational research requires patients, and revenue production also requires patients, so I suggest that serving patients is at the heart of what every university clinic does and central to its mission.

Another way to give order to the clinic's mission is to think about customers. Customers are people who value your service and must be satisfied. They have the choice to accept or reject your services. All your customers must want what you deliver (Drucker, 1993). Every university clinic has more than one customer. You can think of your patients as primary customers, students and researchers as secondary customers, and referral sources such as physicians, patients' friends and families, insurance companies, and donors as support customers. While patients are the primary customers to succeed, all customers must be satisfied, and they all have the choice to accept or reject your services. Marketing will ensure your services are well accepted.

A university clinic's mission should be focused on serving patients and built on opportunities, clinic competences, and commitments. As a start to creating your mission, consider what community opportunities or patient needs exist that match your clinic's competencies and for which the people in your clinic are passionately committed (Figure 7–1). This process can be facilitated by considering and creating a value proposition at the same time.

The thing that makes your clinic exciting is purpose. Your mission should clarify what your purpose is; it should be operational and state who will benefit. A good mission statement will focus on what your clinic is trying to do and for whom, so everybody in the clinic can say, "This is *my* contribution to the goal" (Drucker, 1990). For example: *Elite University Audiology Clinic's mission is to provide and expand the highest quality, evidence-based, hearing health services to the community by providing direct service, training future doctors of audiology, and participating in research.* In this example, the purpose is clear: *to provide and expand the highest quality, evidence-based, hearing health services.* It is clear who will benefit: *the community.*

Figure 7–1. A nonprofit clinic's mission is defined by the intersection of the patient needs and opportunities in the community with the core capabilities of the clinic and the passion and commitment of the clinicians.

How the mission will be operationalized is also clear: *by providing direct service, training future doctors of audiology, and participating in research.* To succeed, *Elite University Audiology Clinic* must provide evidence-based services to the community. It must also expand those services by increasing new patient visits, producing new well-trained audiologists, and participating in research to create new services and provide the evidence base for those services. With a simple and clear mission statement like the example above, you are ready to plan your marketing and measure your success.

MARKETING PLANNING

What Is Marketing?

The best definition of marketing for university audiology clinics and other nonprofit clinics is John Jantsch's definition in *Duct Tape Marketing* (Jantsch, 2011). He states that marketing is "getting someone who has a need, to know, like, and trust you." It is the inclusion of the word *trust* that makes this definition so correct for nonprofit organizations. And, it is turning *know*, *like*, and *trust* into *try*, *buy*, and *repeat* that makes marketing successful.

The Case for Marketing

Many universities, especially state-funded universities, are operating with scarce resources, and even some private universities with billions of dollars in endowment operate as if their resources are limited and have no resource slack in their operations. Studies have shown that resource constraints hinder growth and lower the probability of survival (Becchetti & Trovato, 2002; Musso & Schiavo, 2008). In strong contrast, more abundant available resources improve financial performance (Daniel, Lohrke, Fornaciari, & Turner, 2004), buffer environmental shocks, and allow for more discretion and flexibility in responding to competitors (George, 2005). Therefore, an important role for the clinic director is to convince the university hierarchy to release resources for marketing and other clinic needs. This is problematic because marketing may be seen as an expense rather than an investment. This section provides you with evidence and strategies to help win approval of an annual marketing plan and a realistic marketing budget.

While not focused on universities or nonprofits, Phonak's 2013 Survey of Dispensing Practices published in *Hearing Review* (Phonak Marketing, 2013) demonstrates the importance of creating, funding, and executing a marketing plan. Gross revenue is an indicator of the size and success of a practice. The survey of 268 practices showed that in the lowest quintile of gross revenue, only 22% of the practices had marketing plans compared to 78% in the largest quintile. As seen in Table 7–1, the larger the gross revenue, the more likely the practice was to have a marketing plan, marketing calendar, and a marketing budget, which they funded with a higher percentage of their gross revenue. Universities and other nonprofit clinics not planning and allocating resources to marketing have fallen behind the competition. When using these survey data to demonstrate to decision makers up the hierarchy that marketing works, it

Table 7–1. Phonak Marketing Survey 2013

Phonak Marketing Survey 2013	Smallest 20%	Moderately Small 20%	Median 20%	Moderately Large 20%	Largest 20%
Median gross revenues	$96,000	$350,000	$606,788	$919,000	$2,250,000
% Practices with marketing plans	22%	32%	36%	48%	78%
% Practices with marketing calendar	22%	32%	36%	48%	78%
% Practices with marketing budget	33%	36%	35%	50%	67%
% Gross revenue spent on marketing	0%	0.6%	3%	8.5%	13%

is important that all involved understand that marketing does not work its magic overnight but requires a culture that supports persistent marketing, taking risk, and modifying marketing goals and strategies to meet constantly changing environments and opportunities.

Because the survey data are ranked on gross revenue, they are easy to interpret in financial terms and to make financial arguments to decision makers up the hierarchy. Increasing gross revenues also indicates increasing patient volume. In universities where the audiology clinic can play an important role in providing early patient contact and clinical experience for the AuD training program, increasing patient volume is often crucial to providing the students with required experience. Recognizing the interdependencies of the clinic and the AuD training program by collaborating with the training program to make the argument that clinic marketing will help the university's training goals is an additional strategy that could benefit the clinic and the training program.

Universities are often faced with a "town-gown" problem in which the university's effects on the community are seen as negative. From not paying local taxes to creating too much traffic, there are always several arguments that disgruntled local citizens will make against the university. To counter these arguments, universities are looking to be constructively active in the local community. Providing quality audiologic services to the community on a regular basis and providing the community with educational lecture series fit a university's need to be an active and constructive partner with the community. Many universities have explicitly stated in their strategic plans that one of their goals is to participate more in assisting the local community. If this description fits your university, then the value of a successful clinic is more than the financial and training measures indicate. It is community service publicly valued by the university. Collaborating with the university administration to visibly provide community outreach, audiology services, and educational opportunities is a textbook strategy to seamlessly align clinic and university success in the minds of the decision makers upstream while also educating the community about your value proposition.

How to Get Your Marketing Accomplished With Limited Resources

Marking requires not only planning and financing but also human resources—someone to do it. In universities, resources including human resources are too often limited. Here are three suggestions for accomplishing marketing responsibilities with limited human resources and one suggestion about using limited financial resources:

Shift the Burden

Several management groups will assist you with your marketing challenges and opportunities; many are owned by manufacturers. Manufacturers can offer useful business management advice and connect you with a network of consultants who can help you. I have found them useful. However, manufacturer-owned groups present three problems when used for marketing assistance: One is that it is in your interest to stay free of manufacturer influence, and if a manufacturer, or a manufacturer-owned management group, is subsidizing your marketing, you cannot state in your marketing you are free of manufacturer influence. The second is that manufacturer-based marketing uses product-focused cookie-cutter designs so every clinic using their services looks alike. Differentiation from the competition and separation from those who profit from hearing aid sales are both important strategies to remember for universities and other nonprofits. Third, manufacturer-subsidized marketing usually includes a pricing advantage and puts your clinic in a price-based competition. More about this in a later section on value propositions, but know that price-based is not where you want to be. There are also management groups like Audigy and Fuel Medical (the author consults with Fuel Medical), which will help you manage the clinic and provide business development and many marketing skills such as design of materials at no cost to you. Don't underestimate the power of professional-appearing custom marketing materials that management companies can provide to you. Historically, Audigy has focused mainly on private practices and promotes Audigy's brand and feel. Fuel Medical focuses on university clinics and large ear, nose, and throat (ENT) practices and creates unique branding focused on an individual practice. Both Audigy and Fuel Medical keep your clinic at arm's length from manufacturers. You can discuss your marketing needs and goals with them and develop a value proposition, marketing plan, calendar, and budget with their help. They can even help you evaluate your key performance indicators or provide complete business development services. Someone from the clinic must be involved, but the involvement is much less than going it on your own. Importantly, the university might look favorably on using these sources of assistance that lower costs and demand for human resources while providing sophisticated marketing services resulting in professional marketing strategies and products.

Use University Resources

Universities have public relations (PR) departments that focus on getting public visibility for the good the university creates. While the PR department may not assist with a total marketing plan, it can increase your clinic's visibility in the community and solidify the link between the clinic and the university in the community's mind-set. To work with your university's PR department, you first must make the case that providing PR for your clinic is important to the university. Aligning clinic and university community service strategies is the best course of action to build this case. Establishing a relationship with the PR department and educating them about what the clinic does and how people benefit from your services, outreach, and educational events will help you gain needed visibility in the university and the community. In addition, you can work with your university's human resources (HR) department to make your clinical services better known to current university faculty and staff and their families. Offering special considerations for university faculty, staff, and their families will help to gain HR support and publicity for the clinic. With strong HR support, you can even create a university hearing benefit plan for employees—a plan where university hearing health care services are provided in your clinic. Finally, you can work with the university alumni relations office to identify local alumni who are potent patients and may serve as good referral sources in the community. Letting these alumni know that they are exceptional through some special consideration will increase the success of this effort and increase its popularity with the alumni office.

If your university has a business school, create a relationship with it. If you have no business school in your university, or if you are operating a nonuniversity nonprofit, then find a local nearby university that has a business school. In my experience, business schools like to work on business development projects with community nonprofit organizations, including clinics inside or outside of their university. These projects help bolster the university's community reputation, provide a challenging experience for students, and meet the millennial students' need for social action and involvement (Winograd & Hais, 2011). At Northwestern University, the audiology clinic worked with first-year MBA students from the Kellogg School of Management for clinic strategic planning and for marketing. Northwestern primarily recruits first-year MBA students with 5 years of experience or more, and our recent group had students with varying experience, including experience with a major consulting firm, marketing experience, and financial experience, and one was a medical student in Northwestern's combined MD, MBA program. At Stanford, the business school alumni created a consulting service for local nonprofits, and our local nonprofit worked with these successful alumni to diversify our revenue streams. These university services provide their communities with experienced teams of experts to tackle nonprofit business development projects. In my experiences, they succeeded and were free. They require a well-thought-out project that can be accomplished in a short time period. They work best if you are committed and involved enough to meet weekly with the team or team leader to maintain focus and progress. Figures 7–2 and 7–3 show the initial work plan and work streams developed by the Kellogg Impact Consulting Club (KICC) at Northwestern University for the audiology clinic. The KICC volunteers for the Northwestern Audiology Clinic were Katherine Hartley Rehberger, team leader, and Alyssa Sivanich, Joseph McDevitt, Yu Teraoka, and Jaclyn

High-level work plan

	Market research and customer needs	Action plan development	Tactical plan and financial impact
Timing	Weeks 1-5	Weeks 6-8	Weeks 9-10
Actions	• Review existing research and knowledge base, including benchmarking against similar clinics • Perform employee interviews • Perform customer & potential customer interviews / surveys	• Identify several specific initiatives that would improve clinic utilization / hearing aid purchases • Prioritize initiatives using several criteria (e.g. impact, feasibility)	• Model financial impact of action items • Develop implementation / roll-out plan
Deliverables	• Customer segmentation (types of customers) • List of factors driving lack of audiologist visits / purchases, specifically around Evanston	• Prioritized list of potential initiatives • Key challenges / risks for each action item	• Tactical plan for implementing action items (timing, etc.) • Estimated financial impact of chosen action items
Key meetings	Mid project read-out	Action plan review	Final read-out

Figure 7–2. The sophisticated work plan of the KICC volunteers gives a high-level view of the research they were planning to do, as well as how they would convert research findings to action plans and create estimates of the financial impact to the clinic. Republished with permission of Kellogg Impact Consulting Club.

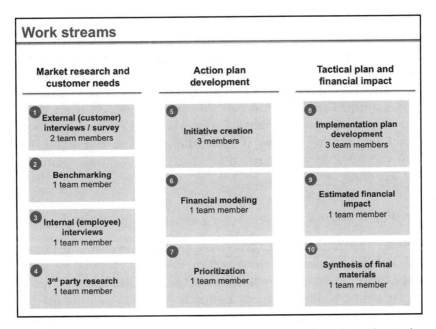

Figure 7–3. The proposed KICC work streams show how the tasks were divided among team members and demonstrate how much of the market planning effort can be shifted to volunteers. Republished with permission of Kellogg Impact Consulting Club.

Gray Rivara. They were assisted by Diane Novak, clinic manager; Sanreka Watley, clinic physician liaison; and Efoe Nyatepe Coo, AuD student. You can see from Figures 7–2 and 7–3 the project sophistication and amount of work this team planned to do and did accomplish in 10 weeks.

Taking advantage of these excellent business school services, often available only to nonprofits, greatly extends your marketing and business development resources. Having the team of volunteers present their findings and recommendations to the whole department and the administration helps to establish a marketing culture and increases understanding of your marketing plan. These free high-level services give you a distinct advantage over the competition, creating sophisticated professional marketing strategies and increased new patient flow to the clinic.

Even without a business school, many universities have planning facilitators who will help you organize a strategic planning session or a change management effort. Because strategic planning includes defining your mission and doing an analysis of your internal strengths and weaknesses, as well as external opportunities and threats, the information gained from these exercises will be important to your marketing efforts and help build a marketing culture. If your administration will support it, you should start your marketing efforts with strategic planning for the clinic.

Involve Students

Another source of human resources are your own AuD students. Involving AuD students in marketing efforts is especially significant for those students who wish to go into private practice or to be a future clinic director in any setting. These students can be assigned marketing tasks as part of their practice management training. They can work with your practice management consulting group, attending the weekly phone conferences and accepting responsibility for tasks they may help develop and put into action. Student capstone projects can focus on needed market research, analysis of the research results, and development of a plan of action and its implementation. Such projects involve students in educational opportunities while advancing the clinic's marketing efforts.

Marketing dollars are too scarce to spend unwisely.

Spend Wisely

As we have seen above, clinics with marketing plans, calendars, and established budgets do better than those without. Planning your marketing will also keep your marketing spending focused and within established limits. Careful tracking of the return on each of your marketing expenditures will guide future spending to omit ineffective strategies, emphasize effective strategies, and create innovative new strategies. More than a 100 years ago, marketing guru John Wanamaker said, "Half the money I spend on advertising is wasted: the trouble is I don't know which half." Today, smart marketers in successful clinics know which half isn't working, and they eliminate it. Understanding your marketing cost, knowing your return on marketing investments, and communicating these numbers intelligently will impress financially focused decision makers upstream and increase your chances of long-term financial support.

Your Clinic's Value Proposition

A well-thought-out value proposition is essential to your marketing success because it helps you break through marketplace chaos and get the patient's attention. For audiology clinics, a value proposition is a succinct statement that summarizes a collection of reasons a patient should use your clinic's services or buy hearing aids and other products from your clinic rather than from any other clinic. At the core of your value proposition is the uniqueness of your clinic that sets it apart from all competitors.

With a strong value proposition, your marketing efforts will be more effective and efficient, and it will avoid the trap of viewing your services and products as commodities. With a strong, valid value position, the reasoning that the patient can get the same service from the guy down the street cheaper is no longer useable. Clinics with no value propositions will find their services commoditized and their clinic competing on price rather than value. Clinics with weak value propositions will consume greater resources to use the strong force of marketing to overcome the weakness of their value proposition.

A strong value proposition comprises three necessary elements (Parker, 2012):

1. Potential patients must want or need your services. It has to *resonate* with them.
2. Potential patients must understand why you stand out from the other available options. *Differentiate* your clinic.
3. Potential patients must believe that you can deliver on your promises. *Substantiate* your proposition (Figure 7–4).

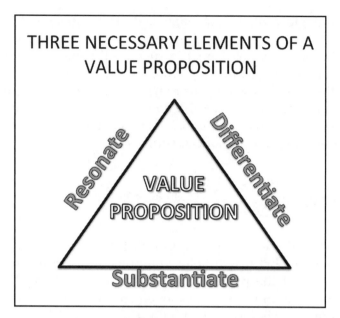

THREE NECESSARY ELEMENTS OF A
VALUE PROPOSITION

Resonate

Differentiate

VALUE
PROPOSITION

Substantiate

Figure 7–4. To be effective, a value proposition must resonate with patients, differentiate you from the competition, and substantiate that you will deliver on your promises.

As shown in Figure 7–5, if your value proposition does not resonant with the potential patient, he or she will think your services are not important enough and not needed. Without adequate differentiation, potential patients will think they can do without you and focus on price. And without substantiation, potential patients will be skeptical and not take the risk of doing business. It is critical to your clinic's marketing success that your value proposition contains all three elements.

In addition, a winning value proposition will be easy to understand and communicate the concrete results a patient will get from purchasing and using your clinic's services or products. It should be able to be read and understood in about 5 seconds and avoid hype (like "never seen before amazing miracle product"), superlatives ("best"), and business jargon ("value-added interactions").

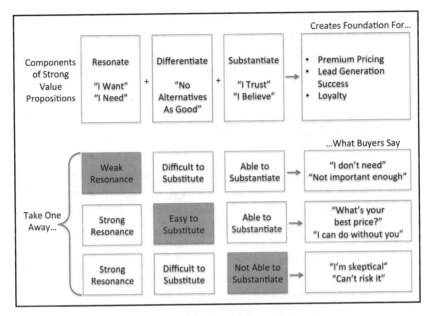

Figure 7–5. The significance of the three necessary elements of a clinic's value proposition (Parker, 2012). Republished with permission of Shawn Parker.

Finally, your value proposition should relate to your mission:

■ The *resonate* element should relate to the *needs and opportunities* you considered in creating your mission statement.

■ The *differentiation* element should relate to the *core competencies* and *capabilities* you considered in creating your mission. What is your clinic the best at?

■ The *substantive* element will have its basis in the everyday *commitment and passion* expressed through how services are provided in the clinic.

Because the mission and the value proposition have so much in common, and both should be created prior to your marketing plan, do them together early in your marketing efforts. Your value proposition should be consistently used as a starting

point for developing, positioning, and marketing messages for
services and products because it is the essence of your brand
or the total experience a patient has with you that makes you
different and better than competitors.

Creating a Value Proposition

In creating your value proposition, start with making a list of
what you are good at and be certain it is a list of what you do
well not what you want to do well. What makes you superior
to your competitors, and what do you do exclusively that your
competitors do not? Consider more than the hearing health care
services and products you provide. Maybe you have a proud
heritage, provide leadership for the profession of audiology, provide a relaxed clinic environment, or focus on educating your
patients better than your competition.

> Goal of Marketing = Awareness + Differentiation + Action

Also, approach the value proposition from your primary
customer's point of view. Value propositions must be tailored to
ideal patients (see below). What is the job they want you to do
for them: Help them with their changes in hearing? Make a list
of these jobs, focusing on the ones your patients tell you that
you do well or do better than the competition. Refine these lists
by using the wording of your patients to state them as values.

Study your top three or four competitors to see how they
market themselves. Do they have a value propositions? What
are they? Can they defend their value propositions? What are
their core competencies as seen by them and by their patients?
If their genuine competencies overlap with yours, you cannot
use those competencies in your value proposition unless you are
undisputedly superior.

Prioritize the remaining core values and pick three or four
that best differentiate you from the competition. Be certain these
also send a clear message to potential patients why they should

use your services and products. These core values will additionally remind the clinic faculty and staff what is important and on what they should be focused.

Critically access if you can support these top values across every part of your clinic from reception to service and ongoing support. Include only those that meet this criterion. If you identify areas where your desired value chain is broken, then set in motions actions to correct these issues, but don't include those values in your value proposition until they are working well for a period of time.

Now refine your value proposition into a concise statement that communicates who your patients are, what you provide to them, and why they should come to your clinic.

For example: *Elite University Audiology clinic is a nonprofit clinic that focuses on patient care, not profit. For over 40 years, we have been providing leadership in the profession of audiology and personalized hearing health services to the local community, helping people reconnect to the world by providing precise solutions for their changing hearing needs. Our services are free from manufacturers' influence, and we continue our leadership at the forefront of the audiology profession as we train future doctors of audiology and conduct cutting-edge research.*

Finally, test your value proposition with patients to see if it resonates with them. Be certain you are being honest and not using wishful thinking for your core values. To be certain, discuss with clinic faculty and staff what proof you would use to defend the values and how you would quantify them to patients. Do testimonials and online reviews support the use of these values?

Let's review how our example meets the three criteria listed above:

1. *Resonate*—Focusing on patient care, not profit, resonates with those afraid that they will be sold something they do not need or from which they will not benefit, as does being free from manufacturers' influence. Reconnecting people with the world resonates with those who feel isolated by hearing loss. People who feel their condition is unusual or difficult will especially resonate with the clinic providing personalized service and precise solutions for their changing hearing needs.

2. *Differentiate*—Being nonprofit, succeeding for 40 years, being a leader in the profession, training future doctors of audiology, doing cutting-edge research, and being free of manufacturers' influence separate Elite University Audiology Clinic from the competition.

3. *Substantiate*—Providing service successfully for 40 years substantiates that Elite University Audiology Clinic has been consistently delivering on its promised service. Training future doctors of audiology substantiates that the clinic staff are knowledgeable. Conducting cutting-edge research substantiates the clinic can read, evaluate, and apply relevant new research.

The example also conveys the benefit the patients will receive from Elite University Audiology—namely, reconnecting with their world. The example fails in one respect: It takes over 5 seconds to read. Can you make your value proposition more concise?

Ideal Patient

In John Jantsch's book *Duct Tape Marketing* (Jantsch, 2011), he introduces the concept of an ideal client. Here we build on that concept to define an ideal patient. Ideal patients are those who are perfectly suited for your clinic. Your ideal patient has a frustration, need, or desire that your clinic can solve. With your clinic team, discuss your best patients. What are the characteristics of the patients who are most satisfied with your services, the ones who write testimonials and refer new patients? With what problems did they present? Do they share similar demographics? Do they have common referral sources? Do they live within a certain radius?

The outcome of this exercise is to arrive at a description of your ideal patient that will make him or her easy to identify. While your patients will never see this definition, you can use it to narrow your marketing efforts and keep expenditures under control by focusing on the ideal patient. By using this description, you also make it easier for referral sources to identify your best potential patients and refer them to you. Your physician liaison should understand this description and have it memorized.

For example: *Elite University Audiology Clinic's ideal patient is frustrated by his or her changing hearing and resulting communication difficulties in a variety of circumstances and is self-motivated or motivated by others (spouse, physician, adult children, etc.) to do something about his or her difficulty. He or she is most likely a well-educated baby boomer or older, is of at least moderate wealth, and leads an active life and considers social inclusion important.*

It may surprise you to see the *"of at least moderate wealth"* phrase in the description of the ideal patient for a nonprofit focused on patient care, not profit. The reference to moderate wealth is there because the treatment for hearing loss is most often hearing aids, and the patient must be able to afford the treatment, which is expensive. A patient diagnosed with a hearing loss but who cannot get the treatment is not ideal. Remember that a nonprofit must reinvest its profit into the clinic to advance its mission. One use for profit realized from ideal patients is to pay for hearing aids for patients who cannot afford them.

Your marketing must be tailored to appeal to your ideal patient, and you must know what these patients value. For the example above, it is important to know the high value older patients place on trust. The survey by *Strategy & Consumer Survey* (Estupianan et al., 2014) found that at different stages of a consumer's life, the considerations, priorities, and trade-offs in health care vary significantly. The key driver of decision making among respondents older than 65 years was the ability to trust their provider's advice.

Marketing Goals

As with any planning, setting goals is an early and necessary step. Goals provide direction for marketing. Goals are clear statements about what you want to accomplish. Goals, when converted to strategies and action items and given timelines and milestones, will create your marketing calendar. They can be action goals that relate to things you can count such as producing a specific measurable result. For instance: *increasing total patient visits by 20%*. Goals can also be image goals to make your clinic be better known or change or improve how your clinic is seen (Stern, 1996). For instance: *Increasing overall visibility or growing your reputation as a world-class evidence-based audiology clinic*. Goals can be categorized as being strategic, tactical, or business focused. Clarifying your goals provides direction for your marketing efforts. Below are examples of goals pertinent to university and other nonprofit clinics:

Strategic goals:

Create a marketing culture—Marketing is everybody's business, and as universities create, perfect, or grow their marketing efforts, they need to consciously build an inclusive marketing culture. This effort should be a marketing goal and a strategic planning goal.

Provide adequate patient diversity—For training programs at many universities, providing the needed diversity of patient contact experience will oblige them to include attracting certain types of patients as an important marketing goal and a strategic goal for the training program. Setting a goal of "*20% of new clinic patients will be pediatric patients*" helps to ensure there will be enough pediatric patients for student training.

Diversify and grow referrals—University audiology clinics not in medical settings use patient referrals as their primary source of patients, so a smart strategic goal would be to diversify and grow the clinic's referral sources and overall referrals.

Tactical goals:

Increase visibility—Most university clinics have little or no marketing and therefore lack visibility, so an important goal for university clinics is to increase visibility. These changes in visibility can be measured directly by surveys and indirectly by increased new patient volume and growing referrals.

Automate marketing—Sadly, too many university clinics still work in a pencil and paper world. As these clinics acquire electronic patient management and medical record software, an important marketing goal should be to automate much of the clinic's marketing without losing personal contact and warmth.

Business goals:

Increase new patients—Many universities now require clinics to support themselves financially from clinic revenues. Most clinic revenue comes from hearing aid sales, and new patients are the primary source of hearing aid sales. The university's focus on revenue translates into new patient goals for university clinic marketing plans. Clinic directors must be able to calculate how much revenue can be expected for each new patient visit to meet department and clinic business plan revenue requirements and to set marketing goals.

Increase total patient visits—There is a strong interdependence between university audiology clinics and AuD training programs. Therefore, an important goal of university clinic marketing is to attract enough patients to the clinic to give students the needed supervised patient contact hours. To determine the needed total patient visits, clinic leadership should work closely with AuD program leadership to calculate the total number of patient visits needed for the student class size being recruited. That resultant goal is easily measurable.

Monitor marketing outcomes—Because many universities have no marketing plan or activity, and because it takes time, monitoring marketing outcomes is mostly nonexistent. Good business practice and the university's growing focus on clinic financial self-sustainability require that marketing outcomes be routinely measured and changes made based on those results.

Your goals may differ from those above, but most marketing goals have as an endpoint to increase new patient visits and patient flow, so let's consider where to find these patients and along what paths those new patients may journey on their way to your clinic.

Markets

We look for the ideal patients in various locations or market-places. The audiology marketplace can be divided in two: an internal market in your clinic and organization and an external market outside of your clinic and organization, and each of these can be further subdivided in two. These four marketplaces should be remembered when planning your marketing, planning strategies to achieve your goals, and creating a marketing calendar. A strong marketing plan will market to all four (Table 7–2).

Internal Markets

Patient Internal Market

Current patients are the easiest market to comfortably reach. All clinics and dispensaries have current patients. One clinic's internal market of current patients is another clinic's external market of potential patients. So you must work to hold on to this internal patient market by keeping in contact with them and maintaining trust by making certain that they are solicited to come into the clinic only because it is in their interests, not to increase profits. Referrals from current patients are a crucial source of new patients and should be solicited and used system-atically. These patients are also the source of testimonials used to build trust in the marketplace.

Potential Patient Internal Market

A second internal market is the market of potential patients in your organization. Private practices lack this internal market, so you have a competitive advantage over private practices. The internal university market made up of faculty, staff, students, and alumni can be large and worth pursuing. Only dispensaries in

Table 7-2. Four Types of Markets, With Only University Clinics in Nonmedical Settings Having Access to All Four

Markets Available to Practice Types	Nonmedical School University Clinic	Private Practice	Big-Box Dispenser	Manufacturer-Owned Dispensaries
Patient internal market	Yes	Yes	Yes	Yes
Potential patient internal market	Yes—university faculty, staff, students, alumni, and medical school departments	No	Yes—in store with members	No
Potential patient external market	Yes	Yes	Yes—in stores not requiring membership	Yes
Professional external market	Yes—should be clinic of choice to professionals	Yes—they hire physician liaisons to accomplish	No/rare—not a good culture fit	Yes—they hire physician liaisons to accomplish

big-box stores requiring memberships have larger potential patient internal markets due to large memberships. When pursuing this internal market, focus on those market segments that have the most ideal patients. Depending on their definition of the ideal patient, most university clinics should focus on older faculty, staff, and alumni, not on students.

For universities with medical schools, the medical school is an important potential source of new patients. Within the medical school, the otolaryngology department may have its own audiologists to serve their medical staff, but search out other medical school departments that serve large numbers of your ideal patients and, through education and building trust, establish those departments as consistent referral sources.

External Markets

Potential Patient External Market

Potential patients in the external market are a large and very competitive market being pursued by every clinic and dispensary of every type, except big-box stores, which require membership. This is the marketplace to which we most often refer. It is good business practice to pay attention to the competition in this market, and clear differentiation of your clinic from the others is the best antidote to this competition. There is also wisdom in knowing that as a profession, audiologists have not done well convincing the majority of external potential patients with hearing difficulties to seek treatment. Being innovative, educating the public, increasing accessibility and affordability of products and services, and strategic marketing are critical to opening up your clinic to the large numbers of untapped potential patients in this marketplace, approximately 60% to 80%. If your marketing could convince this untreated portion of this marketplace to actively seek treatment, there would be an excess of patients and no competition.

Professional External Market

Besides patients, the external marketplace includes local physicians and other professionals, such as those administering senior centers and residences, which have patient bases that include large numbers of ideal patients. For university and nonprofit clinics, this is a critical but untapped source of patients being actively solicited by private practices clever enough to retain physician liaisons for this purpose. There are even a few medical practices that will refer patients to big-box stores because of their low product prices. To limit that problem, you must differentiate your clinic from the big-box store and use your value proposition and differentiation-focused brochures to educate medical practices that audiology is about more than just providing a hearing aid. Because of their status, university and nonprofit clinics have a natural advantage to win this professional external marketplace. For university or nonprofit clinics desiring growth, adding an active program to win the professional external marketplace referrals may be the best investment they can make.

Demographics and the Geographic Marketplace

A useful method for locating ideal patients, potential professional referral sources, and competitors in the external marketplace is demographic analysis. We used Fuel Medical to gather this basic marketing information for our clinic. Their demographic analysis defined our business market boundary as the area defined by a maximum 40-minute drive time, which included 98% of our current patient population. With their data analysis, we could see how the population was distributed within our market boundary and a 5-year projection for changes in total population. Focusing on our ideal patient, they provided us with the distribution of the market population older than 45 years and another for those older than 65 years. Again, 5-year growth projections for these populations were included with a distribution of median age. Another very useful distribution was median household income distribution, which was combined with the age distribution to show us the distribution of median household income for people older than 65 years within our business marketplace boundary and a 5-year projection for how that would change. This distribution was useful in making informed decisions about the areas or zip codes in which we would distribute our marketing materials targeting our ideal patients. All of the information in these geographic map distributions was also provided in detailed tables for easy analysis and utilization.

The demographic analysis also showed us where our competitors were within our business market boundary and was accompanied by a list of these competitors separated between businesses primarily focused on sales of hearing aids and those with ENT specialties. Knowing who the competitors were and their locations allowed us to know the size and nature of the competition, helping us to shape our marketing materials to emphasize our most competitive advantages to differentiate our clinic from local competitors.

A separate demographic analysis was done to identify medical practices within our business market boundaries. This analysis let us know that we were rich in nearby medical practices and could benefit from a physician liaison. The analysis also informed us of the surrounding medical practices and their specialties so we could focus on those that served the largest number of ideal patients.

Demographic analysis is an excellent way to reduce marketing cost and increase marketing effectiveness because it tells you whom the local competitors are and where to best focus your marketing resources to reach the most ideal patients and ideal referral sources in your business marketplace.

Leading potential patients down the path of calling your clinic by defining, understanding, and using marketplaces is critical to success.

Patient Pathways and Strategies for Using Them

Another way to look at marketplaces is to consider the five pathways patients may take from the marketplace to your clinic and to build a strategy around each of these pathways to ensure success and avoid depending on a single source for patient recruitment (Lyon, 2012). For university and other nonprofit audiology clinics, some pathways will be more productive than others. Lyon's (2012) five pathways are as follows:

1. Database—your patient database
2. Retail—print (newspaper, magazine), radio, direct mail
3. Third-party referrals—patients, physicians, senior centers
4. Grassroots—community outreach events
5. Digital—Internet, call tracking, email

> Successful marketing depends on potential patients receiving a consistent message from a variety of sources.

1. Database

Your clinic database is a valuable marketing asset. To best use this asset, you need to segment your approach.

- *Test loss no treatment*—Patients who demonstrate the need for hearing aids but did not purchase them
- *4+ Users*—Patients whose hearing aids are over 4 years old
- Treatment interval *reminders*—Patients you have not seen in a timely manner for checkups and hearing aid maintenance and repairs

Personal hand-addressed and hand-signed letters to a handful of these patients each week thanking them for using your clinic, letting them know you understand how important hearing is to them, and how recent advances in hearing aid technology since their last visit might make a difference to them should increase patient visits. Make offers to let them try the newest technology at no costs, but always put the patient's interest before making a sale so you can continue to differentiate your clinic from the competition. Even without a sale, it is good business practice to stay in contact with these patients so they continue to trust you and feel comfortable coming into the clinic when needed and in making referrals to you. Selection of these patients can be routine with modern patient management software, but a clinician should review the patient records to personalize the letter and make certain it is appropriate before sending out a form letter. Some clinics follow up the letters with a phone call. The number of letters sent each week can be easily adjusted to counter seasonal and other variations in patient flow. Costs are about a dollar a letter, and returns are much higher than direct mail, even direct mail to targeted segments of the public.

Your patient database should also receive newsletters from you two to four times a year to help nurture the patient-clinic bond. Because you are a university, there should be at least one educational article, such as the relationship between diabetes and hearing loss or explaining how loops work and in what local public venues they can be found. Devote a column in every issue to introducing a different clinical faculty or staff member or an article about the AuD students. This keeps the newsletter personal and very different from product-focused stock newsletters. Many clinic directors like to write a personal message for each edition. Newsletters around holidays should contain an article on how hearing treatment can cause a happier, more inclusive holiday. The articles of a specific type, introducing staff, education background, and so on, should appear in the same location in the newsletter so interested readers easily find them. Management companies and other companies can help you with a newsletter design that conforms to your branding requirements, and they have libraries of articles, which, if used sparingly, can help you spend less time on the newsletter while also maintaining its personal feel.

2. Retail

Retail venues for marketing have a broad reach to a large audience of potential patients and are effective in promoting time-sensitive advertisements that require an immediate response. Because your marketing dollars can be best spent targeting your ideal patient rather than a large nonsegmented audience, it is wise to use retail venues sparingly and in as targeted a manner as possible. Time-sensitive advertisements will be used by your competitors to drive patients to their door with a bargain that expires soon such as a "Free $50 Gas Coupon" that you are eligible for only if you come to the clinic in the next 3 days. Patients find these offers very plentiful because manufacturers encourage them and your competition overuses them. But some patients who are not price focused do not believe clinics that promote these "deals" are trustworthy and consider them greedy and desperate. So stay away from those types of ads in retail venues to maintain your differentiation from competition and your trustworthiness.

> Retail marketing: Choose wisely—spend carefully.

Because it is necessary to reach potential patients through a variety of venues, it is appropriate to use retail venues. But you must choose wisely. Know that direct mail is a mainstay of your competition and that seniors receive several direct mail offers about hearing aids each week—so many offers that seniors resent them and do not trust those who send them. Leave direct mail to the competition that overuses this price-centered venue. While the "deals" may vary, all direct mail offers appear the same to potential patients who look past the "deal" and see no meaningful differentiation among offers. Patients tell me the senders "just want to sell them something."

My experience with magazine ads is that they are expensive and not targeted. Newspaper ads done differently than the competition can be effective, but they are expensive. The older demographic still reads newspapers. In my experience, newspaper inserts work better than ads on the pages. Insert ads are more expensive but offer a two-sided opportunity to present your case to the potential patient. They also have the added advantage they are easily removed from the newspaper and set aside for future use to present to a colleague, friend, or family member who could benefit from audiologic services. Using Call Source, we have tracked phone inquiries to newspaper inserts that appeared many months previous to the call. With a two-sided insert, you can make two contrasting or two complementary presentations to the potential patient.

For two contrasting presentations, you can, for example, focus one insert side on what the potential patient will gain from hearing health care treatment and the other side on the negative consequences that may occur if hearing loss is not treated early. For a complementary approach, you could focus one side on how to tell if you have a hearing loss and the other on the top 10 reasons a person with a hearing loss should come to your clinic rather than go to the competition. Your case being presented two ways will resonate with more people and result in more calls to the clinic. You will need to experiment with frequency and messaging in your ads and carefully track responses to see what works and for how long it works.

Radio ads alone are not very effective for audiology clinics because they are expensive, strong radio signals are not targeted, and your message has a high probability of being presented to someone driving and not able to jot down a phone number or Web address. But for university and nonprofit clinics, radio can play an important role in increasing clinic visibility and reinforcing your messages from other venues. Universities often have their own radio stations. Work with these stations to get discount pricing on drive-time ads or ads during the university's popular sporting events. Public radio being a nonprofit organization is a good venue for your nonprofit clinic. People who listen to public radio trust it, and if you sponsor public radio, that trust will generalize to your clinic. Public radio uses sponsors, not traditional advertisements, so work with the station representative to arrive at a properly worded and effective sponsorship announcement. Also, use a simple Web address in your message that people can remember even if they are driving, such as *Audiology.EliteU.edu*. Radio used this way is a good secondary reinforcer of your other marketing. It primarily builds brand awareness.

3. Third-Party Referrals

Referrals are your most valuable source of patients. Strong referral networks are the best way to ensure a steady patient flow.

Patient Referrals

Most university and nonprofit clinics depend exclusively on patient referrals, but not all have a systematic approach to growing patient referrals. In some clinics, patients who refer other people are given a reward such as a $50 gift card. But giving monetary rewards for patient recruitment seems out of place for nonprofit clinics. We should not be buying referrals; we should earn them through our excellent service and patient transformation. By flipping the reward to the patient being recommended, we can create a much better arrangement in alignment with a nonprofit value proposition and a patient-focused mission. With this strategy, the friends and family referral program encourages patients to refer people putting off having their hearing tested. In discussing your friends and family program with current patients, you can explain that most people wait 7 to 12 years to make an appointment, and your clinic is trying to help people sooner, so you are rewarding first-time patients for coming into the clinic sooner. That is, you are helping patients obtain needed help sooner, not buying patients. When first-time patients come for their appointment in the clinic, they are given a $50 discount on their first clinic visit. This makes the referring patient look like a hero to the new patient. The current patient who makes the recommendation should receive a thank you note from the audiologists, but you cannot mention the new patient's name in the thank you note due to Health Insurance Portability and Accountability Act (HIPAA) regulations. A good source of thank you notes that can be easily personalized and appear to be handwritten is http://www.senoutcards.com. No matter what system you use, it should be carefully documented. The current patient should receive several friends and family referral cards that have clinic contact information, the audiologist's name, and the referring patient's name on them. When the referred first-time patient arrives at the clinic, the card should be given to the receptionist so he or she can note who referred the patient, give the discount, and remind the audiologists to send the referring patient a thank you card. Also, you should keep track of which clinicians have patients actively referring to reward clinicians in their personnel evaluations. Patient referral summaries can be presented monthly at clinic meetings to keep the activity fresh in everyone's mind and publicly demonstrate its importance. A good practice is to have the clinician with the most referring patients periodically talk about how he or she promotes the program.

Physician Referrals

Physician referrals are another important but independent source of patient referrals. Taylor and Tysoe (2014) tell us, "The growing awareness of age-related hearing loss as a public health concern represents a monumental opportunity for hearing care professionals to touch the lives of more patients in need of their services. This can only occur if we are willing to form partnerships with primary care physicians around the triple threat of untreated age-related hearing loss and the comorbid conditions associated with it." These partnerships lead to productive physician referrals that can rival or exceed patient referrals, but it takes planning and a large financial investment to make physician referrals work. It also takes patience and understanding because it can be a year before earning a positive return on the investment (ROI) and 2 to 3 years to maximize that return. To succeed requires a long-term commitment and an understanding of the job that physicians want you to do. Medical practices want to understand which of their patients are at the highest risk for hearing loss, how to identify them quickly and inexpensively, and to send patients seamlessly on to where they will get excellent care and be pleased with the service.

Physician referrals are becoming more difficult because private physician practices are being rapidly consolidated into health care systems. To control cost and increase profit, these systems are becoming stricter about keeping all referrals within their system. Luckily, there are still independent practices remaining and practices only loosely affiliated with a health care system. Also, some systems do not have audiology within them and are looking for competent, trustworthy audiologists to whom to refer. Because university clinics are not profit focused and have prestige and credibility from being part of a university, they often engender the most trust and frequently are the preferred clinics to which physicians refer. To build on this advantage, you need a plan to constantly keep local physicians and their staff aware of the availability and need for your services and make that referral process easy and rewarding. The plan should be carried out by a physician liaison who must build personal trust with the referring group to add to the trust of your clinic's brand. The liaison must be capable of evaluating the physician group to determine who in the group has the most influence over referrals and to win that person's trust and friendship. The liaison must be sensitive to the needs of the physician group and be able to produce what is needed, be it Pocket Talkers, 5-minute hearing tests, peer-reviewed articles, or an educational handout explaining the relationship between diabetes and hearing loss. The liaison's work is never done; he or she must rank the local physician groups according to those that have the most ideal patients and then prioritize those groups that refer the most patients or who have the potential to refer more patients and be in constant contact with them. Audiology referrals must be seen in a timely manner and the results reported to the referring physician within 24 hours. Beyond the primary care physician, a good place to look for physician referrals is to physicians who treat patients with diseases that have hearing loss as a comorbid condition (see Chapter 5 for likely practices and strategies). Like patient referrals, the physician referral process must be documented and tracked to best allocate resources and refine strategies. The receptionist should carefully track which physicians are the source of referrals and give this information to the physician liaison regularly. Your physician liaison should report monthly at clinic meetings about who is referring and give feedback from the referring physicians about patients' experiences in your clinic and timeliness of reports. Physician referral expenses for travel "lunch and learn" and other costs should be carefully tracked and documented to allow accurate determination of the ROI.

Physician liaisons are usually found in private practices, not university clinics. As a result, university clinics have been losing physician referrals to private practices unnecessarily despite the advantages universities and nonprofit clinics offer. Physicians are too often not well trained about hearing loss and unaware of the importance of hearing screening for seniors and for those patients who have diseases with hearing as a comorbid condition. University audiologists, as well as their physician liaisons, need to use current peer-reviewed research articles to raise physicians' level of awareness of the importance of early intervention for hearing loss and its potential to allow their patients the ability to pursue a dynamic and participatory life. By doing this, you can position your clinic as a valuable resource and extension of the physician's practice, creating a mutually beneficial relationship.

Physician liaisons are often former pharmaceutical representatives skilled at physician office relationships and interactions. They can be difficult to find and expensive. Physician liaisons are an excellent investment for most university clinics whose goal is to increase new patient visits. Successful physician referral marketing requires an established marketing system and a person responsible for implementing that system and constant communications with the physician practices. If you need help to start, even with a smaller effort such as using clinicians one morning a week to visit local physician practices, you can have a management company or a consultant like Bob Tysoe, marketing consultant with Hearing Healthcare Marketing Company, plan the process with you, help you start, and continue to work with you as needed. If your marketplace is sizable with many nearby physician practices, you should aim long term to hire a full-time physician liaison to capture this bountiful physician referral market. Taylor and Tysoe (2014) tell us that market research and testimonials from audiologists who have implemented a physician outreach program support the conclusion that the risk is worth taking and that you will be adequately rewarded, and that has been my experience in a university clinic also.

Senior Niche Referrals

Another third-party referral strategy is to focus on centers, which house many ideal patients who need your services such as retirement venues, senior centers, or primary care homes in which a team of physicians deliver health care. These centers are very suspicious of people who sell hearing aids. Being a university or other nonprofit will create trust to diminish that suspicion if your actions and marketing materials constantly reinforce a nonprofit, patient-focused approached.

To create an effective strategy to attract patients from the senior niche, we must first understand what job it is that senior residences want from us. Identifying a hearing loss is usually not the first job needed in this environment, where many residents already have a hearing loss. Instead, the more likely jobs the senior centers' professionals need done are educational: learning how to communicate most effectively with residents with hearing loss and learning how to repair and maintain hearing aids and assistive hearing devices. They also need easy access to high-quality hearing health care services.

If you have a physician liaison, a good initial approach to these centers is through the physician group providing medical services to the center. The liaison can make the physician group aware of the availability, importance, and superiority of your services in treating their patients with hearing (or balance) difficulties. Also, your audiologists working with the center administration and nursing staff to present in-service educational workshops on relevant topics, such as routine care and maintenance of hearing aids or how to communicate with patients with hearing loss, can demonstrate your concern and knowledge and build trust that could lead to providing the regular hearing health care for these centers. Access to hearing health care can be difficult for this population, so to provide easily accessible health care to these patients, you should plan to go to the center and provide the service there using their equipment or bring portable equipment. This growing market niche is ripe for servicing by university and nonprofit audiology clinics. It should be part of your marketing plan.

4. Grassroots

Grassroots outreach events are not the most dependable source of new patients. Events like farmers markets and 5K runs that are not health focused are rarely worth doing. Events like health fairs and senior fairs that are more likely to include your ideal patients are more productive. It is best to think about grassroots events as an excellent tool for long-term education of the community about your value proposition and to increase exposure to your brand but not as a significant source of new patients. Costs are usually low for these events, but they often consume human resources, and that should be included in your calculation of ROI. Two to four grassroots events a year is a reasonable limit unless you have a special strategy using this pathway.

5. Digital

Digital marketing is becoming more effective as more people are connected digitally. Today, the majority of people search for health care information online. Pew Research shows that 59% of adults, ages 65+ years, use the Internet. Of these adults, 53% use the Internet for health information (Zickuhr, 2014). To use this pathway successfully, you must consider how your ideal patient uses digital technology by talking with your patients and discovering their desired methods of engagement. Ask them if they use digital technology (Internet, smartphone, etc.) and, if so, how.

Having a well-developed website as part of your marketing efforts to facilitate the patients' task of finding your website and knowing what services you provide, your value proposition, where you are located, and your hours of operation is essential. Your site should be mobile friendly so it adjusts to the size screen on which it is being viewed: computer monitor, tablet, or smartphone. Search engine optimization (SEO), which can facilitate your website being found, is a good investment and is best purchased and maintained through someone with expertise. This is not something you want to do in-house, although the staff may participate in suggesting phrases that potential patients may use in their search. With a maximized SEO strategy, your clinic will be the first one that appears in response to an inquiry. You can also consult with the same expert to advertise on the Internet using Google AdWords and pay per click (PPC) ads targeted to your ideal patient. You only pay when someone clicks on your ad. Remarketing is when a person leaves your site and your ads appear on other sites they visit. Remarketing is a cost-effective way to advertise on the Web; discuss it with your expert. Review the summary reports of these SEO, PPC, and remarketing website projects with your expert monthly and make changes based on those data. Your expert will use Google Analytics to tell you how your website is being used by viewers. Without SEO, PPC, and remarketing, even the best website will go unnoticed, and patients will go elsewhere. Patients expect universities to have superior websites and to have relevant educational materials easily accessible on their site.

Because you are a university clinic, patients may go to your website for education and guidance about many topics: how to buy a hearing aid, advances in hearing aid technology, communication strategies, care and maintenance of hearing aids, or which local venues are looped. You can provide these educational materials and videos, or you can link to other sites where they already exist. When linking to other sites, try to do it in a way that the patient never leaves your site.

Mukti Khaire of Harvard Business School argues that people are so confused by the overwhelming choice the Internet brings, as well as the cacophony of user reviews, that the need for trustworthy guides and other sorts of intermediaries is increasing (Schumpeter, 2014). Universities and nonprofits should take note and position themselves as the preferred trustworthy guides for hearing health care.

Growing numbers of seniors use email, and you should capture patients' and potential patients' email addresses for communicating with them and sending out forms and instructions if they agree. A tried-and-true way to capture new email addresses on the Internet is to offer your educational materials online as PDF documents to be emailed to those who are interested.

Many hospital systems now have Internet portal systems that allow patients to make appointments, order prescriptions, or view test results, and more seniors are now learning to use these digital technologies. As your clinic gains more digital patient management technology, a patient portal would align you with this trend and also help you win acceptance from more technologically sophisticated adult children of senior patients.

Young consumers want to hear from their providers through digital channels. In the *Strategy & Consumer Survey* (Estupianan et al., 2014), respondents younger than 45 years identify digital as their preferred means of engagement to manage their health. Four in five younger than 35 years said they embrace care provided via virtual marketplaces, whereas 47% of seniors "hated" the idea. My experiences reinforce this finding. For seniors with whom I interact in and out of the clinic, social media are great for seeing what the grandchildren are up to and maybe to keep in touch with old friends from high school, but social media play little or no part in their health care. So although Pew Research shows that of the 59% of seniors who use the Internet, 46% use social networking sites (Smith, 2014), that does not mean that seniors prefer or are even using digital media to manage their health care. Only 27% of all seniors even use online social networks (Smith, 2014). Social media are not very effective in generating new patients. Talk to your existing patients and determine if social media are a useful connection to potential ideal patients before investing in them.

Although you should not keep your patients waiting, lobby televisions can provide educational videos for patients and their families and explain your value proposition. They should have the speakers off, provide subtitles, and be connected to a loop system for sound. An intriguing practice is to let your patients try out their new hearing aid's loop connections, if they are willing, with the lobby televisions where other patients can hear their unsolicited testimonials. It is best to not include news on these lobby televisions, especially bad economic news that may discourage a needed purchase. If your audiology clinic shares space with the speech-language pathology clinic, the lobby televisions can be shared. To further support your alignment with the university, many university events can be advertised on these televisions. Often, other university entities that want to advertise on your televisions will in return advertise your services in their venues.

Digital technology by itself will not deliver results. The work involved in managing the technology and content and its integration cannot be underestimated. You must have a powerful message to begin with and a commitment to expend the required resources if technology is to amplify your brand and drive patients to your clinic.

> If it can be tracked, it can be measured and you can learn from it.

A digital technology that has proven useful to our clinic is a call tracking technology called Call Source. For just under $20 a month, you can rent a phone number to use in your marketing and advertising. You put the number in, for instance, your newspaper ad, and this rented number rings on your main phone line at your reception desk just like any other call, but it is has some distinct advantages: You can track the number of calls that your receive from your ad, and you will receive a recording of the call, useful for hearing what about the ad was important to the caller and how the receptionists handled the call. The latter point is very useful in training and monitoring front desk staff and seeing how well the staff is converting calls to appointments. If you are running two ads at the same time, you can use two Call Source numbers to see how effective each ad is.

Because potential patients and their families may save these ads or numbers, it pays to rent the same number or two for a long period and reuse them.

Other Strategies

Some strong marketing strategies may combine pathways or otherwise not fall into the above discrete pathway categorization, such as the powerful *astonishing guarantee strategy*. Jantsch (2011) tells us his favorite way to create a unique difference is to offer an *astonishing guarantee*—a guarantee so strong no one else would dream doing it. This is an established way to reduce a potential patient's risk. An example of an astonishing guarantee is Gravel Rock Company in Northern California that put at the bottom of customers' bills a statement that the customers could pay the prepared bill, and if they did not think the price was reasonable, they could pay what they thought it was worth.

At Northwestern University, we knew that, like other clinics, we were reaching only ~20% of the people with hearing loss who could benefit from treatment. We wanted to attract more people in need and at an earlier age. Our attempts to reach these goals were further inhibited because we did not accept insurance. Without insurance acceptance, we were challenged in two ways: one, to attract insured patients directly whose insurance we did not accept and, second, to attract patients referred by physicians who preferred to send patients to providers that accepted the patients' insurance.

Because diagnostic testing produced only about 11% of revenue, we considered offering free diagnostic testing to reach more people who needed our services, but that was counter to professional ethics, which promotes charging for all services. The Gravel Rock Company example showed us how we could offer an astonishing guarantee: Hearing Test with Voluntary Payment Options for adult patients.

We marketed that adult patients could tell us what they wanted to pay for their hearing test based on our philosophy that every adult should have his or her hearing evaluated regularly—even those who cannot afford it. And we explained that untreated hearing loss diminishes quality of life and is linked to dementia and other chronic diseases, while early detection and treatment are vital to good health. We told potential patients that at the end of their hearing testing, they would be given a bill with our standard prices for services rendered and that they had three options:

1. *Pay nothing* if you cannot afford to pay. We are a nonprofit clinic focused on patients, not dollars.
2. *Pay what you think it's worth* to allow us to cover costs.
3. *Pay it forward* and pay more than the services are normally billed. Your generosity will help others.

We first marketed this strategy for 3 months to see if it would help us reach more and younger potential patients and if it was a financially viable approach. The results were astonishing. We tripled the number of potential patient phone calls to the clinic and converted 100% into appointments. Most patients paid the traditional price for the diagnostic hearing testing. A few patients paid more to help others, and a few patients paid less but bought additional services and products. The plan was financially sound in our clinic.

We had an extraordinary physician liaison who heavily marketed this strategy to physicians who had wanted to send us patients but were deterred by insurance issues, which were removed by this approach. Our liaison also marketed senior centers that had many ideal patients as residents or clients but who were strongly suspicious of people selling hearing aids or other transactions that might take advantage of the elderly. This *"pay what you want"* strategy importantly reinforced our brand as a university nonprofit clinic focused on patients, not profit, and provided hearing health care services patients trusted. Our new patient appointments soared to 45 new patients a month by the fourth month. We had successfully recruited more patients for student training.

Although the percentage of new patients needing hearing aids declined slightly, many of those not needing hearing aids were younger patients in their 40s or 50s who now are our patients for their future hearing health care needs, and they also potentially will become great referral sources who can attest to our superior service and to the fact that the clinic did not sell them a hearing aid they did not need. We hope to serve their parents. Despite reporting a history of hearing difficulty, many patients who responded to the marketing had previously delayed getting a hearing test because of the cost of diagnostic testing. We had successfully reached potential patients at an earlier age than previously.

No one else had dreamed of this strategy, and it was risky to implement, so we tried it for a quarter and succeeded, and then continued it. This strategy allowed us to reach and serve more and younger patients sooner, provided more patients to participate in patient referrals, increased positive patient feedback to referring physicians, provided more patients for student patient contact hours, and provided the clinic with more potential hearing aid purchasers, even with a lower percentage of new patients needing hearing aids, and it was cost-effective.

If your university or other nonprofit clinic does not accept insurance, provides extraordinary service people will voluntarily pay for, and has strong marketing support, especially among professional referral sources, this is an approach that should work well for you as it did for us. If you run a free clinic and realize that patients are more likely to follow treatment if they pay something, this "pay what you want" approach may allow you to capitalize on that fact and to recover a little revenue. If you accept insurance, you need to check insurance regulations, which govern equal payment policies for all to decide if or how to implement a plan like this. You cannot collect payments from insurance companies that differ in amount from what you charge others.

The success of all strategies for recruiting patients depends on not only marketing and the people involved but also establishing a strong marketing support culture.

Creating a Marketing Culture

In learning about the five pathways above, you have acquired a good understanding of how to accomplish your business goals of increasing new patient visits, overall visits, and monitoring and modifying marketing strategies. Now let's consider accomplishing the goal of creating a marketing culture: a strategic goal too often ignored yet so important to long-term marketing success.

Every clinic member, from the receptionist to students, clinicians, and the clinic director, must market your clinic and take responsibility for its visibility, credibility, and success. Marketing should be a regular topic at clinic meetings. The entire clinic must know of ongoing market strategies. Let's look at how the clinic faculty and staff and other department personnel play important roles in making marketing successful. Your marketing plan should include actions taken to strengthen the marketing culture throughout the clinic, department, and administration. These strategies and all marketing strategies should be summarized with their costs on a marketing calendar.

Marketing is everyone's business.

Receptionist

The front desk staff are the most important in the clinic and crucial to marketing. The clinic lobby (we try not to have a "waiting" room) is an extension of the consultation process, and the front desk staff are the minders of the patients in the lobby. The receptionist is the first point of contact with your patients. Potential patients call in response to ads or referrals from doctors, friends, and families, and the receptionist must understand why they are calling, provide them with requested information, and convert their call into an appointment. Without a high conversion rate, your marketing dollars are wasted. Keep the front desk staff well informed about ads and other marketing efforts, including articles given to physician offices. Patients and their families must be convinced that, in addition to the clinicians, the front desk staff also have the patients' best interest as their first priority. Front desk staff also are the last clinic staff with whom a patient interacts. They are critical to collecting marketing outcome data. They can informally collect valuable patient feedback or administer formal surveys. Front desk staff can collect written testimonials and record video testimonials. They can remind the exiting patient of the family and friends program or of an upcoming lecture series. They can ensure that the patient leaves the clinic smiling. The front desk staff must be included in clinic meetings where marketing is discussed, which ideally is every meeting.

Several sources can clarify the role of the front desk staff, such as Chapter 4 in Brian Taylor's book, *Quality in Audiology* (Taylor, 2013). Others to help train your receptionist, such as Kevin St. Clergy's FontDeskAcademy.com. To make your marketing strategies successful, use these or similar resources as an important part of your marketing strategy.

Clinicians

For marketing to succeed, clinicians must understand the marketing strategies and be active participants in determining and achieving marketing goals. They should be knowledgeable about the peer-reviewed articles your liaison is proving to physician groups. Clinicians are the sources of authority in the clinic and the minders of the patients, so their active participation is critical to success. They should actively encourage the friends and family referral program and respond quickly to physicians' request for referral reports and send them thank you cards. Spending a day or two a year with the physician liaison visiting physicians is an excellent use of clinician time. Their participation is required at grassroots events, especially when developing a promising new market niche such as senior centers. Their photographs and short biographies should appear on the website and in brochures. They need to participate in educational lecture series. They must ensure the patient and his or her family that they have the patient's best interests as their highest priority to give authenticity to the marketing strategies and to best serve the patient.

Physician Liaison

Your physician liaison is critical to increasing and maintaining referral sources and is most often out of the clinic nurturing those referral sources, so special efforts must be made by everyone in the clinic to have her or him know they are an integral part of the clinic team. Good liaisons will not limit themselves to just physician referrals but will also assist in developing the senior market and in grassroots marketing. Thank him or her when referrals increase. Ask what you can do to help. Liaisons often need special brochures or other marketing materials to win referral sources; make sure they get what they need and in a timely fashion. Meet for lunch and discuss strategies and referral source feedback. Include your liaison in every important meeting and be certain this vital team member is kept current about clinic activities.

Researchers

An active department research program often needs patients with hearing losses or needs to test translational ideas in the clinic. The clinic team should work closely with researchers to see where their needs overlap. The clinic may build a marketing niche to increase the number of older patients by giving lectures at senior centers. Researchers who need seniors as research subjects should present lectures, and with institutional review board approval, research subject-recruiting material can be combined with clinic marketing efforts and also appear on clinic lobby televisions to share the recruitment cost and increase benefits to both.

Department Faculty and Administration

Administrators and department faculty must be constantly educated about the need for marketing, what marketing strategies are being used, and what does and does not succeed. Quarterly clinic progress reports given to the whole department will create transparency while educating faculty and administration and include them as part of the clinic team. You will find this group can become very interested in your clinic and its marketing efforts if they are educated and included. Their support may be critical to gaining the resources needed to succeed.

AuD Students

What better way for students to learn marketing than to participate in it? Students are very helpful in community outreach efforts where they can create handouts, do screenings, and present talks. They should understand your value proposition. They can participate with your outside marketing management team or consultants. They can accompany your physician liaison. As they participate and learn the nuts and bolts of marketing, they should also be taught its importance and its ethics. It is critical to explain why you are doing the marketing you are doing. It is appropriate to open your department's quarterly clinic report for students to attend. Presenting your annual marketing plan, its successes and failures, to students should be routine and, with their active participation in marketing activities, make them part of the process.

Marketing Calendar

One of the most useful but often overlooked tools for successful marketing is the marketing calendar, which summarizes all of your marketing activities and their costs on one page as a yearlong timeline. Successful clinics use marketing calendars (Phonak Marketing, 2013).

Marketing calendars are created from your marketing plan and its budget for the fiscal year. Put your three or four most important marketing goals at the top of the calendar to keep you focused during the year, especially as opportunities and finances change. Down the left side of the calendar are the months starting with the first month of your fiscal year. Across the top are the five pathways: database, retail, third party, grassroots, and digital, as well as columns for your strategic and tactical strategies that may not appear in the five pathways. A column for monthly notes is useful. Marketing strategies are put in each cell along with their estimated cost. Costs are totaled at the bottom of each column, and the total marketing cost is summed in the lower right-hand cell. Cost and budget totals can be compared in the top right corner. An example calendar grid is shown in Table 7–3.

For each month in the database column, enter how many tested not sold (TNS) and 4+ letters will be sent out and the monthly costs. In up to 4 months, enter the newsletter and the costs associated with creating, printing, and mailing newsletters.

Table 7-3. Sample Grid for Entering Marketing Calendar Actions and Costs

Sample Grid for Marketing Calendar								
FY20??	Marketing goals: 1 2 3						Marketing Budget = \$ Marketing Total Cost = \$	
	Database	Retail	Third Party	Grassroots	Digital	Strategic	Tactical	Notes
September								
October								
November								
December								
January								

							Total $
February							$
March							$
April							$
May							$
June							$
July							$
August							$

Allow at least 3 months between newsletters and be careful to avoid sending out newsletters between the middle of November and the middle of January, when junk mail levels are high and people are preoccupied with holiday matters. Holiday-focused newsletters must arrive at the patient's home before November 15.

For each month in the retail column, enter your retail strategies such as radio public service announcements, NPR sponsorships, and newspaper insert ads. Enter the radio station or newspaper in which the ad will appear, as well as its focus and costs. The focus should relate to the goals listed at the top.

In the third party column, enter physician outreach in each month with the cost associated with that effort, such as "lunch and learns." About once a quarter, enter MD marketing collateral and its costs because your liaison will need article reprints and other new materials quarterly to reach the physicians and educate them with something new. A friends and family program should be entered each month. The cards and signs needed for this program have minimum costs and can be estimated as an annual cost and distributed evenly over the 12 months. If you are developing special new professional referral sources such as senior residences, you can budget monthly cost for the courtship period, during which you will give lectures and in-services and be purchasing pocket talkers, materials for maintaining hearing aids, brochures, and other items. Enter the costs for each month for senior referrals or your choice of referral growth projects.

The grassroots column will have the names and costs of quarterly community outreach events and lecture series on site at the clinic. Onsite lecture series may include advertising and refreshments costs. Screenings at senior centers and other venues should appear here with the costs of marketing collateral such as banners, handouts, brochures, small prizes, and treats.

The digital column is where you enter SEO and PPC and their costs for each month. If you have milestones for website development, they should be entered in this column with their costs. Monthly costs for Call Source numbers should also be entered here.

While most marketing calendars focus only on business goals and their cost, including your strategic and tactical marketing goals will keep you aware of the bigger marketing picture. If one strategic goal is to increase marketing within your organization, it does not fit easily into one of the five business-focused columns. Instead of spreading it over more than one column, it can go in the strategic column. There you can include university health fairs, mailings, and email blast. Lecture series and open houses for the university community can be scheduled in the months with their costs. Starting negotiations with university HR to establish hearing benefits at the university and related subsequent events can be entered. Creating a marketing culture is strategic. Monthly clinic meetings, quarterly department presentations, and presentations educating students about marketing can be scheduled here to keep this effort on track.

If you are beginning to use your patient management software to automate identifying TNS or 4+ patients, those tactics can be entered in the tactical column with any efforts to increase visibility not included in your business goals.

Once the calendar is complete, add up the costs in each column, and then add the columns and get a total cost figure to enter at the top and compare with the amount budgeted for marketing. The numbers should be equal, or cost should be below the budget numbers; otherwise, you have work to do to reduce the costs.

The success of all strategies on your marketing calendar depends not only on establishing a strong marketing support culture and on the strategies and people involved but also on your success at differentiating your clinic, as well as the professionalism and quality of brochures and other collateral support materials produced by the clinic. Have professional assistance in creating and producing your marketing materials to appear professional.

Creating Content to Communicate Your Brand

Your brand is the total experience a patient has with you that makes you different and better than competitors and is summarized by your value proposition. Creating an extraordinary clinic and communicating your points of differentiation clearly and consistently in your marketing materials is basic to creating and promoting your brand and to your marketing success. Because your value proposition states critical differences between you and other clinics, you can use it as a starting point to create differentiation-focused content for marketing materials. Consider the following ways to communicate your clinic's differences:

We are the university—By being part of a university, the clinic will take on the magic that comes with being in a house of intellect. Most people in the community like to be associated with your university. Receiving your university-branded marketing materials and services and products is one way of becoming part of the university. University association also improves patient referrals because the patient feels comfortable making the university recommendation and becomes an active participant with the university. Universities with medical schools often have alumni physicians in the community who are happy to refer to their university's clinic. And don't forget the aging local alumni who would prefer to come to the university clinic and who already have loyalty that your competition must work hard to duplicate.

University clinics have the distinct advantage of having additional brand elements that the university has spent much time and money developing. These are the university's name, logo, colors, and possibly other graphics. These should all be used consistently in developing your marketing materials. All of your material should be in your university colors. The university logo and name using the proper font must also appear on all marketing materials to capture this advantage. Finally, using professional photographs (sorry, no smartphone photos) of landmark campus structures will reinforce a solid connection between the clinic and the university.

We are a patient-focused nonprofit organization—Being a nonprofit makes it easier to convince potential patients that their hearing health is your main focus, not profit; that they can trust you to provide services and products at a fair price; and that you will stand behind your services. The competition will vary in how patient versus profit focused they are, but even those responsible, patient-focused, for-profit audiologists with whom you compete will have to work hard to convince patients they are not just after their money.

We teach other professionals—Because universities train future doctors of audiology, the public sees universities as being more authoritative and knowledgeable, and this is one reason university audiology clinic services are highly valued and should not be commoditized. Unless you are competing with another university training program's clinic, this sets you apart from the competition. Offering CEU courses for other clinicians in the community and using this in your marketing materials can improve this competitive advantage.

> Your actual value proposition—the collection of reasons patients buy from you—is woven into the fabric of the practice and your relationships with patients. Then it's communicated through the collection of messages you bring to the market.

Heritage—Brand heritage is defined as "a dimension of a brand's identity found in its track record, longevity, core values, use of symbols and particularly in an organizational belief that history is important" (Urde, Greyser, & Balmer, 2007). Stephen Greyer, Harvard Business School Professor Emeritus, further explains: "When heritage is relevant, one should identify it, try to activate it, and then leverage it. All brands have a history, many brands have a heritage, but only a few brands use their heritage as the heart of the value proposition they put forth" (Nobel, 2014). Although people in general may be bored with your clinic's history, university audiology clinics often have a strong heritage (track record, longevity, core values, use of symbols, and an organizational belief that history is important) they can use as the core of their market differentiation and at the heart of their value proposition.

Cordia C. Bunch may have been the first clinical audiologist. He tested air conduction audiograms on otology patients in the 1920s and 1930s using an electric audiometer he developed for Western Electric (Jacobson & Jerger, 2014). C. C. Bunch came to Northwestern in 1941 with his audiometer to start an audiology laboratory and teach. Unfortunately, he died in 1942. World War II created an immediate growing need for audiology during and after the war. In 1946, Northwestern University established the first academic program called "audiology," and the profession was born. In the postwar period, other universities quickly followed with their audiology programs. Because the profession was born and developed in universities, many university audiology clinics have a richer heritage and have existed longer than the clinics with which they compete. Patients like to do business with well-established clinics with a rich heritage, so if you have a rich heritage and have been in business longer than the competition, let potential patients know. When this latter point is made, it is important to also include a statement that communicates that you are using up-to-date cutting-edge services and products and not providing the same services you did 40 years ago. For example, you can state that one reason you have stayed in business for this long is that you use the most modern equipment and teach the most up-to-date techniques to train future doctors of audiology.

We have an active research program—If you are in a department that conducts audiologic research, this point will convince potential patients that you have the latest equipment, techniques, and services. Conducting research to improve hearing or to better identify hearing loss tells patients you have their interest at heart and are working for them. Many potential patients will also be impressed if you are using diagnostic testing developed at your university. If so, you must be the expert. By publicly valuing your research, local physicians will know you can read, evaluate, and apply relevant new research, increasing the possibility of their referral. Most of the competition does no research, so this is a wonderful differentiator.

We are independent of manufacturers—Most patients don't realize there are thousands of hearing centers/clinics out there that are owned wholly or in part by the companies that manufacture hearing aids. Nor do they realize that some providers earn rewards from manufacturers based on how many hearing aids they sell. When patients learn these facts, they are appalled. So tell them. University audiology clinics should distance themselves from manufacturers and let patients know they provide a wide range of hearing devices from many manufacturers and don't compensate staff based on sales performance. "We will sell you only what you need and from the best manufacturer available."

We provide rehabilitation—Few would dispute the benefits of a good aural rehabilitation program. Such programs help the patient successfully use his or her hearing device, and patient satisfaction is increased. But chances are good that few of the other practices in your area offer aural rehabilitation. If they don't, and you do, then you have yet another way to differentiate your practice from your competition. Patients who attend these classes are often so well pleased they will give strong testimonials and refer new patients.

We take the time needed—Patients do not want their time wasted. But profit-focused practices, including hospitals, are notorious for moving patients in and out too quickly and patients are dissatisfied. University training clinics must take more time with patients because of ongoing training and additional procedures such as real-ear calibrations. Many patients, especially older patients, appreciate the extra time you spend with them and understand the additional time as a more thorough, caring, and personalized experience. That is a magnificent way to differentiate your clinic from others.

Not all of the above list of differentiators will work for your clinic, but after giving it some thought, you will create additional differentiators of your own. Do you specialize in tough cases? Are your patient satisfaction ratings exceptionally high? Are you the only training program in the state? One great way to create a list of the most important differentiators that applied to your clinic is to regularly ask your patients why they chose your clinic. The answers you receive may surprise you and will help you to understand how patients view your clinic as different from the competition. By interviewing patients, ours and others, the KICC team at Northwestern found the top five attributes patients were looking for in an audiology clinic:

1. Trustworthy
2. Quality of care
3. Price willing to pay
4. Leading researchers
5. Extra appointment time

Note how all lend themselves to nonprofit and university settings. We were pleased.

Marketing evolves—What works now won't always work.

Marketing Materials

Previously, our marketing focus has been getting materials in front of the right audience. Here we focus on creating specialized content by offering those audiences something they will value and act on to use with previously suggested marketing strategies. If you have little or no marketing materials, these ideas will help you to get started. If you already have marketing materials, hopefully they will stimulate new and better-focused materials.

If your existing materials are hand drawn, black and white, done on a copy machine, out-of-date, use jargon, focus on products, look like everyone else's, or are just boring, don't even think about using them. Your marketing materials are part of your brand and must be as exciting, unique, and professional as you and your clinic are, containing carefully crafted messages, professional designs, and professional photographs.

All of the clinic's marketing materials should look like they came from the same place with a distinctive design feature, uniform university colors, and university logo, and they should contain easily found clinic location and directions and clinic contact information, including a source for more information. Your value proposition and mission statement will most often have a place in these materials, supplementing the customer problem-based content described below.

Because successful marketing requires that the audience consistently receives the same message from a variety of sources, your marketing material takes a variety of forms, such as trifold brochures, newspaper inserts, flyers, educational materials, radio ads, and your website. Despite the range of materials, all content works best when it is ideally tailored to the target audience.

Marketing wisdom (Brinckerhoff, 1997) says that in your marketing, you should "focus first on the problems, *not* the solutions" to "demonstrate that you understand what your market wants, what their problems are, and that you can solve them." This is good advice, and the first impression your materials make can be to communicate the problem. For example: *Having trouble hearing in noise?* With the tremendous amount of ongoing hearing health care marketing, I have also found that potential patients realize that many, if not all, clinics understand their problems, and a combined problem/solution statement like, "We can help you hear better in noise" is an effective approach that says we understand your problem and we can help you solve it.

Marketing materials should be developed as they are needed to capture a targeted audience, identify the job that customer wants done, and convince that customer that the clinic is uniqvely qualified to do the job. The four types of markets presented earlier nicely differentiate targeted audiences into four general types, and marketing to one, the professional external market, may be more specifically targeted according to the profession. Each audience has a different problem they want solved, and some have more than one problem for your clinic to solve. Here are some examples:

Patient internal market—Your clinic's internal patient market consists of current and previous patients. One of their problems is keeping up with technological advances in hearing health care such as hearing aids and assistive devices. Is there a new technology that would be helpful to them? Presenting in-house lectures on technological advances, and explaining the types of patients who may benefit, works well to solve this problem and increases contact with the patient. Encourage these patients to bring friends to the lecture and spend a few dollars on refreshments to solidify the bond. A newsletter article announcing the coming lecture and an article afterward summarizing the lecture with testimonials of how useful attendees found the lecture are ways to extend the number of patients who get this problem answered or know that you are eager to help them solve this problem.

Another well-tested approach is to send out letters to patients who have had their hearing aids for more than 4 years as described in the database marketing section and include a flyer on advances in technology, which explains a number of types of technological advances and how they can help people communicate better. Illustrate some points with colorful photos of happy people using the technology.

Potential patient internal market—Members of the university community, as well as their colleagues, family, and friends, with hearing loss are a population whose first problem may be they don't know you exist. Solving this problem may be as simple as increasing visibility on campus through several venues such as campus-wide email blast, campus newspaper ads, alumni magazine articles, and spots on televisions and monitors in other departments and in the campus exercise facility. Other problems that this market needs solved are the same as those of the potential external market addressed below. With the internal potential patient market, make certain they know they are special patients by offering them a special consideration such as a clinic open house or special lecture series designed for them.

Potential patient external market—This is a large and competitive market where identifying the problem must be followed with powerful and unusual solutions that align with your clinic's strengths. Marketing for this group must often first deal with the problem of denial of the hearing loss. Having a short quiz that helps people understand they may have a problem can help with denial and assists friends and family in getting potential patients to your door for testing. Some potential patients use the costs of testing as the problem that keeps them out of the clinic. If so, the "Pay what you want" approach explained on 5-by-7–inch cards or as a newspaper ad can be an effective way to increase clinic calls by these patients. A continuing problem for this marketplace is how to deal with changes in hearing. A first solution to this problem is to educate the potential patient, as well as those around him or her, that an audiologist should test his or her hearing because of the significant problems that hearing loss causes and the benefits treatment of hearing loss provide. There is a powerful and growing body of knowledge to support these arguments; use it. Drawing from your discussions of your clinic's strengths, which differentiate it from the competition, you can then create a list of 5 or 10 reasons why the potential patient should come to your clinic to be tested. A few well-stated testimonials will also help. This solution on to how to deal with hearing changes will fit nicely into a trifold brochure, which is useful in the external professional marketplace also.

Professional external marketplace—The main customer in this market is the medical practice that serves your ideal patient population. A recurring problem the medical practice wants solved is how to identify which patients are at the highest risk for hearing loss and how to do it quickly and inexpensively. Fortunately, there are several solutions for this problem, so the solutions can be distributed through time to maintain an ongoing relationship with the medical practice. My favorite solution is a bifold brochure entitled, "Recognizing Hidden Hearing Loss in Your Patients." The cover uses a photo of a physician and a patient and presents a list of six questions the doctor or his or her staff could ask patients to initially screen for hearing loss along with a brief explanation why detecting hearing loss is important. Inside are eight reasons to send patients to our audiology clinic. These reasons were drawn from our list of strengths and differentiators. Each item had a one- or two-sentence explanation followed by why patients thought that reason was important. For example: We Specialize in Tough Cases—*As a well-established leading research and training site, we are perfectly prepared to successfully diagnose and manage your most complicated cases. We often receive compliments from patients who were previously disappointed elsewhere. Your patients will appreciate the superior care.* Patient satisfaction at referred sites is a problem medical practices want to solve, and it is key to getting regular referrals, so relating each reason to patient satisfaction is important. Our value proposition and mission appeared on the back of the brochure along with location, directions, and contact information.

Another solution to this problem is to distribute the 15-question multiple-choice test developed by the American Academy of Otolaryngology, presented as a 5-minute hearing quiz. Medical practices can have the patient fill out this quiz while waiting in the lobby or in the exam room. Any office personnel can easily score it. The brochure also contains a summary of the types of patients the clinic serves and the services offered along with location, directions, and contact information.

If you offer the "Pay what you want" plan, physicians and their staff will quickly shift the burden of detecting patients with hearing loss to your clinic.

Chapter 5 presents disease state marketing and interventional audiology approaches to medical practices that also serve to provide solutions to questions common to medical practices. Those approaches will work for university and nonprofit clinics also.

The professional external market will consist of other professionals, such as those administering senior centers. The approach is the same no matter what profession; find out what problems they want solved and develop the best solutions possible for them and let them know why you are the best solution to their problems.

FINAL THOUGHTS

The fast-paced changes in hearing health care and increased competition from a variety of new venues have raised the importance of well-reasoned marketing strategies to university and other nonprofit clinics to a critical level that cannot be ignored.

In this chapter, you have been provided with an approach to clinic marketing customized to university and other nonprofit audiology clinics' needs, intended to increase your understanding of marketing and to stimulate your thinking about starting or improving your marketing strategies so you can respond effectively to this critical need and prosper.

Now you must develop your own integrated plan that works in your unique nonprofit setting. The summary, which follows, can help you with this process. As you go through the steps to create a successful marketing experience, it is important to constantly to see that all components of the planning—mission, value proposition, ideal patients, strategies, goals, budget, and culture—are integrated and consistent. If you do, potential patients will receive a powerful and consistent message from a variety of sources and from all their interactions with the clinic —key elements for marketing success.

SUMMARY

"In times of change learners inherit the earth, while
the learned find themselves beautifully equipped
to deal with a world that no longer exists."
—Eric Hoffer

Due to fast-moving changes in hearing health care, including increased competition and transparency, university and nonprofit audiology clinics must now incorporate marketing as a critical strategy for their success and long-term sustainability. Marketing is necessary and requires a long-term commitment of resources, human, and capital. Marketing the clinic is an investment that requires dollars and hard work. Everyone involved must have the proper expectations for success, and ROI must be constantly monitored and adjustments made according to outcome data. Monthly ROI will not turn positive until about a year, and ROI will maximize only after about 3 years. Starting a marketing effort requires much initial planning and building a marketing culture where everyone accepts responsibility for achieving success. To assist you with that effort, the approach presented in this chapter is summarized below with references to the pages containing content about each step in the process. Adjust the ideas suggested here to meet your unique clinic and markets. Knowing that marketing is necessary to clinic viability should motivate everyone involved to approach this challenge with enthusiasm. You will find achieving success is extremely rewarding.

Steps to marketing success for university and nonprofit audiology clinics are:

1. Conduct strategic planning to identify the clinic's strengths, weaknesses, opportunities, and threats, and define the mission (pp. 293–295).
2. Based on strategic planning results and resources suggested in this chapter, create an argument in a case statement to justify to the decision makers upstream that marketing the clinic is a good investment and will accomplish objectives important to them and to the clinic (pp. 295–298).
3. Research ways to accomplish needed marketing tasks with the least resources by using existing internal resources, such as PR, HR, students, and the business school, and external resources such as free management services (pp. 299–305).
4. Create the clinic's value proposition: a collection of reasons a potential patient should use your services or products rather than any others. To be effective, a value proposition must resonate with patients, differentiate you from the competition, and substantiate that you will deliver on your promises (pp. 305–310).
5. Define your ideal patient: the patient who has a frustration your clinic is best at solving and on whose patronage the clinic can succeed. Use this ideal patient and the job he or she wants done as the target of your marketing strategies to limit marketing expenditures and efforts (pp. 310–311).

6. State marketing goals to be accomplished to provide milestones and direction for marketing strategies (pp. 311–314).
7. Define the ideal customers in each of the four marketplaces in which you will promote the clinic: (1) patient internal market, (2) potential patient internal market, (3) potential patient external market, and (4) professional external market. Include all four marketplaces in your marketing strategies (pp. 314–317).
8. Conduct a demographic analysis to locate ideal patients, potential professional referral sources, and competitors in the external marketplace (pp. 317–318).
9. Decide on strategies you will use to reach potential patients through each of the five marketing pathways: database, retail, third-party referrals, grassroots, and digital. Put the most resources into third-party referrals, then database marketing and website development. For university or nonprofit clinics adding an active program to win the professional external marketplace, referrals may be the best investment that can be made (pp. 318–331).
10. Develop a unique astonishing guarantee strategy no one else would dream of and include it as an active marketing strategy on your marketing calendar (pp. 331–333).
11. Constantly create and renew an active marketing culture throughout the clinic, department, and administration (pp. 333–337).
12. Construct a marketing calendar, which summarizes all of your marketing activities and their costs on one page as a yearlong timeline (pp. 337–341).
13. Develop a set of marketing materials for each event in each pathway on your marketing calendar. These materials must clearly differentiate the clinic from the competition and focus on the ideal patient. Heritage, research, and training are especially effective and unusual differentiators that most universities and nonprofits have over the competition (pp. 341–349).
14. Check to make certain the clinic culture reflects the values in your marketing strategies and materials. Immediately make changes if needed.
15. Execute marketing strategies as a team making corrections based on constant feedback from monitoring each strategy's progress, success, and ROI.

16. Have fun! Marketing gives the team clear goals and feedback; celebrate the successes often and inclusively.

REFERENCES

Becchetti, L., & Trovato, G. (2002). The determinants of growth for small and medium sized firms: The role of the availability of external finance. *Small Business Economics, 19*(4), 291–306.

Brinkerhoff, P. C. (1997). *Mission-based marketing: How your not-for-profit can succeed in a more competitive world.* New York, NY: John Wiley.

Collins, J. (2005), *Good to great and the social sectors: A monograph to accompany good to great.* New York, NY: Harper Collins.

Daniel, F., Lohrke, F. T., Fornaciari, C. J., & Turner, R. A. (2004). Slack resources and firm performance: A meta-analysis. *Journal of Business Research, 57*(6), 565–574.

Drucker, P. F. (1990). *Managing the non-profit organization: Principles and practices.* New York, NY: Harper Business.

Drucker, P. F. (1993). *The five most important questions you will ever ask about your nonprofit organization.* San Francisco, CA: Jossey-Bass.

Estupianan, J., Fengler, K., & Kaura, A. (2014). The birth of the healthcare consumer: Growing demands for choice, engagement, and experience. *Strategy & Consumer Survey.* Retrieved January 4, 2015, from http://www.strategyand.pwc.com

George, G. (2005). Slack resources and the performance of privately held firms. *Academy of Management Journal, 48*(4), 661–676.

Jacobson, G. P., & Jerger, J. F. (2014). James F. Jerger, PhD, responds to five questions. *Journal of the American Academy of Audiology, 25*(4), 308–309.

Jantsch, J. (2011). *Duct tape marketing: Revised and updated.* Nashville, TN: Thomas Nelson.

Lyon, S. (2012, July). *Building a marketing plan you can use. Amplify your future.* Paper presented at the Fuel Medical Summit Meeting, Las Vegas, NV.

Musso, P., & Schiavo, S. (2008). The impact of financial constraints on firm survival and growth. *Journal of Evolutionary Economics, 18*(2), 135–149.

Nobel, C. (2014, November 3). Brand lessons from the Nobel Prize. *Harvard Business School Working Knowledge.* Retrieved January 4, 2015, from hbswk.hbs.edu

Parker, S. (2012, July). *Building a value proposition—Part 1. Amplify your future.* Paper presented at the Fuel Medical Summit Meeting, Las Vegas, NV.

Phonak Marketing. (2013, December). 2013 survey of US dispensing practices. *Hearing Review*, pp. 24–32.

Salamon, L. M. (1999). *America's nonprofit sector: A primer.* New York, NY: The Foundation Center.

Schumpeter. (2014, October 18–24). Pointers to the future. *Economist*, p. 72.

Smith, A. (2014, April 3). Older adults and technology use. *Pew Research Center.* Retrieved January 4, 2015, from http://www.pewinternet.org/2014/04/03/older-adults-and-technology-use/

Stern, G. J. (1996). *Marketing workbook for nonprofit organizations.* St. Paul, MN: Amherst H. Wilder Foundation.

Taylor, B. (2013). *Quality in audiology: Design and implementation of the patient experience.* San Diego, CA: Plural.

Taylor, B., & Tysoe, B. (2014, June 23). Forming strategic alliances with primary care medicine: Interventional audiology in practice. *Hearing Review.* Retrieved January 3, 2015, from http://www.hearing review.com

Urde, M., Greyser, S., & Balmer, J. (2007). Corporate brands with a heritage. *Journal of Brand Management, 15,* 4–19.

Winograd, M., & Hais, M. D. (2011). *Millennial momentum: How a new generation is remaking America.* New Brunswick, NJ: Rutgers University Press.

Zickuhr, K. (2014, February). *Older adults and technology.* Presented at JASA's Seminar on Advocacy and Volunteering in New Landscapes, New York, NY. Retrieved January 3, 2015, from http://www.pew internet.org/2014/04/29/older-adults-and-technology/

INDEX

Note: Page numbers in **bold** reference non-text material